The
London
Grants
Guide

A guide to sources
of funding for voluntary organisations
and charitable purposes in the
Greater London area

Edited by **Lucy Stubbs**

A
Directory of Social Change
publication

THE LONDON GRANTS GUIDE
A guide to sources of funds for voluntary organisations and
charitable organisations and charitable purposes in the
Greater London area

Edited by Lucy Stubbs

Designed by Michael Norton

Published by the Directory of Social Change,
Radius Works, Back Lane, London NW3 1HL
(071-435 8171)

Typeset by Jane Wood

Printed and bound in Britain by the Bath Press

ISBN 0 907164 85 4

Contents

▬▬▬ Part Two: Local Funding Sources Borough by Borough

▬▬ Index

Preface

The London Grants Guide lists the sources of funding that exist specifically to help organisations and individuals in London. The intention is both to provide a convenient handbook for London charities and also to make better known those older, endowed trusts that have disappeared from sight over the years. As readers will note, a number of them are substantially underspending their charitable income.

What the Guide covers

This book has information on local authorities, other statutory funding sources and grant-making trusts and charities. It also gives details of the main sources of advice and information available to local organisations. In all it covers about £200 million a year in statutory funding and a further £42 million from charitable sources, mainly endowed grant-making trusts. Of this, about £six million is given to help individuals; the rest is given in grants to London voluntary organisations.

Details are given of over 300 London grant-making charities. These vary from the large, well-known and well-endowed trusts such as the Sir John Cass Foundation, to smaller, unknown but very effective bodies such as the 'Duckett' charities.

The guide does not cover national grant-making trusts or companies unless they have a specific London priority or allocation. These are covered in three companion volumes, *A Guide to the Major Trusts, A Guide to Company Giving* and *The Major Companies Guide.*

Sources of funding for subscriptions, donations, collections or payment of services are not included. The vast network of local fund-raising activity, centred on bodies such as Rotary Clubs and Lions Junior Chambers of Commerce rarely have a permanent office and cannot be listed; often the local Council for Voluntary Service will be able to advise how to identify them.

The City Livery Companies are not listed separately. A few of these companies have identifiable London orientated charities, some of which are very important and admirably conducted bodies. These are included individually in our guide. But there are probably other livery companies which support voluntary organisations, especially when these can show a connection with the trade concerned. Unfortunately these companies are often secretive about their charitable work, even when this is carried out through publicly-listed charities. The accounts held on file at the Charity Commission are often out-of-date and do not contain precise details of projects supported.

Acknowledgements and Requests for Further Information

I am very grateful to the many people from organisations of all kinds who co-operated in the preparation of this guide. However, I am fully aware that it is not comprehensive and would welcome further information and suggestions. Please write in or telephone me on 071-284 4365.

Lucy Stubbs, The Editor
August 1992

Local Authorities and Grant Aid

This article provides some background information on how the allocation of grants is carried out within local authorities. It is not the 'be all' of how to go about applying for a grant but gives a few essential pointers to those in pursuit of funding.

Local Authorities

Local authorities exist as a vehicle through which services can be delivered at a local level.

The range of services provided varies from authority to authority although many are statutory and determined by central government. Educational and social services are among those which must be provided whereas leisure and recreational facilities are discretionary.

Local authorities conduct their business through a series of committees which reflect either departments or local areas of services. These committees, comprising elected councillors, meet at regular intervals throughout the year. Each committee has specific responsibilities. It considers issues and makes recommendations which are then ratified or rejected by the council which meets several times a year.

Most local authorities invite applications for grants during autumn and requests for decisions on funding are often put to the appropriate committees well before the start of the financial year in April.

Organisations should also remember that committee meetings are public forums and members of the public have every right to attend.

Why Grant Aid?

There are often areas where the services provided by a local authority do not fully meet the demands or expectations of the local community. Sometimes voluntary organisations fill these shortfalls in return for local authority funding.

Certain acts of Parliament empower local authorities to

make grants, such as the 1977 Housing Act which lets local authorities fund organisations working with homeless people.

Traditionally the voluntary sector has had a policy development and quality control role. It has often been at the forefront of promoting new ideas and services on behalf of its clients. Concepts such as client advocacy and the independent inspection of residential homes would not be so far advanced as they are today if it was not for the innovations of certain voluntary groups.

Local authority attitudes to funding the voluntary sector have been varied, normally according to the political philosophy of the party controlling an authority at any given time. In some councils the provision of funding for voluntary organisations has developed in a haphazard fashion. Others have been quicker to realise the benefits of grant-aiding local organisations and established grants units which deal with applications in a coordinated and consistent way.

However, local authority attitudes are changing. The voluntary sector's innovations and responsiveness to the demands of its clients has brought about an increased recognition that it can provide a range of services in a more efficient and cost-effective way than local authorities.

This change in philosophy has come at a time when local government is required to look at the efficiency of its services because of Compulsory Competitive Tendering (CCT) and the NHS and Community Care Act. Further opportunities have arisen for voluntary organisations to undertake services in return for grant-aid or contracts.

However the uncertainty of local authority finances means that voluntary organisations still struggle to secure funding for new and innovative projects. There is also a certain reluctance on the part of local authorities to relinquish the role of service provider.

Applying for Grant Aid

As many voluntary organisations will already know, the current restrictions on local authority funding have led to a sharp decline in the funding available.

So it is more important than ever before that organisations are well-informed. It might sound like stating the obvious but organisations must make themselves aware of when application forms are available, what information should be provided and when forms should be returned. These should be key questions.

The grants officer should be your first point of contact. This is the person in a local authority who can enlighten organisations as to the best way to proceed on the tricky road to obtaining financial assistance.

Procedures and application processes should be mastered; quite often voluntary organisations cannot be considered for financial assistance because they fail to apply to the right committee at the right time.

Thought should be given to the application itself. Often it is an organisation's only chance to sell itself and its services. Time and care should be taken in completing all the sections and providing all the relevant supporting information. Nothing irritates a grants officer more than receiving half-completed application forms. It immediately reduces an organisation's chances.

When applying groups must differentiate between bids for funding for existing 'core' services and bids for new 'growth' services. They must provide details of their fund-raising activities.

Lobbying councillors can contribute to the success of an application. Time taken to identify and enlist the support of relevant committee chairs and committee members should be seen as time well spent. It is also worth establishing a rapport with the officers whose responsibility it is to advise the committee.

Reports containing the officers' recommendations are prepared two or three weeks prior to a committee meeting and authorities are legally required to ensure that reports must be available at least seven days before the meeting.

The reports are public documents and voluntary organisations should make sure they know what the recommendations are affecting them. A vast amount of lobbying can be carried out in seven days.

More than ever councillors favour organisations that do not rely totally on local authority funding but have a robust attitude towards fund-raising from a variety of sources. They have become more value-for-money conscious and this is often mirrored in their approach to the voluntary sector. Organisations should show an ability to provide cost-effective services, an established set of objectives and targets and a mechanism for reviewing the effectiveness of their services.

Contracts

The NHS and Community Care Act obliged statutory authorities to adopt a more contractual relationship with the organisations they funded.

Many voluntary organisations dislike contracts but they should remember that although the local authority holds the purse strings, negotiating a contract is a two-way process.

Terms and Conditions of Grants and Contracts

When a local authority awards grant-aid or a contract it will require adherence to its terms and conditions. Groups should examine these in detail and decide if they are compatible with their objectives and principles. This can save trouble and recrimination. It may well be that adherence to the terms and conditions is simply not worth the money offered and that they should look to some other source of funding.

Where to get help

Applying for financial assistance can be daunting, especially for new groups. It can be a complex and time-consuming exercise. However, there are always people on hand to ask. Your borough's grants officers are usually 'user-friendly' and will understand your concerns and problems. Alternatively your local association for voluntary service should provide you with helpful advice.

Conclusion

The future funding of voluntary organisations is uncertain. A recent report by the London Boroughs Grants Committee showed a 10% reduction in grants awarded by London Boroughs to voluntary organisations from 1990 to 1992. Although future developments are difficult to predict it is unlikely that there will be a reversal of this trend.

It is probable that in future funds available from local authorities will be targeted towards organisations directly providing services rather than to groups whose main activity is campaigning. Small organisations and newly formed groups will be particularly vulnerable to losing their funding.

Service contracts will gradually become a standard component of the grants process for all groups in receipt of grant-aid. However the contracting out of services will probably develop at a slow pace with contracts only being awarded to larger voluntary organisations.

These developments make it vital for voluntary organisations applying for grant aid to present themselves and their services in a positive and professional way.

Nigel Cramb, Community Resources Officer,
London Borough of Hillingdon, April 1992

Community Care and the Voluntary Sector

Introduction

Under the spotlight of government legislation the voluntary sector has rapidly acquired new clothes. Contracts, community care and active citizenship are our new bywords and we even have a new name, the 'independent sector', placing us alongside the hallowed private sector in the government's estimation. Our language has changed, so that efficiency, competitiveness, quality assurance and marketability are the new measures of success. As icing on the cake, a number of recruiting agencies are now luring 'highly skilled staff' from the private sector to the voluntary sector to show us how it's really done.

Being more 'professional' and 'business-like', some of the large, well-established voluntary groups are now assuming responsibility for mainstream social services. This will impress central government. Both of the main political parties envisage more of a role for the voluntary sector in service delivery and only a cynic would suggest their real motive was saving money.

The NHS and Community Care Act

The NHS and Community Care Act (1990) marks a shift away from long-term hospital care to care in the community, redefines the role of local government and encourages voluntary groups to develop their role in service provision through contractual funding.

The case for community care became overwhelming when a 1986 Audit Commission report exposed the 'perverse incentive' for local and health authorities to place people in residential care simply because the Department of Social Security would foot the bill.

Alarmed by this expense the government commissioned Sir Roy Griffiths to find a better alternative and his proposals for change were incorporated by and large in the NHS and Community Care Act. But this legislation has been a long time in coming for the service users and carers who have had to rely for years upon underfunded and overstretched domiciliary and respite care services.

The Act promotes a 'mixed economy of care', in which private, non-profit and voluntary agencies take over statutory responsibilities. According to the government, services will improve if local people have more of them to choose from. Competition is expected to boost quality. Local authorities are now encouraged by central government to contract out their services to a range of 'independent' providers.

Clearly these ideas are in the ascendency. Under the weight of successive reforms, local government is now transforming its role from one of provider to enabler and purchaser. Having experienced financial crisis in recent years, local authorities have a major incentive to contract out their services at less cost.

Response of the Voluntary Sector

The NHS and Community Care Act was welcomed by voluntary groups but with a few important reservations. Although local authorities were rightly given the responsibility of coordinating community care, the resources identified for the task seemed inadequate. Sceptics immediately interpreted the new policies as cost-cutting measures and warned that community care was a cheap option.

Nevertheless, the voluntary sector threw itself wholeheartedly into assisting local authorities with their community care plans. Determined to make community care a success, voluntary groups mobilised their members, often without any encouragement from the local authority. The voluntary sector played a crucial role in ensuring that the professional planners listened to the views of service users and strove to influence the range of services available.

Preparing for the Contract Culture

Voluntary groups must be prepared for contracting because it may well replace grant-aid as the major form of statutory funding. To participate effectively small voluntary groups need to consider the legal and organisational implications and to prepare themselves for negotiating and managing a contract.

Entering into a contract could affect a voluntary group's charitable status and may require a revision of its constitution. Groups will need to consider becoming a company limited by guarantee to protect individual management committee members from incurring large financial costs if there is a breach of contract.

Contracts will require tighter financial management than grants and longer term financial planning. For further information consult the London Voluntary Service Council's publications on contracts which offer advice on the changes they will bring and are specifically geared to small organisations.

Benefits to the Voluntary Sector

In one important respect the voluntary sector has already profited from the NHS and Community Care Act. For years voluntary groups tried to persuade local authorities to afford them equal status in the planning and delivery of services. Its enormous contribution to community care planning demonstrated to local authorities how much expertise the voluntary sector has to offer. In some London authorities voluntary groups, service-users and carers are now represented at every level of the planning process and exert direct influence over service provision.

For voluntary groups the main advantage of contracting is said to be financial. Since contracts are often negotiated for three year periods, they are expected to provide more financial security than annual grant aid. Greater security will enable voluntary organisations to offer improved conditions of employment and to be more effective in planning and evaluating their work.

Disadvantages for the Voluntary Sector

The government states 'There is no reason why the move from grants to contracts should inhibit the distinctive contribution of the voluntary sector in terms of flexibility, vitality and innovation.' (*The Individual and The Community*, 1992). Strangely enough, this is precisely the reason that many voluntary groups are opposed to contracts.

If contracts impose tight service specifications, how can voluntary groups remain flexible? Innovative work can only develop if funding is given without strictly defined terms. What about voluntary work which does not fit the specifications of local and district health authorities? The evidence so far suggests that large, white, well-established organisations are more likely to receive contracts than small groups, new projects, black organisations, or groups performing non-service delivery roles.

Contracts impose standards upon voluntary groups and define priorities for them. This goes against the grain of voluntary activity. If voluntary groups become more accountable to their funders than to the community, they may begin to resemble statutory authorities and their 'distinctive contribution' may wither away.

The Future

It remains to be seen how comprehensive community care services become in the next few years and much will depend upon how well the reforms are financed. According to the latest Audit Commission report some social services departments are struggling to adapt to their new roles in care management and needs assessment. The Department of Health has also acknowledged that local authorities are unlikely to implement all the community care reforms from April 1993.

If the voluntary sector is only funded to provide mainstream services its greatest strength, the ability to respond to needs identified by local people, may be lost. In order to adapt to emerging needs voluntary groups require a form of 'arms length' funding that enables them to innovate and to establish new services. Quality assurance, from a voluntary sector perspective, is provided by service-user involvement, equal opportunities and a needs-led approach. Contracting may be a cheap option for statutory funders, but it is unlikely to improve the quality of local service-provision.

Steven Phaure, London Voluntary
Service Council, April 1992

Applying to a Trust

I vividly remember trying to raise funds for voluntary organisations which I worked for during much of the last twenty years.
I used to struggle to find out about trusts, thinking what they
wanted to know and how much I could possibly ask for without
seeming greedy. There was the thrill of receiving a cheque,
especially when it was for the amount requested. I also recall
the 'Ah well' feeling when a refusal letter arrived and being
filled with sense of protest and hope when it was suggested
another aspect of our work might interest a particular funder. I
had already put so much effort into an application
for something which was badly needed and this was being
turned down.

When I worked in voluntary organisations it was assumed
that everyone knew how to raise money and keep the accounts.
If you did not, then you either hoped you never would be called
upon to do either task or like me you quickly went on a course
in order to learn. Not so many years ago raising money did not
pose the enormous problems it now does. There used to be less
competition, and more money was available from a wider
range of sources. The amounts which many organisations
needed to raise were not as huge as is frequently the case now.
Often only top-up money was needed to build upon a basic,
established income. Now it is not unusual for organisations to
be raising considerable amounts and to have no guaranteed
funding at all.

In the current environment people working in organisations
must know how to raise funds and keep accounts. These are no
longer tasks to be done half-heartedly or avoided though they
still seem to strike fear into many hearts. Working for two
charitable trusts, I find that there is still a long way to go before
the voluntary sector becomes professional in this regard.

During 1991 the City Parochial Foundation and the Trust
for London made well over 500 grants to London-based
organisations. Whilst many of the applicant groups were small,
fairly recently formed bodies others were long-established,

reasonably large organisations employing staff and working with substantial budgets. Yet in only a tiny number of cases was an application received in a form which could be put straight to the grant-making committee. In the vast majority of these cases considerable work had to be done with individual organisations before the application was ready to go to committee and in some instances the Trust for London supplied additional consultancy to help compile the actual application as well as advise and assist with structures and systems.

This is not to say that there are always doubts about the quality of work of organisations. On the contrary, on many occasions it is the presentational skills which are lacking. It is not unusual to receive letters of application which, on their own, would not elicit a positive response from any funding body but a visit to the organisation conveys a completely different impression and leaves me puzzled.

The puzzle is that for some reason it seems to be a problem for many organisations to put across to funders what needs they are meeting and what excellent and exciting work they are doing. It is not so much that people in organisations do not know *how* to get the message across, it is often more of a question of *which* message to choose. I have known applications be revised and resubmitted which bear no resemblance to the original after a visit from funding staff and perhaps several lengthy discussions. However, applicants cannot rely on always receiving a visit. Organisations must, if they are to survive, do their homework before putting pen to paper and approaching any funder.

When I talk to organisations which are approaching charitable trusts for funds I tend to begin by advising them to know themselves. All voluntary groups have a history; their members should know why the group began, who started it, what were the circumstances, what the aims are, whom it serves, what it does, how it has changed or developed over the years, and the reasons behind the developments. All the members should know how their organisation is managed and how policy is made. Their current financial situation should be common knowledge as well as where their funding comes from and how it is administered.

When communicating with funders applicants should also know why they want funding and be clear that what they are seeking funding for falls within the priorities of the charitable trust being approached. Organisations must study the Directory of Grant-making Trusts and any guidelines issued by individual trusts before making an approach. In the long run this saves time, energy and the potential frustration of finding an inappropriate application has been made.

Strange as it may sound it is important that potential applicants take seriously the information charitable trusts publish. Recent experience prompts this remark.

At the beginning of 1992 both the Trust for London and City Parochial Foundation issued new funding guidelines for the next four and and five years respectively. The guidelines were widely circulated in order to inform prospective applicants. The ensuing deluge of telephone calls and letters revealed that few had actually read the guidelines before making contact.

Some organisations submitted applications which clearly fell outside the grant-making priorities set out in the guidelines booklet and it was common to find that applicants did not enclose the documents which the guidelines identified as a necessary accompaniment to an application. This may sound like a moan on my part but although it is understandable that people might be desperate for funds it is clearly counter-productive to use time and energy submitting incomplete or inappropriate applications and it is the organisation's time and energy more than the trust's which are wasted.

Both the Trust for London and the City Parochial Foundation make a deliberate effort to listen to the views on our policies and procedures expressed by those who receive grants. It is one of the areas on which the Trust seeks comments in its monitoring. The new policies for grant-making have taken into account much of the feedback there has been over recent years as well as the results of several monitoring exercises which were commissioned during 1991. The trustees have taken seriously the comments that funding ought to be targeted rather than general, that guidelines should be detailed and widely publicised. It is not therefore unreasonable to expect that organisations read and accept the end result. In our experience however, many argue that their area of work should have been included in the priorities for the next four or five years or else they go to great lengths to 'make their organisation fit'. This, too can prove to be a non-profitable exercise.

As the economic climate grows harsher for the volun-tary sector as a whole I feel that fund-raising by all voluntary organisations no matter how small must now be seen as a strategic exercise. It must be treated as seriously as all the other activities in which the organisation engages and as part of the overall organisational strategy. It cannot be seen as the job no one wants, which is tagged on the end of the list of things to be done. Neither is it a once a year event. The strategy must be ongoing so that income and expenditure are planned and, as much as possible, (though it may seem a luxury these days) fundraising is not left until the bank account is empty. This is the important link between proper accounting and fundraising so that they work hand-in-hand and are treated as equally important jobs in every organisation no matter what size it is.

Alison Harker, Field Officer, City Parochial Foundation
and Trust for London, February 1992

The Role of a Council for Voluntary Service

A Council for Voluntary Service (CVS) is an independent voluntary organisation which supports local voluntary groups and promotes community action. Nationally there are about 200 CVSs. Some have no paid staff, others have over 100, but about 40% employ between four and nine staff. Most are known as a Council for Voluntary Service, although other names such as Voluntary Action Council or Federation of Community Organisations are also used. The CVS, or its equivalent, usually receives a grant from its local authority to maintain an office and employ staff but other sources of funding, such as charitable trusts, are equally important, especially for starting new projects.

The main functions of a CVS are:

(a) Services and Support for Other Organisations – services may be general, for example, production of a newsletter or a directory of local groups; or specific, such as helping an organisation with a particular problem. The CVS will work with organisations by offering them help, advice and support as appropriate. Some CVSs run projects for the benefit of other organisations, for example, a Volunteer Bureau, a Community Transport Scheme, or an accountancy service.

(b) Liaison - this involves bringing organisations together to share ideas, facilitating the exchange of information, and encouraging joint action. The CVS acts as a focal point, gaining an overall view of needs and resources and may establish working parties on special areas of need such as elderly people or young unemployed people.

(c) Representation - this involves taking the lead in obtaining the voluntary sector's representation on other bodies such as the Community Health Council or the Police Liaison Committee; consulting voluntary organisations on particular issues and acting as a channel through which views can be expressed; and promoting and publicising the work of the voluntary sector.

(d) Development Work - this is often considered the most important function of a CVS and is a process of reviewing existing provision by identifying needs, initiating action to meet those needs, and trying to achieve a better match between needs and resources. In practice, this could mean helping to establish a new, independent organisation or assisting a group in the development of its own work. A CVS, being able to take an overview, is ideally placed to encourage and promote the development of a new project.

The resources of CVSs vary enormously which is reflected in the work they are able to undertake. However to give an idea of how a CVS may operate locally, I have outlined some of the work undertaken by Merton Voluntary Service Council (MVSC) which was set up five years ago and now has two full-time and two part-time members of staff funded by the London Borough of Merton and a full-time Community Care Development Worker funded by a trust. We hope this will illustrate the type of help which your local CVS may be able to give should you contact it.

In our service and support role, we regard the distribution of information to be crucial. We subscribe to an increasing number of national and local bodies and the information from these sources is distributed to local groups via our bi-monthly newsletter, or by special mailings. Every day we get requests for information ranging from simple enquiries about a local group to more complex advice on charitable status, equal opportunities or new government legislation. We publish a Directory of Community Organisations in our borough; we have a small library of books and items of equipment which may be borrowed; and we provide a photocopying service and advice on the production of simple publicity leaflets and posters. We run regular training events on such topics as raising money from trusts, evaluation, the role of a management committee, anti-racism etc. and give detailed advice and guidance on a range of organisational issues such as employing staff, organising an annual meeting, sources of funding, etc. As we understand the grant-making processes of our local authority and know most of the officers and councillors involved, we often advise groups seeking to approach the council.

In our role as development agency, we have been involved in setting up a range of new groups. This involvement has varied from acting as secretary to a steering group to calling a public meeting, negotiating for funding, drafting a constitution, and finding premises. New projects which have been established with our help include developing a multi-agency centre - which acts as the base for a number of local groups, setting up a group for deaf people, starting a community playscheme, initiating a second-hand furniture project, co-ordinating a women's health project, developing a Carers' Support Project, and establishing a Refugee Network. With a new scheme, it is always our aim to withdraw once it becomes self-supporting.

We promote co-operation between local agencies and have set up a number of local networks which bring together those with a common interest or concern. To ensure that we keep in touch with current developments, we meet regularly with staff from other agencies in the borough and with staff from other London CVSs to exchange ideas and consider joint action. Often we are asked to represent the views of the voluntary sector and to facilitate joint discussion. When doing this we consult as widely as possible to ensure that everyone's views are heard.

As you will see, the work of a CVS is varied and wide-ranging and will reflect the needs of the area which it serves and the resources which are available. However, the work of all CVSs is based on a philosophy of promoting good practice in order to give people the power to take control of their own lives and thereby bring about social change.

Christine Frost, Merton Council
for Voluntary Service

Part One
London-wide and multi-borough funding sources

Introduction

This part of the book gives details of all funding bodies that cover more than a single borough. Most of them cover the whole of London. They are listed in three groups:

The sources of statutory or semi-statutory funding

Grant-making trusts and charities

Major London companies, with radio and TV stations.

These sections are followed by a brief listing of the major sources of advice and training available to London charities.

Statutory and semi-statutory funding: This listing includes bodies such as the London Boroughs Grants Scheme, the London Docklands Development Corporation (which covers parts of three boroughs) and the London Arts Board.

Grant-making trusts and charities: This section is divided into two parts. First there are those charities that will consider making grants to relevant organisations. The second part lists those that only make grants for individuals who are in need.

These entries should be read carefully before any application is made. Trusts are much annoyed by applications which show that the information that they have given for publication has not been read and taken into account. In many cases a preliminary telephone call will be helpful to both trust and applicant.

Major London Companies: This section lists companies which are specifically London oriented, mainly the radio and TV stations. Many other companies are given in Part Two of the book where major local employers are listed borough by borough.

Sources of advice: Again, local organisations should look also at the borough by borough entries in Part Two of the book, where the addresses of the local Councils of Voluntary Service are given.

Official Sources

Commission for Racial Equality

Type of beneficiary: Organisations

Objects: Up to 1991 grants were made for ethnic minorities in the following priority areas: training and counselling for young people, employment promotion, legal support and advice centres, the arts, elderly people and women.

Grant details: Because of uncertainty over its own funding, the current outlook for grants is not at all clear.

Applications procedure: Enquiries are still welcome, but applicants should note the above.

Correspondent: Maurice Forsythe, Senior Field Officer (Greater London)

Address: Elliot House, 10-12 Arlington Street, London SW1E 5EM (071-828 7022)

London Arts Board

Beneficial area: The 32 London Boroughs and the City of London

Background: The London Arts Board replaced Greater London Arts in October 1991 and became a fully independent regional arts board in April 1992.

Policy: The London Arts Board, both on its own and in partnership with local authorities, the London Boroughs Grants Committee, and the private sector

- promotes and supports artistic excellence and innovation throughout London
- develops access to the arts for the enjoyment, education and benefit of all who live and work in, or visit, London
- celebrates the richness of London's cultural diversity
- seeks to enhance London's quality of life, reputation and economy

Income: £9 million (1991/92)

Grant total: £8 million

Grant details: In 1992/93 the LAB has a budget of over £10 million. Grants are made throughout the year for dance, drama, literature, music, combined arts, visual arts and crafts, and a number of arts education projects. No further details available. Contact the correspondent for further information.

Correspondent: Claire Martin, Marketing and Information Officer

Address: 133 Long Acre, Covent Garden, London WC2E 9AF (LAB grants help-line, 071-240 4578)

London Boroughs Grants Scheme (LBGS)

Beneficial area: Greater London

Grant total: Approximately £27,400,000 in 1992/93

Background: LBGS was established in October 1985 to deal with some of the funding of London-wide voluntary organisations for which the GLC had been responsible. Now an extremely important funding body in its own right, LBGS is administered by the London Boroughs Grants Unit. All decisions relating to the making of grants and the operation of the scheme are taken by the London Borough Grants Committee, which is made up of one elected member representative from each London borough council. This committee meets eight times a year.

Policy: LBGS funds eligible London-wide voluntary organisations as defined in Section 48 of the Local Government Act 1985. This effectively means that any voluntary organisation applying for a grant from LBGS will have to fulfil the following criteria:

- 'that it carries out its activities otherwise than for profit and that it is not a public or local authority';
- 'that its activities will benefit either the whole of Greater London or any part of it extending beyond the area of any one particular borough'.

In effect, LBGS exists to support London voluntary groups who cannot receive funding from their local council because they cover too wide an area. It is not able to assist local groups which operate inside a single London Borough for the sole benefit of residents in that borough.

Types of grant: Not only revenue, but also capital and other non-recurring expenditure are eligible for funding by LBGS - although help with capital needs is very limited. There is no restriction on the type of activities funded providing it can be shown that they are an essential part of meeting the identified need. LBGS encourages groups to seek joint funding from the Scheme together with other public and non-statutory funding agencies. The grants unit has forged close working relationships with many of London's grant-making trusts. Policy issues are discussed at regular meetings during the year.

Grant-aid is sub-divided into the following main categories:

housing,
social services,
the environment,
training,
arts and recreation,
minorities,
general advice and information.

Grants vary in size from about £2,000 to over £500,000, the latter being awarded in a few cases to very large organisations. Between 650-700 voluntary organisations are funded each year and their range of activity is very broad. Examples of beneficiaries include Thames Reach Housing Association (working with homeless, single people), London Lighthouse, the London Voluntary Service Council, the London Division of the National Association of Citizens Advice Bureaux, Hampstead Theatre, and the Refugee Arrivals Project. There are many others based in all the London Boroughs which benefit large numbers of Londoners.

For the first time in 1992/93, the Grants Committee will have Section 11 funding funds available from the Home Office to support a number of new projects run by black and ethnic minority voluntary organisations. This will involve a number of staff being employed by the Grants Unit and its lead borough (Richmond upon Thames) and being outposted to those projects for three years.

No. of grants: About 650 likely in 1992/93

Exclusions: Main areas of activity which the Scheme will not fund are as follows:

- where 'the organisation seeks to promote or oppose any political party or political causes or otherwise engage in party political activities'

- where 'the service for which the grant is requested covers a policy field or geographical area much broader than London, and does not separately identify and specifically provide a service for a significant number of people in London'

- where 'the grant application is to support a campaign aimed primarily at persuading central government to change one of its national policies.'

Longer Term Funding: The committee has been considering how to bring greater stability to the funding of the voluntary sector. Once individual reviews of funded organisations have been approved and the committee is satisfied they are operating effectively, longer term grants, usually over three years, will be awarded. The first of these approvals was given in 1992.

Applications Procedure: Application forms are available from July onwards in any one year, to be returned by the last Friday in September. Between November and January the boroughs agree the annual budget, which includes an amount for grant-making and an amount for the Scheme's running costs (in 1992/93 about £27,455,000 and £1,745,000 respectively). Decisions on grant-aid may not be finalised until well into the year for which grant-aid is being considered. The funding year runs from 1st April to the 31st March.

Correspondent: Gerald Oppenheim, Director

Address: London Boroughs Grants Unit, 5th Floor, Regal House, London Road, Twickenham, Middlesex TW1 3QS. (081-891 5021)

The Grants Committee also assists the voluntary sector in non-financial ways.

Training for the Voluntary Sector
In 1990/91 the LBGS gave its backing to the start of a series of training courses for management committee members of voluntary organisations. This direct training provision aims to improve the effectiveness of voluntary managers and the services they oversee. In addition the Grants Committee training initiative gives new skills to people who volunteer their time to work on these committees and have to carry out the complex and demanding tasks of managing the financial and human resources of London voluntary agencies.

To support this initiative the Grants Unit has also compiled a select list of trainers and consultants to carry out these training courses. It has also compiled a number of consultancies for voluntary organisations funded by the committee where the

Unit and/or the organisation believe there would be major benefits. The Grants Committee has renewed both programmes for 1991/92 to build on the successes of the first year.

Funding Development Strategy: In 1990 the Grants Committee approved a Funding Development Strategy and during 1990 to 1991 work began on developing a computerised Funding Resource Database which will allow the analysis of funding practices and aid the identification of funding partners and areas of common interest amongst funders.

A key element of the work has been to help build a strong partnership between the public and private sectors, to help trusts meet London's needs and keep them briefed on the committee's work.

Consultation: The committee consults with the voluntary sector through its representative body, the Voluntary Sector Forum, twice a year on a formal basis.

The Grants Unit also takes part in several working parties which involve voluntary organisations and these include the Refugee Working Party and the Legal and Advice Working Party. The Unit provides a home for the Policy staff of the Single Homeless in London (SHIL) Working Party.

Sectoral Reviews: The committee has started a rolling programme over three years of looking in depth at the funding it provides to the voluntary sector. These sectoral reviews help the committee to define its funding priorities and policies from the perspective of a London-wide funding agency.

Review of Needs: The committee is required by its legislation to keep London's needs under review. Sectoral reviews contribute to this process but the committee also commissions research into specific concerns, looking on a broader basis at social and economic trends, legislative developments affecting the voluntary sector and local government and assessing needs and demands.

The 1991/92 review *Capital Concerns* was published in February 1992 and was carried out for the committee by the London Chamber of Commerce and Industry.

The Sports Council Greater London Region

Beneficial Area: 33 London boroughs

Objects: To support the capital costs of schemes:

1. which increase participation in sport and recreation;

2. which improve performance in sport;

3. which alleviate recreational deprivation in areas of special need.

Type of Beneficiary: Statutory, commercial and voluntary organisations

Total given to voluntary organisations: £304,650 in capital grant aid, £98,000 in interest free loans

Grant details: The Sports Council Greater London Region is advised on its allocation of its capital grants and loans by the London Council for Sport and Recreation whose membership includes voluntary and statutory organisations with an interest in sport and recreation.

Grants and loans are determined according to financial need but loans can only be made up to a maximum of £10,000. Grants can be made to statutory, commercial and voluntary organisations but only the latter are eligible for interest-free loans.

The Sports Council tends to concentrate its capital grants on projects of wider than local significance and local, small-scale schemes are unlikely to be supported. Applicants are advised to contact the Sports Council directly for advice as to whether or not their scheme would be likely to receive support.

Applications Procedure: Contact the Field Officer for your London Region for advice on eligibility, likelihood of support, timescales and applications procedures (see below).

Address: The Sports Council Greater London Region, PO Box 480, Crystal Palace National Sports Centre, Ledrington Road, London SE19 2BQ (081-778 8600)

London Docklands Development Corporation

Grant total: Unknown, see below

General: The funding of the London Docklands Development Corporation is itself uncertain and consequently it is difficult to know how far the LDDC will be able to fund local projects in the future.

However, as part of its responsibilities for the regeneration of the London Docklands Urban Area, the LDDC currently operates a programme of grants to voluntary organisations serving the area.

Voluntary organisations wishing to apply for funds from the corporation must:

• Contribute to the regeneration of London Docklands

- Have a constitution and elected committee
- Demonstrate a commitment to equal opportunities in the areas of staffing, management, and service delivery
- Provide evidence of local need
- If it is a long-term project it must demonstrate plans for becoming financially independent of the LDDC within three years
- Identify goals for monitoring and evaluation purposes.

Voluntary organisations can apply for grants for various activities including the following:-

Arts: There is limited funding available for some arts projects, especially those related to Education and Training.

Water Recreation: Grants to voluntary organisations are available towards the costs of staging events and activities, or the cost of safety items and other equipment.

Health: There are grants of up to £6,000 for organisations which support health promotion and healthy living in Docklands and encourage business involvement and sponsorship of these activities.

Community: Grants are made to organisations which provide various services in the community and are administered through two programmes: The Community Support Programme makes revenue or capital grants in excess of £1,000 and the Minor Community Grants Programme awards small one-off capital grants of up to £1,000.

Community grants are generally administered through the three area teams. These are the East Team which covers the Royal Docks, the West Team which concentrates on Wapping and the Isle of Dogs, and the South Team which comprises Surrey Docks.

The corporation is normally limited to providing support to organisations within the Urban Development Area (UDA). However, support can be given to groups working outside the UDA if it is shown that their work significantly benefits people living and/or working in Docklands. Funding will usually be 75% of the costs incurred whilst providing services for people in the Docklands.

Grant details: In 1991/91 funded organisations included: The Alpha Grove Community Centre (£36,450) which provides services to the local community; Cambridge University Mission to provide a skills training facility for underprivileged women (£21,628); Ellen Elizabeth Marine Venture for salaries and running costs of a boat which is used for the educational and recreational facilities for young children; Friends of Chaucer Hospital for a facility for the support of people within the community who have received hospital treatment for mental illness (£17,442); and the Island History Trust which collects and disseminates historical information on the Isle of Dogs.

Applications Procedure: Voluntary organisations interesting in applying for a grant should contact the Grants and Voluntary Liaison Officer in the first instance.

Correspondent: Kofy Asante, Grants and Voluntary Sector Liaison Officer

Address: Thames Quay, 191 Marsh Wall, London E14 9TJ (071-512 3000 ext 3337)

Trusts which make Grants to Organisations

The Alexandra Trust

Beneficial area: Principally the East End of London

Objects: Relief of poverty

Type of beneficiary: Organisations

Latest figures: 1990

Grant total: £15,000

Grant details: The following information is based on the 1984 accounts on file at the Charity Commission. Grants ranging from £2,000 to £3,800 were made to organisations which included the Trevor Huddleston Fund for Children, St Botolph's Evening Centre, St George's Men's Care Unit, the Salvation Army and Providence Night Shelter.

The trust previously made 'Crisis Fund' donations direct to individuals – the present secretary has told us that the trust now supports only organisations involved in care for poor and dispossessed people.

Applications procedure: In writing to the correspondent. The trust's resources are already stretched.

Correspondent: Mrs I G Sharp, Secretary

Address: The Alexandra Trust, PO Box 436, 1 Watergate, London EC4Y 0AE (071-822 6203)

The Assheton-Smith Charitable Trust

Beneficial area: London; Sussex and North Wales

Objects: General charitable purposes

Type of beneficiary: Organisations

Income: £8,100 (1990)

Grant total: £8,200

Grant details: Grants are made to registered charities only, especially those involved with the elderly. In 1990 159 grants were made, most of them for £50 and often to small organisations.

Applications procedure: By letter to the correspondent – handwritten and signed letters are favoured.

Correspondent: Colin Moore, The Senior Trust Officer

Address: Coutts & Co, Financial Services Division Trustees Department, 440 Strand, London WC2R 0QS (071-379 6262 ext. 1673)

The Baring Foundation

Beneficial area: National, with a special interest in the London area

Objects: Social welfare, medicine, the arts, education, conservation, religion and youth

Type of beneficiary: Organisations only

Grant total: £7,285,494 nationally and £1,523,285 to London charities; (1990)

Grant details: The foundation gives grants only to national charities or to those that are 'local' to Greater London, Merseyside or Tyne and Wear.

The foundation is the sole holder of the Ordinary Shares in Barings bank. Barings has prospered greatly in recent years and as a result there has been an increasing stream of dividend income available to the foundation for grantmaking. Donations of about £25,000 in 1970 grew to 1.8m in 1986 to £7m in 1990.

David Carrington, Director of the foundation, and former Principal of Morley College in Southwark describes the policy of the foundation as follows:

'The foundation makes grants across all the areas of charitable giving which are categorised as the arts, church and religion, conservation, education, international, medicine, social welfare and youth – though youth has tended to receive a low priority since a number of the other large foundations specialise in youth matters.

In general the Council likes where possible to

support causes which for one reason or another have less popular psychological appeal than those more obvious or 'safer' charities which will find ready support in the popular mind or among donors who do not have the time to carefully consider their giving.

'A third policy premise governs the work of the foundation. We are willing to support the 'core' funding of an agency (i.e. its central running costs) rather than concentrating on more temptingly glamorous specific projects which tend more easily to receive help from some foundations and many firms and companies.'

'A small organisation cannot responsibly give more than temporary employment if it has only a year's funding in hand, so in these circumstances a three-year grant is a godsend. The Foundation is therefore open to giving three year grants of up to £7,000 p.a. – or sometimes to making three year grants on a tapering basis'.

During 1990 the foundation had 135 three year grants running, compared with 51 in 1989.

Social Welfare (£2,871,760 nationally in 1990)

Social welfare covers an enormous field from major national appeals (often connected with an anniversary such as a centenary) by such bodies as Age Concern to a tenants' association in Hackney. This means that the foundation has to be particularly stringent in assessing priorities in the field of social welfare, looking at both the areas of need which a project is addressing, and the effectiveness of the work.'

Examples of social welfare grants given to London organisations in 1990: the Griffins Society, for its rehabilitation work with women ex-offenders (£17,500); the Shalom Justice and Peace Association in Newham to help a redundant church adapt its premises for multi-ethnic use (£29,000).

Medicine (£612,000 nationally in 1990)

'Medicine some years ago featured low on the list of donations but it will be of no surprise that matters have now changed. The foundation does not support much medical research. On the other hand, appeals for hospitals and their equipment are constantly with us. Another source of medical appeals to which the foundation on occasion responds is the associations concerned with a particular disease. Recently, however, in the field of medicine the foundation has started to emphasise primary health care, that is, the first line provision of health services, general practitioners, district nurses etc.'

Examples of grants given for medicine in London: The Royal Free Hospital School of Medicine to support alcohol related work (c£50,000), British Home & Hospital for Incurables to enable it to complete the modernisation of its home in Streatham (£25,000).

Education (£1,346,000 nationally)

Educational projects were the major beneficiaries of the foundation's increased donations in 1990 with 19.3% of grants being made in this category. The foundation is keen to support the work of adult or continuing education and has started to make sizeable grants to universities.

Examples of grants made to educational projects in London: the Foundation of Young Musicians to maintain the practice of music in the disbanded ILEA (£25,000); to the Department of Philosophy, King's College, London, for its outreach work (£25,000); the Institute of Community Studies to start a teaching programme on environmental issues in primary schools in Tower Hamlets (£15,000).

The Arts (£521,000 nationally in 1990)

Over half the grants in this category were awarded to organisations in London, with The National Portrait Gallery receiving a grant of £125,000 towards its ambitious programme of extension and refurbishment. Other grants to London organisations are as follows: The English National Opera for a new production of Wozzeck (£60,000) the Half Moon Young People's Theatre in Tower Hamlets towards converting and refurbishing a Victorian town hall (£25,000); Camden Arts Centre (£18,000); English Concert was awarded a grant towards its programme celebrating the bicentenary of Haydn's visit to Oxford (£15,000); the Almeida Theatre for its festival of contemporary music (£10,000).

Conservation (£479,000 nationally in 1990)

This was a category which would appear higher in the league table of donations if a number of environmental projects such as population concerns were not listed as international.

Conservation includes religious and secular buildings, environmental work and even the establishment of relevant museums.

No grants were made to organisations for specifically London projects.

Youth (£141,000 nationally in 1990)

'The Foundation feels that it does not have to give youth causes high priority, mainly because a number of major trusts and foundations concentrate in the field of youth work. Where youth work is supported it is mainly where it is connected with training and employment, or with special projects for young people at risk.'

During the year one of the grants awarded was to the London Youth Advisory Centre to extend their premises for work with young people throughout London (£20,000) .

Church and Religion (£18,000 nationally in 1990)

Very few donations are given for church renovations but grants are made annually to the Historic Churches Preservation Trust and the Council for the Care of Churches.

Applications Procedure: There is no application form and the foundation does not see applicants personally until after the receipt of written information. Guidelines for applicants are available from the correspondent.

Correspondent: Rosemary Hawkins, Secretary

Address: 8 Bishopsgate, London EC2N 4AE (071-280 1000)

The Belvedere Trust

Beneficial area: South London

Objects: To support housing and community projects in the voluntary sector

Type of beneficiary: Organisations

Income: £106,890 (1990/91)

Grant total: £98,660

Grant details: The trust makes grants within the following areas of priority:

Resources Development, Training and Consultancy: to support and stimulate work designed to increase resources and skills.

Housing Cooperatives: one-off grants for work that has not been supported by the Housing Corporation or other statutory organisations.

Furniture Projects: to sustain and expand the work of recycling and providing furniture for those in need.

Small Grants Programme: grants mainly in the range of £200 to £500 with a rare maximum of £1,000 to be given:

    to initiate a new piece of work

    to fund a one-off event

    to provide an extra facility

    to respond to an emergency or unexpected need

Homeless International: In recognition of the common concerns of the homeless and inadequately housed throughout the world, the trust reserves a small proportion of its grants budget for proposals submitted by Homeless International.

In 1990/91 the trust made 45 grants ranging between £100 and £8,700, and the average grant was £2,500. The most significant funding was given for salaries with the largest grants going to Lewisham Furniture Project (£8,700), Croydon Housing Aid Society, (£7,000) and Centre '70 Community Association (£7,000). A grant totalling £11,000 over three years was awarded to the South London Homelessness Project.

Correspondent: The Administrator

Address: 1st Floor, Rochester House, 2–10 Belvedere Road, London SE19 2HL (081-653 8833)

Benevolent Society for the Relief of the Aged and Infirm Poor

Beneficial area: London

Objects: Alleviation of the hardships of the aged and infirm poor.

Type of beneficiary: Individuals and organisations

Income: £6,500 (1991)

Grant total: £6,000

Grant details: Quarterly assistance and Christmas and Easter gifts to pensioners, and lump sum grants of up to £500. The society's committee has recently turned some of its resources to helping small charities actively engaged in projects and work for the benefit of the elderly, particularly in deprived areas of London.

Application procedure: In writing to the correspondent

Correspondent: TJ Berner, Honorary Secretary

Address: 107 Elborough Street, Southfields, London SW18 5DS

Other information: This charity was founded in 1761 and is now run by a committee whose chairman is the parish priest of St Mary Moorfields, Eldon Street, London EC2.

The Benn Charitable Foundation

Beneficial area: London

Main grant areas: Housing and accommodation for young people in need

Type of beneficiary: Organisations

Income: £7,700 (1989)

Grant total: £7,000

Grant details: Each year most of the trust's income is granted to St Christopher's Fellowship.

Applications procedure: In writing to the correspondent

Correspondent: Ann Hithersay, Secretary

Address: 53 Warwick Road, London SW5 9HD

Rowan Bentall Charitable Trust

Beneficial area: Southern England

Objects: General charitable purposes

Type of beneficiary: Organisations

Income: £35,900 (1990/91)

Grant total: £32,460

Grant details: The trust supports hospitals, churches, youth organisations, care of the elderly, the armed forces, education and preservation of the environment. Grants, both one-off and recurrent, are made for sums between £20 and £1,500.

Applications procedure: In writing to the correspondent in July and November. There is no application form.

Correspondent: L E Rowan Bentall

Address: President's Office, Bentalls plc, Anstee House, Wood Street, Kingston upon Thames, Surrey KT1 1TS (081-546 2002)

The Brixton Estate Charitable Trust

Beneficial area: National; in practice those areas where the company has a presence i.e. EC1–EC4; Kennington, Oval and Brixton (where the company was once located); West London

Objects: Any charitable purpose

Type of beneficiary: Organisations

Income: £41,000 (1988/89)

Grant total: £55,500

Grant details: Grants are given to registered charities, both to national charities and to smaller local organisations, but not to local branches of national organisations. Both one-off and recurrent grants are made, usually in the range of £300 to £700, exceptionally to £1,000. Charities working in most areas can apply, particularly those working with handicap and children. The trust does not sponsor the arts, and applications from groups working with homelessness and addiction are unlikely to be successful.

Applications procedure: In writing to the correspondent

Correspondent: Mr G Leversedge

Address: 22/24 Ely Place, London EC1N 6TQ (071-242 6898)

Other information: The last accounts on file at the Charity Commission are for 1988/89.

The trustees did not want this trust to be included in the guide.

Sir John Cass's Foundation

Beneficial area: The former Inner London Education Area. This covers the London Boroughs of Camden, Greenwich, Hackney, Hammersmith, Islington, Kensington and Chelsea, Lambeth, Lewisham, Southwark, Tower Hamlets, Wandsworth, Westminster and the City of London.

Objects: Educational grants (see below)

Type of beneficiary: Organisations and individuals

Income: £1,650,000 (1990/91)

Grant total: £887,000

Grant details: The work of the foundation falls under three main categories:

1. Support of the Sir John Cass Foundation schools, the City of London Polytechnic and Church of England voluntary schools as prioritised by the Diocesan Boards of Southwark and London. £240,000 was given in donations in 1990/91.

2. Support of organisations in Inner London involved in promoting education, including strategic projects concerned with the development of education and the enhancement of the school and college curricula. This category accounts for the largest part of the grants total.

Current priorities for the period 1992/95 include:

projects aimed at improving literacy, numeracy and English as a second language

projects promoting science education

strategic projects aimed at developing physical education within the curriculum

education and training work with young offenders

strategic innovations in the development of health education and nursery education at a policy-making level

arts enrichment programmes tied into a course of study

Grants may be considered for capital or revenue purposes not exceeding three years. The trustees do not consider applications from schools or institutions for which statutory provision should be available. This includes the provision of teachers' salaries, school books, equipment and payment of building works. Trustees prefer to encourage educational initiatives of an experimental or innovative nature which may offer a future model of 'good practice'. Such work would not normally be within the remit of the local authority. However, trustees also recognise that many sections of the community in Inner London are severely educationally disadvantaged and that 'complementary' or 'supplementary' education packages which may not in themselves be innovative are also extremely valuable additional services, providing they are developed by voluntary organisations.

In 1991/92 a total of £540,000 was awarded to organisations in this category. Major grants include £25,000 to the Nuffield Mathematics Project, which is developing a broad-based 'A' Level maths course to encourage a greater number of students to study maths at a higher level. A grant of £25,000 was also made to another 'strategic project', The Earth Science Process Centre at the Institute of Education. This resource enables hundreds of students and children in Inner London to observe complex physical processes including river formation, rainfall simulation, and soil erosion with the help of specialised apparatus. Smaller grants were awarded for supplementary education work with ethnic minority groups, artist-in-residence projects in schools and environmental work.

3. Educational grants for further and higher education, including limited support for post-graduate study. To be eligible applicants must be under the age of 25 and must have lived in the former Inner London Education Area for at least three years. As this foundation is for the benefit of young residents of Inner London the trust does not support those who are studying in London but whose permanent address is outside it. It is not sufficient to be living in London solely for the purposes of study. Priority is given to students on one year courses or about to complete a course. Students receiving mandatory awards will only be considered exceptionally and will need to demonstrate that they have applied first for loans and Access funds available to them. Limited support is available to students studying the performing arts, providing they can offer a significant contribution to their expenses. In 1990/91 181 grants totalling £107,000 were made to individuals.

The 1991 annual report states: 'Once again our help has assisted young people to follow a wide variety of courses – A-levels, BTEC, fashion and design, dance, drama, medicine, veterinary medicine, law, accountancy, business studies, computer science, nursery nursing, hairdressing, catering and furniture design'.

Applications procedure: An initial letter of application must be submitted to establish if the need or proposal falls within the foundation's policies. Applications for individuals and projects are considered in March, June, September and December (but applications are requested at least four weeks before).

Correspondent: The Clerk to the Governors

Address: 31 Jewry Street, London EC3N 2EY (071-480 5884)

Other information: See also the entries for Aldgate and Allhallows Barking Exhibition Foundation, Aldgate Freedom Foundation and Samuel Butler's Educational Foundation.

This is one of the largest educational foundations in the country. The surplus of income over expenditure was £400,000 in 1990/91. The annual report states, 'Our review of our scheme of Administration has been completed and application made to the Charity Commission for an amending scheme which will reduce the size of the Governing body, bringing in new expertise, redefine the area of benefit and give governors more flexibility in their grant giving.'

City Educational Trust Fund

Beneficial area: London

Objects: Grants to organisations only (no grants to individual students), through:

1. Assistance for the City University and educational activities connected with it;

2. The advancement of education generally by the promotion of research, study, teaching and training in various arts and science subjects.

Type of beneficiary: Organisations

Latest figures: 1991/92

Income: £164,800

Grant total: £150,000

Grant details: Grants ranging between £500 and £15,000 were made to a variety of educational groups and institutions including Alleyn's School (£7,500), Young Person's Concert Foundation (£5,000), and the Community Language Centre (£500).

Application procedure: To the correspondent

Correspondent: Mr Lee, Town Clerk's Department

Address: City of London Corporation, Guildhall, London EC2P 2EJ (071-260 1405)

Other information: This charity was originally known as the Coal Market Fund, and was established after the 1949 City of London Coal Market Acts in order to pay for costs incurred by this public market for the sale of coal. These Acts were repealed in 1967 and the charity was renamed.

City of London Police Children's Fund

Beneficial area: London

Objects: To raise money for the benefit of children and young persons

Type of beneficiary: Organisations and individuals

Income: £15,770 (in 1988/89 but variable because the bulk of the trust's income is raised through raffles, lotteries and parties)

Grant total: £1,840

Grant details: 8 donations ranging between £25 and £530. Beneficiaries included Clerkenwell Parochial School, St Mary's Primary School, St Bartholomew's Hospital , and the National Holiday Fund.

Application procedure: To the correspondent

Correspondent: Jon Meredith, The Secretary

Address: City of London Police HQ, 26 Old Jewry, London EC2R 8DJ (071-601 2707)

Other information: This entry was not confirmed by the trust.

The City Parochial Foundation

Beneficial area: The Metropolitan Police District of London and the City of London

Objects: Social welfare

Type of beneficiary: Organisations

Income: £5,931,708 (1991)

Grant total: £6,142,000

Background: The City Parochial Foundation was founded by The City of London Parochial Charities Act of 1883. This provided that the charitable funds for all but the five largest City of London parishes should be administered by a new corporate body,

the trustees of the London Parochial Charity. The members of the governing body are nominated by a variety of further bodies, including the City of London, the Church Commissioners, London University and the City and Guilds Foundation, and normally hold office for six years. They are trustees of three major funds. The City Church Fund is managed entirely for the benefit of the church commissioners, to whom all surpluses are transferred. The Central Fund, with which this entry is concerned, was endowed with all non ecclesiastical funds of the city parishes and this is now the source of income for general charitable purposes. The foundation has undertaken the administration of the Trust for London, which has a separate entry in this book.

Since 1935 the trustees have undertaken reviews of policy at five yearly intervals. In 1991 the foundation undertook a major review of its grant-making policies and developed a strategy for 1992 to 1996. With a significantly increased grant income, over £5 million p.a., and the prospective increase in the number of applications to the foundation, the trustees decided to establish a wider range of funding responses.

General: This foundation sets a standard of approachability and openness to potential applicants which is a model for other trusts. It is also committed to carrying out an annual monitoring of the geographical spread of the grants made to enable the trustees to keep under review the area distribution of its grants and secondly, to undertaking an annual monitoring of the ethnic minority organisations funded to enable the trustees to see the extent of its support to such organisations.

General Criteria for Grant-making:

all grants must benefit the poor inhabitants of London;

all applicants must know in practice they are developing services for all sections of the community;

grants made should have an impact on a particular need or problem;

applicants must show they can tackle the problem realistically;

wherever possible the users of services should be part of the designing, planning and delivery of services;

partnerships with other funders are very welcome, and applications involving joint funding are encouraged;

monitoring of work funded is important for both the beneficiary and the funder; the foundation will monitor grants made, and will require the cooperation of the beneficiaries.

Grant-making Strategy 1992-1996, Priorities for Funding:

There are four main elements in the strategy for 1992 to 1996:

Programme funding

Strategic funding

General funding

Funding of exceptional needs and interests

There will be a mid-term review in 1994 to assess how far the programmes have been on target.

Programme Funding: The trustees have highlighted three areas of concern for programme funding:

carers	(1992-1995)
mental health	(1993-96)
penal work	(1993–96)

A budget of approximately £500,000 a year for three years for each of the above fields will be set aside, for capital or revenue funding of projects submitted by registered charities. All the grants will be made in the first year of the three-year period. Revenue grants can be for three years and will vary when given over the three year period. They are likely to be in the range of £25,000 to £75,000 a year for three years. Capital grants are unlikely to exceed £75,000.

Proposals should relate to new work. Other needs within these areas may be better addressed by other parts of the foundation's funding strategy, described later.

The staff concerned with these three programmes are:

carers:	Timothy Cook
mental health:	Alison Harker
penal work:	Evelyn Oldfield

All grants made will be closely monitored, as will the whole programme; from time to time all beneficiaries will be required to meet to discuss lessons learned.

Strategic Funding: The foundation states in its latest document on grant-making policy and procedures, 'It is clear that some issues may be best looked at across London, and grant making practice developed accordingly. The trustees and staff may from time to time initiate across-London work.'

The foundation, together with the Trust for London (see entry further on), will be earmarking funds, and taking initiatives to help maintain and develop the necessary support services for voluntary organisations.

As part of this, applications are invited which focus upon:

1. 'Training opportunities for staff and committees, especially in new areas such as community care developments, or providing services under contract.

2. Implementation of equal opportunity policies. Many organisations do not find it easy to move from written equal opportunity policies to practical implementation, despite every good intention; as cuts are made in statutory services, it is vital that all voluntary sector services are open to everyone at all levels.

3. Support structures for refugee communities. These are often lacking not least because of the speed with which people from some communities have arrived and been dispersed throughout all the boroughs.

4. Proposals which aim to help a group of voluntary organisations come together to develop a more coherent strategy in one borough, or to meet a particular need of one client group across several boroughs.

5. Proposals to address London-wide issues concerning the poor of London.'

General Funding: The general funding programme will have three elements to it:

1. Major concerns

2. Sustaining organisations recently funded by the foundation

3. Small grants

Major Concerns: In its 'Grant-making Priorities and Procedures' the foundation states it 'will during at least the first three years of the quinquennium give high priority to work in the following areas:

1. Disability – where the emphasis would be on support for organisations managed or led by people who themselves have disabilities.

2. Education and training – of particular interest, though not of exclusive concern, are services tackling under-achievement, supplementary education, English as a second language especially for women, and access provision to post-school education and training.

3. Elderly and frail people living in the community.

4. Homelessness affecting both families and single people: street work, outreach work, and work with

14

homeless people with addictions, being of special interest.

5. Young people – within this area, priorities are restricted to schemes providing after-school care, holiday care, work with young people with special needs, and daycare for young children.

6. Welfare rights work with special emphasis on money advice and debt counselling.'

Sustaining Organisations Recently Funded by the Foundation: A major priority is to consider applications from some of the organisations recently grant-aided by the foundation. Further grants will not be given automatically, but staff will discuss with organisations what is required to continue the organisation's work.

Small Grants: A small grants programme is to be introduced, so that any charitable organisation can apply for grants of up to £10,000, which will normally be one-off grants. For these applications there will be an application form, available on request.

Exceptional Needs and Interests: The trustees will always be ready to consider exceptionally interesting proposals in any area of work helping the poor of London. A strong case would have to be made, amply supported by relevant experts in the field of concern. Any such applications should be submitted in the usual way.

Black and Ethnic Minority Organisations: The foundation wishes to encourage applications from charitable organisations working within and managed by the black and ethnic minority communities, and is particularly aware of the opportunities to assist Section XI initiatives.

Lesser Concerns: Areas of work which the foundation considers of less concern are only considered if there were insufficient take-up on its major schemes. It should be emphasized though that some projects within this category may well come within some of the grant-making strategies mentioned previously e.g. sustaining grants or small grants. Lesser concerns are:

arts, open spaces and recreation

community transport

youth and community centres

counselling

health

general advice

special needs housing

Exclusions: The following areas cannot be funded under any circumstances:

community business initiatives

medical research and equipment

individuals

fee paying schools

trips abroad

general holiday playschemes

one-off events

publications

sports

major capital appeals

the direct replacement of public funds

endowment appeals

Application procedures: The following guidelines generally apply to all funding schemes though the timetable and, in some respects, the application procedure for the Programme Funding scheme, are different and are listed further on.

The foundation will normally only consider applications from organisations which are registered charities, except where

1. the organisation is newly established and is still in the process of obtaining registration; in such a case the release of any grant for a second year will be conditional upon registration as a charity.

2. the applicant is exempt from registration.

3. the applicant is registered as a Friendly Society.

In very exceptional circumstances applications from statutory bodies may be considered.

There are no application forms, except for small grants. Prior to submitting a detailed application it is advisable to discuss the proposed application with one of the staff.

It is required that all applicants adopt the following basic format:

statement about the organisation: legal status, aims, brief history, staffing and management committee details, and current activities; reference to any previous grants from the foundation or Trust for London should be made.

detailed financial position of organisation listing main sources of income.

statement on the particular need for which funding is being sought.

full costing of the proposal.

details of other funding sources, especially applications to other trusts.

details of monitoring to be carried out on the scheme for which funding is being requested.

The above should be accompanied (where available) by a copy of the constitution (if a new applicant to the foundation) and:

most recent annual report

most recent audited accounts

budget for the current financial year

the job description, if application concerns a post

equal opportunities policy

list of names and addresses of office holders

The application should not exceed three sides of A4 paper, exclusive of necessary appendices.

Timetable: Apart from the three priority areas of special programme funding, all applications must be completed by:

31 January for April meeting

30 April for July meeting

15 August for October meeting

15 November for January meeting.

An application is only completed when all documentation has been received, staff have no further questions to raise, and where necessary a meeting has taken place between the applicant and a member of the foundation's staff.

Applications Procedure for Programme Funding: Registered charities only should apply (but see criteria for organisations applying, listed earlier on) and there are several stages in the procedure. The initial outline application should not exceed two typed sides of A4, with basic costings in an appendix. (See details on basic format of application form in previous pages). This should be accompanied by copies of the applicant's constitution, most recent annual report, audited accounts, the names and addresses of the management committee, and a statement from an independent referee on the need to be met and the capability of the organisation to address that need. The work proposed should be achievable within three years.

The deadline for submission of the draft applications are:

Carers	30 May 1992
Mental Health	30 April 1993
Penal Work	30 April 1993

These outline applications will then be considered by the advisory committee within each particular programme. When the foundation is considering funding an organisation, a discussion is arranged between the applicant and members of the foundation. Please note that applicants are not necessarily asked to proceed to the next stage.

Discussions are to be completed by:

Carers	30 July 1992
Mental Health	30 July 1993
Penal Work	30 July 1993

Applicants proceeding to the second round will be asked to submit a revised and final application showing clearly the analysis of the need being addressed, the proposed means to address that need, the time-table and targets to be achieved, the likely impact of the project, the lessons that might be learned and the monitoring that will be undertaken.

The deadline for receiving final submissions are:

Carers	30 August 1992
Mental Health	30 August 1993
Penal Work	30 August 1993

The advisory committees will meet in October and through the Clerk give advice to the foundation's Grant Committee. The foundation's decisions will be known to all applicants by 30 October 1992 and 1993.

Correspondent: Timothy Cook, Clerk

Address: 6 Middle Street, London EC1A 7PH (071-606 6145)

Isaac Davis Trust

Beneficial area: London

Objects: Benefit of Jewish charities or members of the Jewish faith

Type of beneficiary: Individuals and organisations

Income: c£11,000 per annum

Grant details: Most of the income is given in grants to organisations, but around £2,000 is given to individuals.

Correspondent: Miss E Cashdan, The Secretary

Address: United Synagogue Trusts Ltd, Upper Woburn Place, London WC1H OEP (071-387 4300)

Delmar Charitable Trust

Beneficial area: London

Objects: General charitable purposes

Type of beneficiary: Organisations

Income: £25,200 (1987)

Grant total: £8,300

Grant details: Organisations which have been assisted in the past have been involved in medical treatment, mental or physical rehabilitation, social welfare, children and young people. In 1987 56 grants were made and the most common size of donation was £130.

Applications procedure: In writing to the correspondent. Grants are usually allocated in October to November.

Correspondent: Miss M L Knott, Secretary

Address: 9 Bridle Close, Surbiton Road, Kingston-upon-Thames KT1 2JW

Other information: Latest accounts on file at the Charity Commission are for 1987.

The Drapers' Charitable Fund

Beneficial area: Unrestricted, but see below

Type of beneficiary: London charities; also national charities, disaster and emergency appeals, and textile related charities

Latest figures: 1990/91

Grant total: £543,229, only partly in London.

Grant details: The Drapers' Charitable Fund was established in 1959 for general charitable purposes. It should not be confused with the Company's other hundred or so charities of varying sizes, many originating in the sixteenth and seventeenth centuries. The Drapers' Consolidated Charity, with the Company's Charities General for the Poor, and Sir William Boreman's Foundation have their own entries in this book. The Drapers' Company Educational and Charitable Trust is described in the companion book, *The Educational Grants Directory*.

Consideration of applications from London charities is restricted to those where the area of benefit includes the City of London.

Grants in 1990/91 to London charities included those to: St Paul's Cathedral Choir School (£3,000); London Federation of Boys' Clubs (£1,000); City of London School (£750); City and Guilds of London Art School (£10,000); Royal Hospital and Home, Putney (£5,000); London Enterprise Agency (£1,400); City of Guilds London Institute (£250); Kingston Grammar School (£250); Imperial War Museum (£500); St Bartholomew's Hospital (£1,000); Westminster Abbey Trust (£1,000); Wimbledon Guild (£1,000); Hackney and City of London Victim Support Scheme (£500); Royal Marsden Cancer Appeal (£2,500); Westminster Cathedral (£500) and Toynbee Hall (£4,000).

Applications procedure: In writing to the Secretary

Correspondent: G C Watts, Secretary

Address: Drapers Hall, Throgmorton Street, London EC2N 2DQ (071-588 5001)

The Fishmongers' Company's Charitable Trust

Beneficial area: National, with a special interest in the City of London

Objects: The relief of hardship and disability through national bodies; education; the environment; fishery related charities and City of London charities.

Type of Beneficiary: Organisations

Grant total: £250,000 (1991)

Grant details: Approximately £250,000 is available by way of annual donations though it is not known what proportion of these grants are made to organisations in the London area. Grants and donations are normally made on a once-only basis and do not exceed £10,000 for general charitable purposes. Preference is given to charities seeking to raise funds for a specific project or for research but most of the Company's £1,000,000 a year income is needed to fund existing scholarships and to fund work at the Company's own almshouses.

Applications procedure: To the correspondent. Meetings take place three times a year in March, June and October.

Correspondent: M R T O'Brien, Clerk

Address: The Fishmongers' Company, Fishmongers' Hall, London Bridge, London EC4R 9EL (071-626 3531)

French Protestant Church of London Charities

Beneficial area: Unrestricted

Objects: Educational grants, with priority for those

connected with the French Protestant Church.

Type of beneficiary: Primarily individuals, sometimes organisations

Income: c£160,000 (1991)

Grant total: c£140,000

Grant details: The French Protestant Church of London and the charities connected with it derive from the arrival of the emigrés from France in the reign of King Edward VI, though the present church, in Soho Square, was built only in 1893. Many of the books in the library, including the unique collection of manuscripts and records, date from the earliest Huguenot days. In 1747 the first French Protestant School was founded. This continued until 1944 when the vast majority of pupils, having been evacuated during the war, failed to return to Soho. The money was subsequently used for educational bursaries, under a new charity commission scheme. Financial assistance is currently available in the following categories:

1. Grants or bursaries, for fee-paying establishments, for the education of children of members of the Church.

2. Grants or bursaries for French Protestant children attending the Lycee Francais in South Kensington.

3. Special allowances (from a limited fund) for those under 25 years of age of proven French Protestant descent to assist with educational expenses.

4. Bursaries at schools of the Girls' Public Day School Trust.

5. Bursaries at schools of the Church Schools Company Limited.

6. Bursaries at a selected number of independent day schools for boys.

7. Bursaries at schools of the Choir Schools Association.

8. An annual scholarship for Huguenot research.

9. Project grants for those under 25 years of age for help with individual projects.

In all cases awards can only be to those under the age of 25, with priority being given to persons who or whose parents are members of the French Protestant Church and those of French Protestant descent.

Applications procedure: Categories 1 and 2 – to the Secretary of the Consistory, FPCL, 8–9 Soho Square, London W1V 5DD

Categories 3 and 9 – to the correspondent.

Category 8 – to the Institute of Historical Research, The Senate House, London WC1E 7HU

Other categories – to the Head Teacher of the school concerned

Correspondent: John L Gatenby

Address: 35 Great Peter St, Westminster, London SW1P 3LR (071-222 7811)

The Gauntlet Trust

Beneficial area: London and surrounding area

Objects: General charitable purposes

Type of beneficiary: individuals, organisations

Grant total: £32,000 (1989/90)

Grant details: There are modest annuities for necessitous persons and grants to organisations for education, research, youth and general charitable purposes. Sixty-two grants were made during the year, the majority being very small. The largest grants were £8,000 to Undergraduates with Industry, £4,000 to the Sheffield Company and Apprentices Scheme and £3,000 to the Sail Training Association.

Correspondent: Robert Cowe

Address: 81 Coleman Street, London EC2R 5BJ (071-606 1199)

Other information: The trust was established under a settlement laid down by the Worshipful Company of Armourers and Brasiers and has assets of over £0.5 million.

Godson's Charity

See entry in the Greenwich section.

The Goldsmiths' Company's Charities, including the John Perryn Charity, the Goldsmiths' Charitable Donations Fund, Goldsmiths' General Charity, and the Goldsmiths' Arts Trust Fund.

Beneficial area: National, with a special interest in the Greater London area.

Objects: General charities, education, support of the craft of silversmithing and jewellery.

Type of beneficiary: Organisations

Income: About 1.9 million (1990)

Grant total: £985,600 only part of which is to London charities.

Grant details: In 1990 the Goldsmiths' Company's Charities had a combined income of about £1.9 million. 'The Company's grant making policy embraces general charities, education and support of the craft of silversmithing and jewellery. Within the general charities sector, the emphasis is on London-orientated charities and the disadvantaged in society'.

In 1990 John Perryn's Charity had an income of £643,800 and made £395,000 of grants (excluding a donation of £66,000 to the Goldsmiths Art Trust Fund). Many grants were made to London organisations, the largest being £100,000 to Goldsmiths' College. Most grants ranged between £1,000 and £5,000.

Most of the Goldsmiths' Arts Trust Fund is spent on mounting exhibitions but in 1990 it made donations to the Goldsmiths' Craft Council (£15,000) and the Royal College of Art (£4,000).

The Goldsmiths' General Charity made £533,163 of grants in 1990 and most of these ranged between £1,000 and £5,000. The largest grants were made to the St Christopher's Hospice (£65,000), the Courtauld Institute of Art (£20,000) and the National Hospital for Nervous Diseases (£20,000).

£195,690 of grants were made by the Goldsmiths' Charitable Donations Fund and most grants ranged between £1,000 and £5,000.

Any local charity can be considered. For local branches of national organisations to be considered, the application must come through the central governing body, and in some cases applications will be restricted to the leading charity in the field.

Appeals for expeditions must be made through the Royal Geographical Society and are applicable to London Colleges and establishments of further education.

Charities with extensive public appeal already, such as TV appeals, Easter appeals, etc. are unlikely to receive support. Furthermore, the company is unlikely to entertain applications for grants towards endowment funds.

Applications procedure: In writing to the clerk, including in the application:

Registered charity number

Latest annual report and full audited accounts

Name of two independent referees (initial application only)

Object of appeal

Appeal target and amount needed to meet it

Major grant-making organisations approached and results to date

Preference for a single grant or for annual grants for up to three years

No organisation, whether successful or not, will have more than one appeal considered every three years.

Note that applications for the relief of individual need must be made via social services or other intermediary body.

Correspondent: The Clerk

Address: The Goldsmiths' Company, Goldsmiths' Hall, Foster Lane, Cheapside, London EC2V 6BN (071-606 7010)

The Hale Trust

Beneficial area: Greater London, Surrey, Sussex and Kent

Objects: Advancement of education and the improvement of life of deprived or handicapped young people under 25 years old.

Type of beneficiary: Individuals and organisations

Grant total: £33,100 (1989/90)

Grant details: Grants to individuals constituted £8,100 of the grant total and consisted of nine grants for educational purposes of £900 each. The grants may sometimes be recurrent but cannot be made for more than three years.

Organisations working on behalf of deprived or handicapped individuals area are also assisted; grants are made to local groups and projects, not to national organisations. In 1989/90 thirty-eight grants were made and ranged between £40 and £3,700.

Applications procedure: After an initial enquiry, application forms will be forwarded to the applicant if he/she appears to qualify and if funds are available. The trustees usually meet in February, July and November, and in most cases meet applicants before grant decisions are taken.

Correspondent: Mrs J M Broughton, Secretary to the Trustees

Address: Rosemary House, Woodhurst Park, Oxstead, Surrey RH8 9HA

Edward Harvist Charity

Beneficial area: London Boroughs of Westminster, Barnet, Brent, Camden and Harrow

Objects: General charitable purposes

Other information: This charity's considerable investment and rental income is connected with the land on and beside which the Edgware Road was built. The charity is now administered by Harrow Council, and the income distributed to the five London boroughs in direct proportion to the amount of the road that passes through their area. (See separate entries in the boroughs' sections.)

Haslemere Estates Charitable Trust

Beneficial area: Central London

Objects: Welfare of children

Type of beneficiary: Organisations

Latest figures: 1987

Grant total: £30,700

Grant details: The correspondent told us that the stated aim of this trust is to assist organisations involved in the welfare of children in central London. No further information is available. Haslemere Estates plc engages in property development.

Applications procedure: In writing to the correspondent. Applications may take 3–6 months to process.

Correspondent: Miss Helen Bostock

Address: Haslemere Estates plc, 4 Carlos Place, Mayfair, London W1Y 5AE (071-629 1105)

Other information: The grant figure above refers to the company's total giving in 1987. This trust's most recent accounts on file at the Charity Commission date from 1976.

Haymills Charitable Trust (formerly known as The Dudley Cox Charitable Trust)

Beneficial area: National, but particularly Ealing, London, East Anglia and the West Country

Objects: General charitable purposes, grants for the benefit of present and past employees of the Haymills Group of Companies

Type of beneficiary: Individuals, organisations

Income: £48,160 (1990/91)

Grant total: £40,430

Grant details: Four grants were made to pensioners (former employees at Haymills Group of Companies). Grants were awarded to youth and welfare organisations, educational establishments, medical bodies and hospitals. In the past organisations funded in and around London included: Central Middlesex Hospital League of Friends (£5,400), Mount Vernon Hospital Appeal (£1,000), and the Middlesex Association of Boys' Clubs (£1,500)

Correspondent: I W Ferres, Secretary to the Trustees

Address: Empire House, Hanger Green, London W5 3BD (081-997 5602)

Help a London Child Appeal Fund

Beneficial area: Greater London and the Home Counties

Objects: Children

Type of beneficiary: Organisations and individuals

Grant total: £700,000 (1990/91)

Grant details: Help a London Child (HALC) was started in 1975 by Capital Radio as a fundraising appeal to help disadvantaged and underprivileged children in London. Most of the fundraising traditionally takes place over the Easter weekend. In 1991 20 hours of the station's broadcasting time was devoted to an on-air auction, record pledges and other activities.

Many listeners organise their own fund-raising attempts on behalf of the appeal. All the money raised is immediately paid into the HALC Fund, and the trustees aim to pay it out as soon as possible. Most of the administration costs are paid for by Capital Radio.

HALC may only distribute money to registered charities. However, any organisation or individual may apply but must nominate a charity willing to accept the money on their behalf should they be successful.

Projects must be for the benefit of children and young people under the age of 18.

The children benefiting from the grant should live in Greater London, or in the Home Counties (ie the Capital Radio listening area). HALC considers requests for the support of holidays outside London (but not abroad) or for residential homes where the children's parents live in London.

The trust looks favourably on self-help organisations and applications showing a commitment to creating their own fundraising opportunities.

It will consider requests for help with salaries on the understanding that any grant given will be for one year only.

In 1991 several families were helped directly and children's organisations were equipped with minibuses and transport. Groups organising holidays, and outings were supported as well as toy libraries and playgroups. HALC has become concerned at homelessness amongst young people and in 1991 this area of concern received the largest percentage of HALC's funding. The average grant in 1991/2 was £2,000.

Applications procedure: Application forms are available from 1 January from the administrator upon receipt of a 9" x 4" stamped addressed envelope. Would-be beneficiaries should send in their applications by the beginning of May and HALC's Allocations Meeting takes place at the beginning of July. Applicants are informed in early August whether or not they have been successful.

Correspondent: Tamsin Wheeler, Administrator

Address: c/o Capital Radio PLC, Euston Tower, London NW1 3DR (071-608 6203)

Heritage of London Trust Ltd

Beneficial area: London

Objects: The promotion of architectural conservation

Type of beneficiary: Organisations

Grant total: £102,700 (1989/90)

Grant details: The trust has been active since 1981 in promoting architectural conservation. With the demise of the GLC the trust lost its main public sector support, which has been partly replaced by assistance from LBGS. It receives technical help from English Heritage.

The trust's policy is to try to obtain partners to match the funding it provides, thereby bringing together the resources of both the public and private sectors. Grants, which range from £250 to a maximum of about £13,000, are made to conserve listed buildings of interest to the public. About half the grants are made to churches. In 1989/90 Cabmen's Shelters (£13,400), the Dulwich Picture Gallery, (£10,000), the Sick Children's Trust (£7,500) and

Mitcham Parish Church (£6,100) were among the groups supported.

Applications procedure: The initial approach should be made by letter after which a site visit may be made. Board meetings are held three times a year.

Correspondents: Sir John Lambert, Director, and Mrs D Beattie, Honorary Treasurer

Address: 2nd Floor, Chesham House, 30 Warwick Street, London W1R 6AB (071-973 3809)

John Hobby Charity

Beneficial area: London

Type of beneficiary: Welfare organisations

Income: £5,000 (1987/88)

Grant details: The charity is administered alongside the Clothworkers' Foundation, a national grantmaking trust, and an application to one may be considered as an application to both.

Correspondent: C M Mowll

Address: The Clothworkers' Company, Clothworkers Hall, Dunster Court, Mincing Lane, London EC3R 7AH (071-623 7041)

The Antony Hornby Charitable Trust

Beneficial area: Primarily London

Objects: General charitable purposes

Type of beneficiary: Organisations

Income: £38,400 (1990/91)

Grant total: £37,400

Grant details: About 100 grants are made each year to organisations, both national and specific to London, with an emphasis on handicap and disability, medical research and the arts. Some recurrent grants are made but most are one-off and in the region of about £100-£200.

Applications procedure: In writing to the correspondent, preferably enclosing a sae. The trust has stated that it is fully committed and does not normally add new names to its lists unless it is a charity known to the trustees or a very special appeal.

Correspondent: Miss June King, ref. RAH/JK

Address: Messrs Cazenove & Co, 12 Tokenhouse Yard, London EC2R 7AN

The King's Fund (King Edward's Hospital Fund for London)

Beneficial area: Mainly London

Objects: Health care

Type of beneficiary: Organisations

Grant total: £2,530,657 (1990)

Background: The fund was founded in 1897 and was one of a number of ventures begun that year to commemorate Queen Victoria's Diamond Jubilee. A capital sum was built up and the interest from it formed a permanent endowment.

Although set up initially to make grants to hospitals, which it continues to do, the fund's brief has allowed it to widen and diversify its activities as circumstances have changed over the years since its foundation. Today it supports research and development in all aspects of health care and management, except clinical; publishes books and reports, some stemming from work supported by the fund, provides education for management and health care at its College; and provides facilities for research and discussion at its Centre.

Grant-making ranges from sums of a few hundred pounds to major schemes costing more than £1 million, such as the Jubilee Project which was the fund's commemoration of the Silver Jubilee of Queen Elizabeth II. That project helped ten London hospitals to renovate some of their oldest wards. The problems of health care in the inner city areas are the concern of the London Primary Health Care Group (formerly called The London Programme), for which, to date, some £1,415,000 has been made available. Another new venture concerns the assessment and assurance of quality in health care.

The King's Fund College was established in 1968. Its aim is to raise management standards in the health care field through seminars, courses and field-based consultancy.

The King's Fund Institute was established at the beginning of 1986. The primary aim of the Institute is to contribute to improving the quality of public debate about health policy through the production of impartial analyses.

Policy: While the London hospitals, which the fund was founded to support, remain the focus of the fund's concern, this also includes the wider spectrum of care for the sick and handicapped in London, and the prevention of ill health.

The amount available for grants each year is entrusted to the following grant-making bodies, each with its own remit.

Grants Committee promotes the better delivery of health care in and for Greater London though projects of national relevance may occasionally be considered. This committee currently distributes about £1,000,000 a year, or just under half the total amount of the fund's grant-making.

In 1990, with the impending changes in the organisation of the NHS, the Grants Committee supported schemes to encourage the early development of the community care proposals contained in the government's white paper, 'Caring for People'. It awarded several of its largest grants to this end. The Spinal Injuries' Association and Thames Polytechnic received £69,300 to demonstrate the feasibility of an on-call personal support and user-directed case management service. The University of Bristol, Norah Fry Research Centre was awarded £70,300 to explore the feasibility of a service brokerage system and the University of Kent at Canterbury received £61,300 to develop quality indicators for use by purchasers in contracts/service agreements in residential services. Gloucester Social Services received £70,000 to develop a case management service which is sensitive to the needs of the black and ethnic minority communities in Gloucester, and the South West Thames Regional Health Authority received £35,000 to develop a management simulation of the implementation of the Community Care Act.

The Fund continued its support of organisations assisting homeless people, particularly in London. Nine grants totalling £350,000 were made; the two largest grants in this category went to the London Homelessness Forum (£78,000) to provide a coordinator for local organisations working with homeless families, and to the Thames Regional Health Authorities (£69,500) to set up a strategic team to develop work on health and homelessness throughout the four Thames regions. Other major grants were awarded to Blackliners' Helpline (£20,000) for a housing support manager; the Hampden Community Association (£25,200) for outreach work and services for homeless families on Sundays; to the London Connection (£46,000) to increase the range of services for young homeless people in central London; to the South East London Consortium (£48,000) to coordinate health and homeless activity between statutory and voluntary agencies; and to the Thomas Coram Homeless Children's Project (£33,700) to help girls from homeless families whose first language is not English.

Other grants of £20,000 and over went to the Community Hygiene Concern for a 'bug busting' project to eradicate head lice in school children in

West London; to the Forbes Trust towards the setting up of a London centre of a charities evaluation service providing support for the voluntary sector on evaluation; to the Foundation for AIDS Counselling, Treatment and Support for a health coordination centre; to Haringey Social Services to establish a multi-ethnic helpline for sufferers from mental illness; to Holloway Neighbourhood Group towards a centre for people with stress/mental illness problems; to the London Acute Services Initiative of the King's Fund, to establish a London Health Monitor to process data about health issues of topical interests, (£85,000); to MIND in Camden for a project which makes mental health services more accessible to people from black and ethnic minorities; to the Somali Counselling Project for their counselling work with Somali refugees. Almost half of the 64 grants made were for under £20,000; a few went to the NHS and over half to voluntary organisations.

Centre Committee encourages innovation and the dissemination of new ideas to help improve health care, with health care defined broadly to include voluntary agencies, carers and clients themselves. Unlike the Grants Committee, the Centre Committee may support an innovative project of sufficient merit wherever it is based, although ultimate relevance to London is still an important criterion.

Its grants are, however, restricted to the fields where the Centre is concentrating its own health services development activities. Each year the Centre Committee sets one or two priority issues where work in the field can strengthen the activities of the Centre. It then seeks to identify and support projects in these areas. In 1990 priority areas included services that are sensitive to the preferences of people with physical and sensory disabilities, services for black and ethnic minorities, and work with carers.

In 1990 the Centre Committee made ten major grants of £7,000 or more. The two largest grants went to the Yorkshire Regional Health Authority (£54,600) towards the appointment of a carers' development officer and to the National Black Mental Health Association (£35,000) towards the appointment of two staff and a small budget for running costs. Grants of £25,000 were made to The Central Manchester Health Authority and the Coventry Health Authority to improve services for black and ethnic minorities through the contracting process. Four grants of £20,000 each were made to the Northallerton Health Authority, Redbridge Practice Locality Team and Wirral Practice Team so that each could fund a development worker and

Wycombe Practice Team received its grant to set up a consumers' group. Smaller grants of £15,000 and £7,000 respectively were made to the British Council for Organisations of Disabled People: disability image/ethical image group and for Clinical Bursaries to enable four delegates to attend a course in the US. 26 grants of £1,000 or under were made to diverse groups such as Behavioural Phenotypes Study Group and Kent Learning Centre for the Disabled.

Small grants, decisions on which can often be taken within a matter of a week or two, cover a number of organisations and individuals. In this, as in the rest of the fund's work, there is a welcome and unusual emphasis on encouraging the dissemination of research results or of good practice following research. For further information, and for details of priority issues, contact Christine Davies, Grants Officer (081-341 0604).

The London Primary Health Care Group (formerly called The London Programme) promotes primary health care in the inner city, with particular attention to disadvantaged groups. Grants are made in close conjunction with development work on primary care, including co-ordination of primary and other health services. As well as considering applications for grants, this programme commissions work to meet specific needs that it has already identified.

In 1990 four grants were made totalling £103,200. The largest grants were awarded to the Croydon Community and Continuing Care Unit (£50,000) to promote work on integrating general practice and community health services on a neighbourhood basis and to the Riverside Department of Public Health (£34,900) to improve health care for homeless users of the accident and emergency services at Charing Cross Hospital. The Primary Care Development and Audit was awarded a grant of £17,400 towards its work on the ways in which professional audit in general practice can be linked to other quality assurance activities in primary care. The Catholic Institute for International Relations received a grant of £1,000 as a contribution to the running costs of an international conference for UK and third world health workers. The Project Director of the Programme is Pat Gordon from whom more information is available (071-267 6111 ext. 201).

Educational and Bursary Grants: The fund has several schemes under this broad heading including:

Medical Travelling Fellowships for London based Registrars, Senior Registrars and (on occasion)

registrars and consultants wishing to work at overseas centres. The amounts of money available for them are quite small. Enquiries should be made to Katherine Melia (071-727 0582).

Educational Bursaries (non clinical) are for nurses and others wishing to develop and broaden their careers for a course leading to a recognised qualification, for example in education or in rehabilitation studies. Priority is given to those working in Greater London. Enquiries should be made to Christine Davies, Grants Office (081-341 0604).

The NHS travelling fellowship scheme is provided in conjunction with the NHSTA where managers within the service are encouraged to broaden their management horizons through a specific project or series of visits. Enquiries should be made to John Smith, Bursar, King's Fund College (071-727 0581 ext 2131).

Management Committee: In addition to the main methods of grant-making, described above, the management committee will itself consider innovative proposals, aimed at raising the quality of health care, that do not fit into any of the schemes described above.

The committee's grants in 1990 totalled £896,100 in 45 separate donations. The King's Fund/Milbank Initiative received the largest grant of £200,000 for a joint health policy review on the future of acute hospitals. The Informal Caring Support Unit received £54,800 towards the running costs of the unit and four donations of £50,000 were also made; the Royal College of Physicians was funded for the cost of a senior lecturer in medical audit, to work particularly in the field of outpatient audit; SANE received support towards the cost of launching a new schizophrenia helpline service to be run by volunteers; St Bartholomew's and The London Hospital were funded towards the cost of a lecturer's post to organise community placements for medical and dental students; National Action on Incontinence received funding towards the cost of launching this first self-support association for people who are incontinent and those who care for them. As well as substantial grants, 30 donations were made for £20,000 and under. Many of these were given towards producing publications and mounting conferences and workshops.

General: The Fund states 'unfortunately we have to refuse many good applications simply because money is limited. In deciding what to support we shall be trying to assess the following:

Does the project have clear and realistic objectives that have been well-thought out?

Is the applicant likely to achieve them?

Does the proposal meet the purposes for which the fund exists?

How well has the financial strategy, for both the long and the short term, been planned?

If the project is successful, how strong an impact will it have?

How effectively could progress be monitored, and (where appropriate) evaluated?

Could any lessons from the projects be made more widely available?'

The details of the grants made suggest a preference by the fund for individual projects which can generate new knowledge or practice in the field concerned. Nevertheless a small number of grants have been made to enable organisations to continue or develop existing work.

Applications Procedure: The initial approach should normally be made to the person responsible for the committee or programme most appropriate to the proposed project. In cases of doubt help should be sought from Helena Whittaker, Grants Administrator (071-727 0581 ext 2202).

'Written applications should not be more than four pages of A4, including the purpose, scope and cost of the scheme, and whatever funding is available or being sought. It is not worth preparing a lengthy submission without previous consultation with an appropriate person at the King's Fund'.

'In general, the fund will not support:

Medical Research (on the ground that others are better equipped to undertake this).

General appeals or applications from large, well-established national charities.

Items that should, in our judgment, form a routine part of mainstream service provision (medical equipment and maintenance usually fall under this exclusion); long term core funding of any service or institution; vehicles and other transport needs; large capital building projects; holidays and outings.'

Correspondent: Helena Whittaker, Grants Administrator

Address: 14 Palace Court, London W2 4HT (071-727 0581)

Lloyds Charities Trust

Beneficial area: National

Objects: Social welfare, health, education

Type of beneficiary: Organisations

Grant total: £561,150 in 1990, only partly in London

Grant details: This large trust is an arm of Lloyds Insurance rather than of Lloyds Bank. A high proportion of its grants are awarded to national organisations, mostly to the better known and well-established. There are, however, a relatively small number of grants which can be identified with a particular locality and these are concentrated strongly in London, which no doubt reflects the home base of the trust in the City. The great majority of these grants is in the range of £500 to £1,000.

Examples in 1990 were: Alone in London Service (£500), British Home and Hospital for Incurables, Streatham (£1,000), Camden Training Centre (£250), Centrepoint, Soho (£500), City of London Sinfonia (£1,000), Dulwich Picture Gallery (£250), Greater London Fund for the Blind (£250), Inner City Renewal Trust, Spitalfields (£500), Intake, Kings Cross (£500), London Association for the Blind (£500), Royal London Society for the Blind (£3,000) and Wimbledon Guild (£250).

Correspondent: M J Crick

Address: Lloyds of London, Lime Street, London EC3 (071-623 7100)

London Aged Christian Society

Beneficial area: London

Objects: Relief of the Christian poor over 55 years old

Type of beneficiary: Organisations and charities

Latest figures: 1990/91

Income: £4,880 (1990/91)

Grant total: £4,000

Grant details: One-off grants can be paid to Christian organisations or charities. Donations were provided to help with the costs of heating, refurbishing old people's homes, outings etc.

Applications procedure: To the secretary through Christian organisations or charities.

Correspondent: The Secretary

Address: 16 Vine Hill, Clerkenwell Road, London EC1R 5EA

The London Taxi Drivers' Fund for Underprivileged Children

Beneficial area: Greater London

Objects: To relieve children underprivileged by reason of health, mental or physical handicap, poverty or lack of parental care

Type of beneficiary: Organisations

Grant total: £55,400 (1990)

Grant details: Grants are made principally to organisations, on the whole to hospitals, special homes and schools for physically and mentally handicapped children. Grants have paid for or contributed towards the cost of medical equipment (infant ventilator machine, cardiotacograph, ultracentrafuge, kidney machine, orthokinetic chairs), equipment for playgrounds and the learning environment, including tapes, projector, musical instruments and toys.

The charity prefers to make grants which will benefit more than one child, but occasionally small grants can be made to individuals for such items as clothing.

Applications procedure: In writing to the correspondent giving full details. Applications are considered once a month.

Correspondent: M Shaffron

Address: 6 Langdon Drive, Kingsbury, London NW9 8NR (081-205 6408)

Other information: This fund-raising charity was founded in 1928; as well as making grants it organizes the annual Southend Outing for over 500 children, the Mad Hatter's Christmas Party at the Grosvenor House Hotel, and a number of other trips and outings.

Lucas Diesel Systems Employees' Benevolent Fund for Handicapped Children

Beneficial area: West London

Objects: Welfare of mentally handicapped children

Type of beneficiary: Organisations

Latest figures: 1983

Income: £5,000

Grant total: £3,500

Grant details: Grants are made to schools and

groups for handicapped children in West London (principally the Acton and Ealing areas) for specialized equipment.

Applications procedure: To the correspondent. The grants committee can arrange to visit the organisation concerned.

Correspondent: Alan Togood, Personnel Manager and Trustee

Address: Lucas Diesel Systems, Larden Road, Acton, London W3 7RP (081-743 3111 ext 2400)

Other information: This entry was not confirmed by the trust and more up-to-date information would be welcomed.

The Marr-Munning Trust

Beneficial area: Unrestricted, but with a special interest in West London

Objects: General charitable grants

Type of beneficiary: Organisations

Income: £262,130 (1991)

Grant total: £44,860

Grant details: Most grants awarded in Britain are for the London areas of Ealing, Acton, Hounslow and Sudbury and some grants are recurring. The main work of the trust is in the field of overseas aid.

Applications procedure: The trust states that all its funds are fully committed to existing projects and that it can neither consider nor reply to unsolicited applications.

Correspondent: Miss J Honor, MBE, Trustee

Address: Harcourt Lodge, 9 Madeley Road, Ealing, London W5 2LA (081-998 9593)

The Violet Melchett Children's Fund

Beneficial area: The former GLC area

Main grant areas: Welfare of poor mothers and young children

Type of beneficiary: Organisations

Income: £38,970 (1989/90)

Grant total: £25,850

Grant details: At present all grants are given as a result of approaches made by the trust itself to projects being undertaken by national charities within the London area. Beneficiaries in 1989 to 1990 included CPAG, Gingerbread, Baby Life Support Systems (BLISS), the Handicapped Adventure Playground Association (HAPA) and the Ashburnham Playgroup.

Applications procedure: Charities, groups and organisations considering applying are advised that there is little chance that additional grants will be made for the time being.

Correspondent: P R H Mond

Address: 14 Falkland Road, London NW5 2PT

The Metropolitan Drinking Fountain and Cattle Trough Association

Beneficial area: UK and overseas

Objects: To promote the provision of pure drinking water for people and animals

Type of beneficiary: Organisations

Income: £25,420 (1990)

Grant total: £17,460

Grant details: Founded last century, the Association has to date provided over 8,000 drinking fountains, cattle troughs and water wells. In 1990, 32 associations, the majority within London and many of them schools, were provided with new drinking fountains. Although the Association does not undertake maintenance work, it is happy to advise and sometimes assist restoration of older fountains.

Applications procedure: To the correspondent

Correspondent: D R W Randall, Secretary and Treasurer

Address: 105 Wansunt Road, Bexley, Kent, DA5 2DN (0322 528062)

Other information: The association has also undertaken work overseas, and provided for the supply of drinking water in villages in the Third World.

Metropolitan Hospital-Sunday Fund

Beneficial area: London

Objects: Hospitals, residential homes, and medical charities caring for sick or disabled Londoners

Type of beneficiary: Organisations caring for the sick and disabled

Grant total: £438,700 (1990)

Grant details: In 1872 Church leaders of various

denominations met to decide how to raise funds to pay for the medical treatment of Londoners. They decided that collections should be made in places of worship of all denominations on one nominated day each year to be called Hospital-Sunday. This practice still continues and in 1990 the fund received £19,130 from collections made in some 300 places of worship. The charity also raises money through collections by voluntary helpers (£2,390), from individual donations and Deeds of Covenant (£8,640), from hospitals and homes (£5,370) and from schools (£135). Now, however, the bulk of the charity's income (about £477,620 in 1990) comes from dividends and interest on its investments.

The fund has four main grant making programmes. The first of these is support for hospital, homes, and medical organisations which are all registered charities and outside the NHS. As the fund explains, such institutions need help to 'enable them to augment the care and facilities required for their patients and residents. Some can only provide additional facilities or maintain and improve their services with our help as the fees charged usually only meet the cost of patients' treatment. Others provide beds for those unable to meet the full fees by subsidising them from charitable sources'.

Specific purpose grants are made to a number of independent hospitals, homes and medical charities each year to meet either the total cost or partial cost of an item or scheme. In 1990 68 such grants were awarded and ranged from a grant of £450 to Mission Dine Club for the Elderly to purchase art and craft materials and a sewing machine to a special grant of £50,000 to a Winged Fellowship Holiday Centre to obtain a replacement coach. The provision of vehicles is still a feature amongst the Specific Purpose grants as the fund is aware of the important part that transport plays in getting residents to day centres and for day trips and other social activities. Five such grants were made ranging from £11,000 to £50,000.

Trustees are keen to award grants for items which will give patients direct comfort and care. For example, in 1990, The Haven received £1,500 to replace a sitting room carpet, Homesdale was given £4,300 to provide special beds and the Mildmay Mission Hospital was awarded £2,000 to purchase window blinds and refrigerators.

The trust is happy to receive appeals from new applicants and thereby 'meet a widening field of care'. In 1990 it awarded grants totalling £59,300 in response to first-time applications from independent hospitals, homes and medical charities.

The second programme enables medical social workers attached to NHS hospitals in London to make grants for under £50 to both in-patients and out-patients using its Samaritan Funds. This programme received support to the value of £19,550 in 1990 but the 1990 Annual Report and Accounts states 'the use made by Social Workers in the NHS hospitals of our Samaritan Fund Grants has continued to fall. The total amount required to renew these grants in 1990 was in fact the lowest for many years'. The trust is introducing a number of changes in administering the funds to encourage social workers to use them.

The third programme enables social workers attached to the NHS to make grants to individual patients of £50 and over for their fares and those of their relatives, debts, and can enable patients to take a convalescent holiday. The fourth programme can help patients in long stay geriatric wards to take a holiday away from the hospital environment that is normally their home. In 1990 about £7,320 of such grants were made.

Applications procedure: To the Secretary in writing by April of each year. There is no restriction on the number of successive years that the same applicant may submit an application for consideration or that the same applicant may be awarded a specific purpose grant.

Correspondent: The Secretary

Address: 40 High Street Teddington, Middlesex TW11 8EW (081-977 4154)

The Metropolitan Police (Property) Act Fund

Beneficial area: London (Metropolitan Police District)

Objects: To assist community and social welfare groups, educational and medical appeals

Type of beneficiary: Organisations

Grant total: Variable, about £350,000 in 1990/91

Grant details: This is not a registered charity; rather the money comes from the sale of unidentified property, including the proceeds of crime, which has come into the hands of the police. Typically several hundred grants varying between £50 and £10,000 will be made to London health and welfare charities, appeals and organisations, including hospitals and community groups.

Applications procedure: The committee of the fund does not actively seek nominations; rather they rely on organisations being put forward by local police officers based on their wide-ranging knowledge.

Correspondent: Mr D Shonfield, Secretary, T.O. 31 Branch

Address: Metropolitan Police Community Involvement Branch, Room 632, New Scotland Yard, Broadway, London SW1H 0BG (071-230 3358)

The Morgan Crucible Company's Charitable Trust

Beneficial area: National, but an emphasis is placed on certain areas including South London

Objects: General charitable purposes

Type of beneficiary: Organisations

Income: £30,000 (1987)

Grant total: £26,000

Grant details: After a major grant of £7,000 to Battersea Arts Centre, cash grants of between £25 and £500 were given to 78 organisations.

Applications procedure: In writing to the correspondent. The Charity Committee meets quarterly.

Correspondent: The Company Secretary

Address: The Morgan Crucible Co plc, Chariott House, 6-12 Victoria Street, Windsor, Berkshire, SL4 1EP (0753 850331)

Other information: This entry was not confirmed by the trust and more up-to-date information would be welcomed.

The New Chasers Charitable Trust

Beneficial area: London

Objects: Welfare of young people in need

Type of beneficiary: Organisations

Income: c£15,000 (1991)

Grant total: c£15,000

Grant details: Grants, the majority for around £100, are given to groups, centres and organisations working with children and young people.

Applications procedure: In writing to the correspondent. Applications will then be forwarded to the trustees for consideration at their meetings.

Correspondent: Mrs Sally Robinson

Address: Marks & Spencer plc, Michael House, Baker Street, London W1 (071-268 3278)

Other information: The bulk of the trust's income is derived from an bi-annual wine-tasting evening at Sotheby's and is roughly the same each year.

This trust did not wish to be included in the guide.

The Noah Trust

Beneficial area: Mainly London

Objects: The prevention of illness and promotion of health

Type of beneficiary: Individuals and organisations

Income: £6,000 (1991)

Grant total: £5,700

Grant details: Grants can be made to organisations and to eligible individuals if they can find an organisation to receive the grant cheque. In 1990/91 grants for £1,000 and over were made to the Carers' Project (mental health), homeless families for playground equipment and Islington Pensioners' Press Foundation for Victims of Apartheid. Smaller grants went to homeless families for the course fee of a health visitor, to a liaison group for caring professionals in Bayswater, to a cello group to play at a pensioners' club and to buy new furniture for sheltered accommodation aimed at elderly Caribbean people.

Applications procedure: On one side of A4, attaching financial reports and projections, and annual report if possible. Sadly, due to the small size of income, unsolicited applications are unlikely to be successful unless they are very much concerned with the wider issues of health promotion.

Correspondent: Dr Richard Stone

Address: 15 Blenheim Road, St John's Wood, London NW8 0LU

Other information: In certain cases the trustees present applications they cannot fund to other trusts with whom they are in close contact.

Peabody Community Fund

Beneficial area: London

Objects: Improvement of quality of life of London communities

Type of beneficiary: Organisations

Grant total: £420,000 (1989/90)

Grant details: Grants are made for the following purposes:

- communal facilities serving areas of high social deprivation
- projects designed to assist groups with particular social deprivation such as the disabled, various ethnic minority groups, the long-term unemployed and young people at risk
- Community facilities on or near the Peabody Trust's housing estates
- Support services for the homeless

Donations recently made by the fund include: £105,000 to Montgomery Hall for the provision of communal facilities for North Kennington residents, £45,000 to Community Service Volunteers for the National Volunteer Network, £25,000 to the Federation of Black Housing Organisations for training and advice services for people working with ethnic minorities, £10,000 to the Soho Family Centre for improvements to provide a play area and a small office, £4,000 to St John's Upper Holloway Primary School towards the provision of play areas and gardens and £250 to the National Houses in Multiple Occupation Group towards the cost of producing printed information.

Correspondent: The Secretary

Address: 207 Waterloo Road, London SE1 8XW (071-928 7811)

Other information: The Peabody Trust is best known for its work in providing housing for people on low incomes but it established the Peabody Community Fund in 1980 to assist the wider needs of communities.

This entry was not confirmed by the trust.

Princess Mary Memorial Trust Fund

Beneficial area: Former County of London

Objects: Relief of poor working women

Type of beneficiary: Organisations

Income: £13,830 (1990)

Grant total: £15,000

Grant details: Donations were made to the Bermondsey and Brook Lane Medical Mission (£5,000), Catifield House (£5,000), the Friends of the Cheyne Centre (£2,500) and the Thomas Coram Foundation for Children (£2,500).

Applications procedure: To the correspondent.

Correspondent: See 'Other information'.

Address: Gregory Rowcliffe & Milners, 1 Bedford Row, London WC1R 4BZ (071-242 0631)

Trustees: Mrs P E Pierrepont, Miss S A Whitfield, C P Masters, A C Winter Miss H J Hipps

Other information: The previous correspondent for this trust has died and attempts to find out who might be administering it proved unsuccessful.

See entry for the King Edward VII Children's Convalescent Trust Fund, in which information about a third trust is also given.

The Christopher Rowbotham Charitable Trust

Beneficial area: National with a special interest in London (NW, SE and NE).

Main grant areas: Assistance of national and local charities

Type of beneficiary: Organisations

Income: £36,000 (1989)

Grant total: £30,000

Grant details: Grants (on average £500) are made to organisations, especially smaller groups with low overheads but never to individuals or to capital building appeals. The correspondent notes that the trust's funds are substantially committed.

Applications procedure: To the correspondent. Grants are distributed in May.

Correspondent: Mrs C A Jackson

Address: 18 Northumberland Square, North Shields, Tyne and Wear NE3 1PX

Other information: No accounts since 1976 are on file at the Charity Commission.

The Royal Victoria Hall Foundation

Beneficial area: Greater London only

Type of beneficiary: Organisations

Objects: The assistance in the provision of mainly theatrical facilities for people who need them due to their social and economic circumstances. These facilities include dramatic performances, concerts, exhibitions and lectures.

Income: £48,072 (1990/91)

Grant total: £32,000

Grants details: The trust supports theatrical organisations only and makes most grants for one-off capital expenditure. No retrospective funding is given and no grants are made for fine arts, music or dance projects which are not in a theatrical context. Applications from individuals are not accepted and no repeat grant applications within three years are considered.

Lilian Baylis Awards are given to talented drama students who are facing financial difficulty in their final year of study and are nominated by accredited drama schools.

In 1990/91 funded organisations included Spare Tyre Theatre (£2,000) towards their musical play for young unemployed people in Newham; Clean Break Theatre Co (£2,000) towards the director's fee for their Spring production; Tricycle Theatre Co (£2,000) towards workshops for children or holiday activities for children or their youth theatre; Path Productions (£1,000) for their workshops and costumes for The Tempest; St James's Opera (£1,000) towards their aim of providing young opera singers with an opportunity to develop stage and acting skills; Sharp Edge Theatre Co (£750) towards their production of Shout Across the River.

Applications procedure: In writing to the correspondent

Correspondent: Mrs C Cooper, Clerk

Address: 120 Green Lane, Sunbury on Thames, Middlesex TW16 7PH (0932-782341)

S Group Charitable Trust

Beneficial area: Mainly Greater London

Main grant area: Support of organisations (see below)

Type of beneficiary: Organisations

Income: £41,450 (1989/90)

Grant total: £36,240

Grant details: About 75 one-off grants of about £400 were made. Organisations working in the following areas were supported in 1990: the community, children and young people, physical disability, mental health, homelessness, the arts. No grants are made to individuals, or to overseas aid agencies, animal charities, research projects, bricks and mortar appeals or religious organisations.

Applications procedure: By letter only, and preferably typewritten, to the correspondent. The trustees meet quarterly in March, June, September and December. Note that three clear years must elapse before re-application.

Correspondent: Mr R Baird, Chairman

Address: Saatchi & Saatchi Advertising, 80 Charlotte Street, London W1A 1AQ (071-636 5060)

Other information: This entry was not confirmed by the trust.

Simon's Charity

Beneficial area: London, with a special interest in the boroughs of Camden, Lambeth, Southwark and Wandsworth; and Oxfordshire

Objects: General charitable purposes

Type of beneficiary: Organisations

Income: £5,000 (1990)

Grant total: £5,000

Grant details: Cash grants are made to registered charities only. In 1990 London beneficiaries included a housing association, youth centre, legal resource project, and Charterhouse in Southwark. Grants are generally in the region of £50-£100 and can be repeated. An associated trust has a special interest in the arts.

Applications procedure: In writing only. Trustees' meetings are bi-monthly.

Correspondent: T R M Simon

Address: 96 Burbage Road, London SE24 9HE

Sportman's Fund for Handicapped Children

Beneficial area: Not defined (possibly Newham, Redbridge and Barking and Dagenham, London generally)

Objects: Benefit of handicapped people

Type of beneficiary: Organisations

Income: £57,800 (1985)

Grant total: £17,150

Grant details: After administration and fundraising costs, £24,350 was available for charitable donations. £17,150 was given in grants, most, as in previous years, to the John F Kennedy School, Hyleford School and Beckton School.

Correspondent: See below

Address: See below

Other information: Ivor Barry & Co (36 Linhope Street, London NW1), used to be the trust's accountants. No information about the current accountants of the trust or its administrator was forthcoming. Further information would be welcomed.

The Truro Fund

Beneficial area: The inner London area

Objects: Grants for young men under 21, preferably resident or attending school or college in the beneficial area, and for organisations involved in employment-related schemes or community activities for young men under 21.

Type of beneficiary: Individuals and organisations

Income: About £6,000 (1990)

Grant total: Not known

Grant details: Grants up to a maximum of £1,000 for the purchase of tools or other equipment for young men intending to start their own business, follow a trade or profession or profession or enter an apprenticeship; bursaries, scholarships or maintenance allowances to help those who wish to further their education; support for charitable organisations helping young men to improve their education or to develop their full potential.

Applications procedure: Application forms (containing full details of the trustees' requirements) are available from the correspondent. Applications are usually considered in May and November. The trustees take a strong personal interest in all applicants and prefer to make small grants to individuals.

Correspondent: Mrs P Clarke, The Clerk to the Trustees

Address: c/o Messrs Wilde Sapte, Queensbridge House, 60 Upper Thames Street, London EC4V 3BD (071-236 3050 ext. 3536)

The Trust for London

Beneficial area: London

Objects: The support of small community-based organisations

Type of beneficiary: Organisations

Income: £840,960 (1990)

Grant total: £613,430

Grant details: The Trust for London was legally formed in 1986, began making grants in 1988 and is managed by the City Parochial Foundation (although the foundation has separate priorities, policies and procedures, and a separate entry in this book). The trust has an endowment fund which will yield an income for charitable purposes of about £600,000 a year. The endowment comes under the authority of Section 49 of the Local Government Act 1985 and arises from the sale of assets of the Greater London Council (GLC). The income is not a replacement for existing sources of grants but is additional money for the voluntary sector in London.

General Policy and Approach: The trust aims to benefit and give priority to small local community based organisations with charitable purposes. 'Small' is defined as usually no more than the equivalent of two full-time posts. The trust is guided by five factors.

> To have an initiating and pro-active role rather than wait for applications
>
> To seek to ensure that its grants make a distinctive and particular impact
>
> To be accessible to small groups
>
> To work to stated priorities
>
> To recognise the value of practical advice and support

The grants will *not* be given:

> For major capital schemes
>
> In response to general appeals
>
> To individuals
>
> For research
>
> As part of a full-time salary
>
> To replace cuts by statutory authorities
>
> To umbrella bodies to distribute
>
> To organisations which have received grants from the City Parochial Foundation

Grants: It is not intended to make grants exceeding £10,000 to any one organisation in any one year.

Revenue and Capital grants will be made. The former can be for two or at most three years, though on a reducing level of grant.

The grants programme for the four year period 1992/95 is in two distinct parts:

– work initiated by the trust for which funds have been earmarked as indicated below

– grants made in response to applications

Work initiated by the trust

The work of the trust in its first four years 1988/91 showed the need for:

• increased training and practical help for the staff and committees of small groups

• provision of opportunities for certain borough

31

based councils of voluntary service to re-establish their developmental role for small groups

- provision for seed-bed office space
- consultancy support for small emerging groups

To help meet the above needs, the trustees are earmarking funds in the region of £150,000 each year and will determine its distribution.

Grants made in response to applications
Continuation Grants

A major priority is to consider applications from some of the organisations previously grant-aided with revenue costs by the trust. Further grants will not be given automatically but Field Officers will discuss with organisations what is required to continue their work. The trust remains concerned to support women's groups, black and ethnic minority women's groups and black and ethnic minority organisations.

A budget of £300,000 a year will be available for such continuation grants.

New Priorities

Applications will be considered from small groups in any London Borough which fall within the following categories:

- self-help groups with special emphasis on women's groups
- supplementary schools
- work with disabled people, children or adults, in the black and ethnic minority communities
- outreach work with women and children in refugee communities

A budget of £200,000 will be available for these new priorities.

Applications procedure: The first step is a discussion with a Field Officer. If you are eligible to apply the Field Officer will arrange a meeting.

Then organisations are required to complete an application form which is not issued prior to this stage.

All applicants must indicate what monitoring they will carry out of the work funded. Successful applicants will be required to co-operate with the trust's monitoring procedures.

All organisations should make sure that they have a copy of the up-to-date guidelines produced by the trust, and are encouraged to talk with staff before finalising any application.

The Grants Committee meets four times a year in March, June, September and December. Completed applications must be received by the Field Officer six weeks before a grants meeting.

'Completed' means that all documentation has been received, staff have no further questions to raise, and a meeting has taken place between applicants and a member of staff.

The deadlines for completion are as follows:

31 January for March meeting

30 April for June meeting

31 July for September meeting

15 October for December meeting

An organisation may make only one application in any twelve month period.

The decision of the grants committee is final.

General: The formation of this trust was a most welcome development. Its policies, procedures and priorities have been worked out in close consultation with the voluntary sector in London. In particular, the emphasis on seeking out the areas of greatest need, rather than waiting for applications to arrive of their own volition, makes it much more likely that the grants finally made will indeed meet the trust's objectives.

Correspondent: Timothy Cook, Secretary

Address: 6 Middle Street, London EC1A 7PH (071-606 6145)

The TSB (Trustee Savings Bank) Foundation

Beneficial area: England and Wales, but with specific regional commitments

Objects: Education, medical and scientific research, social welfare

Type of beneficiary: Organisations

Grant total: £1.6 million (1991)

Grant details: The foundation was formed as part of the restructuring of the TSB Group when it was converted in 1986 into a public limited company. The foundation is independent of the TSB Group but the two work closely together so that to some extent the foundation can still be regarded as a 'company trust'. The board of trustees includes a representative from each of the 8 regions through which the foundation operates. Appeals for a region are considered for recommendation to the foundation by a meeting of a trustee and TSB Bank local representatives to ensure local support for the foundation's donations. The strength of the links between company and foundation are shown by the fact that applications that are small and very local in nature may be made direct to a Branch Manager, rather than in the normal way to the foundation.

The foundation has three main objectives, to which it seeks to allocate funds:

Education and vocational training

Scientific and medical needs

Social and community needs

The funds are principally allocated to social and community needs.

The foundation prefers to support specific or local projects rather than contributing to general appeals.

In 1990/91 the foundation awarded approximately £1.6 million in grants. Of this total, £138,000 was awarded in south east England.

The foundation has issued the following guidelines about the areas of work which it is interested in supporting:

Education and Training

Bringing new skills to deprived areas

Activities which motivate and train individuals to get and keep a job

Disabled people

Initiatives which prepare for life beyond schooling

Help where potential talent or expertise might be lost to the community

Scientific and Medical Research

Particularly research related to maladies which prevent a significant percentage of the working population from remaining in work. Funds are fully allocated until 1993, and no new applications can be considered in 1992.

Areas of research currently supported include:

Arthritis and rheumatism

Asthma and chest or heart ailments

Age-related ailments

Mental health

Social and community needs

Projects in deprived communities, particularly inner cities

Projects supporting activities for the young and the elderly

Crisis and advice centres

Care for disabled people and the infirm

Projects which stimulate civic responsibility

Projects which make the enjoyment of the arts more readily available to the handicapped, the underprivileged and those with special needs.

The trustees meet quarterly. They consider all applications presented to them by the Director General, and decide which of these to approve, the size of the donation and its nature – whether a single donation or a grant spread over a longer period. The majority of grants are for one year only.

Applications procedure: In writing at any time to the Secretary. The foundation only supports charities recognised by the Charity Commissioners or to which the Inland Revenue has accorded charitable status. Applicants are advised to obtain a copy of the foundation's guidelines before making an application.

The foundation does not give grants to: individuals; overseas projects; animal charities; schools and universities (capital, equipment, running costs); building or restoration of the fabric of churches; hospitals and medical centres (capital, equipment, running costs); general endowment appeals; sponsorship or fundraising activities; organisations which collect funds for subsequent redistribution to other charities; specialist studies such as religion, politics, law or medicine; geographic and scenic appeals. No loans are made, nor does the foundation run any charitable projects itself.

Correspondent: Miss Christine Muskett, Secretary

Address: 25 Milk Street, London EC2V 81Y (071-606 7070)

The Sir Mark and Lady Turner Charitable Settlement

Beneficial area: London, especially the Highgate area

Main grant areas: General charitable purposes, especially organisations involved with the elderly, the arts, conservation, medical research and the welfare of children and young people

Type of beneficiary: Organisations

Income: £14,350 (1990/91)

Grant total: £15,450

Grant details: Grants are made to organisations involved in the areas outlined above. Grants may be one-off or recurrent and range between £100 and £400.

Applications procedure: In writing to the correspondent. Applications are considered twice a year and applicants will only be contacted if their appeal has been successful.

Correspondent: Mr Chris Gilbert, Acting Secretary

Address: Kleinwort Benson Trustees Ltd, PO Box 191, 10 Fenchurch Street, London EC3M 3LB (071-956 6600)

Wakefield (Tower Hill Trinity Square) Trust

Beneficial area: One mile radius of 41 Trinity Square, London EC3, (Southwark, City of London, Tower Hamlets)

Objects: Provide general social work and support local charities with general charitable purposes

Type of beneficiary: Organisations

Income: £234,760 (1990)

Grant total: £204,880

Grant details: None on file at the Charity Commission

Applications procedure: To the correspondent

Correspondent: Ms Barbara Moody, Grant Administrator

Address: Attlee House, 28 Commercial Street, London E1 6LR (Tel: 071-377 6614; Fax: 071-377 9822)

Other information: The trust's income mainly comes from rent on its properties (£208,910) with dividends (£18,780) and profit from the sale of investments (£7,080) making a contribution.

John Wates Charitable Foundation

Beneficial area: Mainly South London

Objects: Young people, music and general charitable purposes

Type of beneficiary: Organisations and individuals

Income: £119,770 (1991)

Grants total: £69,530

Grant details: In 1991 most grants were for £300 and made to individuals studying music and drama. The largest grant of £62,930 was awarded to the King's Medical Research Trust and two small grants

of £100 and £50 were given to people pursuing a religious education.

The trust has limited resources and only a very small proportion of applicants are successful.

Applications procedure: In writing to the correspondent

Correspondent: N N J Smith

Address: Messrs Oswald Hickson Collier & Co, 1 Pemberton Row, Fetter Lane, London EC4A 3EX (071-583 5333)

Other information: The foundation was registered in 1984 and the charity's 1991 accounts are on file at the Charity Commission.

The Wates Foundation

Beneficial area: Not formally restricted but primarily London and nearby

Objects: Social welfare, education, environment, etc.

Type of beneficiary: Registered charities

Income: £1,459,158 (1991)

Grant total: £1,426,500

Grant details: The foundation was established in 1965 by members of the Wates family, of the building firm of that name. The foundation maintains its original character as, essentially, a family trust responding to need and encouraging excellence. 'The foundation's aims are the alleviation of distress and the improvement of the quality of life, especially in urban communities. Within these broad aims, which are reflected in a wide pattern of grants, the trustees currently have a special interest in the well being of young people (aged 14-25) in all its aspects, both spiritual and physical, including in particular, youth unemployment, alcohol and drug abuse, young offenders and young people at risk, and opportunities for self-fulfilment through education and recreation and voluntary work within the community.' The foundation is also interested in the elderly.

The majority of grants are made in the South East and in the inner cities, with £470,310 being allocated to organisations in London.

Priority areas were approved at a policy review in 1988, and in 1991 grants were allocated as follows:

Community Projects/Disadvantaged	48.86%
Education and Science	16.26%
Special Projects	13.10%

Overseas	7.02%
Church and Religious Projects	5.42%
Health	3.96%
Arts	3.90%
Heritage, conservation and environment	1.43%

The normal range of grants is from £1,000 to £10,000, but the trustees envisage occasional grants well in excess of this. The maximum length of support is normally three years. While the trustees prefer to support innovative and capital projects, they do not exclude from consideration applications for assistance with salaries or running costs, including costs previously funded from statutory sources.

Examples of grants awarded in 1991 in the London area are: National Association for Gifted Children, Brixton (£1,000), Surrey Docks Farm Provident Society Ltd (£10,000), Trinity Hospice Centenary Appeal, Clapham, (£500), Age Concern, Ealing (£10,000), All Saints Church, Clapham Park, (£3,000), Avenues Unlimited/YWCA in Spitalfields (£2,500), Earls Court Homeless Families Project, (£5,000), Friends of Battersea Churches Housing Trust (£5,000), Jobs in the City, Peckham (£5,000), Centrepoint Soho (£52,000) and People for Action (£130,000).

Applications procedure: Applications can be made at any time, by letter to the director, with a description of the project and the latest accounts of the organisation. Grant allocation meetings are usually held in January, April, July and October. Grants are made only to organisations having charitable status. No grants are made to individuals nor usually to large well-established charities, to national associations or in response to national appeals. Appeals from independent schools, for repair of individual churches and for large building projects are not normally supported. Practical projects involving people are preferred to research. The trustees do not favour indirect funding, e.g. to other trusts, which leaves the recipient discretion over allocation.

Correspondent: Sir Alan Goodison, Director

Address: 1260 London Road, Norbury, London SW16 4EG (081-764 5000)

Woolnoth Society Charitable Trust

Beneficial area: City of London and immediate neighbourhood

Objects: To encourage the involvement of its members in the civic and charitable activities of the City

Type of beneficiary: Organisations

Income: £14,000 in 1991 (partly from members' subscriptions)

Grant total: £13,500

Grant details: Grants are made to organisations that work with the underprivileged either in the City or in areas close by, such as Stepney, Whitechapel and, on occasions, northern Southwark. Recent beneficiaries have included Whitechapel Mission (£4,000), Queen Elizabeth Hospital for Children (£3,130), PHAB (£1,500), Outdoor Activities Initiative (£1,280), Hoxton Health Group (£1,000), and Elfrida Rathbone, Islington (£500).

Applications procedure: In writing to the correspondent, for consideration by the Appeals Committee.

Correspondent: I C Cormack

Address: Citibank NA, PO Box 10, 7 Savoy Court, London WC2R 0EA (071-438 1157)

Grant-Making Trusts which support Individuals in Need London-wide

The trusts in the previous section support charitable organisations and individuals in need. The trusts listed in this section support individuals in need only.

Thomas Arneways Loan Charity

Beneficial area: Greater London (preference to the City of Westminster) and adjacent counties

Type of beneficiary: Individuals

Income: In excess of £40,000 available for advances

Grant total: See below

Grant details: Loans of up to £5,000 may be made at a rate of interest of 6 % on the security of a bond signed by the borrower and two sureties, or on such other security as is acceptable to the trustees.

Those eligible are individuals who are in need of financial assistance and who are preparing for or engaged in any trade, business or profession. Loans are not available for companies or partnerships.

Applications procedure: Phone or write to the correspondent for an application form

Correspondent: I R Adamson, Clerk to the Trustees

Address: 1 Dean Farrar Street, Westminster, London SW1H 0DY (071-222 8044)

The British and Foreign School Society Trust

Beneficial area: Greater London

Objects: Educational grants for students wishing to continue their study to a higher education level but who have not yet obtained any qualification above 'A' Level.

Type of beneficiary: Individuals

Grant total: £13,500 (1990)

Grant details: Grants to help with college or university fees, maintenance, books, equipment, travel to place of study. Preference is given to those on a one year course of study or in their final year. Grants range from £100 to £600 and are one-off.

Applications procedure: In writing to the correspondent by 31st October (for January interviews) or 30th April (for July/August interviews). Applicants should have lived in Greater London for at least two years prior to application.

Correspondent: S M A Banister, Secretary

Address: The Richard Mayo Hall, Eden Street, Kingston upon Thames, KT1 1HZ (081-546 2379)

The Builders' Clerks' Benevolent Institution

Beneficial area: Within a twenty-mile radius of Charing Cross

Objects: To support ex-employees and their dependents by way of a small pension or temporary assistance.

Grant details: Ten or twenty one-off payments are made each year.

Correspondent: Roger Shelton, Honorary Secretary

Address: BEC, 18-20 Duchess Mews, London W1N 3AD (071-636 3891)

Other information: This entry was not confirmed by the trust.

The City and Diocese of London Voluntary Schools Fund

Beneficial area: Diocese of London

Objects: Educational grants for any person under 25 years old who has attended a Church of England school in the Diocese of London for at least two years

Type of beneficiary: Individuals

Grant total: £10,900 (1989)

Grant details: About 135 grants were made to help with educational expenses such as extra tuition, books or field trips. Grants range from £300 to £400 and are usually one-off.

Applications procedure: To the correspondent

Correspondent: The Deputy Director, the London Diocesan Board for Schools

Address: 30 Causton Street, London SW1P 4AU (071-821 9311)

The Cutler Educational Foundation

Objects: Grants for pupils or students under 25 in full-time education, either or both of whose parents were teachers for the former London County Council or ILEA and are unable to help through financial difficulty.

Income: about £4,000

Grant total: about £4,000

Grant details: Preference is given to pupils and students who have been orphaned. No further information is available.

Application procedure: Apply in writing at any time with details of the course or study pursued, grant needed and financial circumstances. After an initial letter of application has been received, a local Voluntary Secretary visits an applicant to discuss his/her financial situation and assess the amount of grant required.

Correspondent: J D Lyn-Jones, National Secretary

Address: c/o The Teachers' Benevolent Fund, Hamilton House, Mabledon Place, London WC1 (071-465 0499)

The Mary Datchelor Trust

Beneficial area: Greater London

Objects: The promotion of the education of persons under the age of 25 who are resident or attending an educational establishment in Greater London, or whose parents are resident there.

Type of beneficiary: Individuals

Grant total: £137,000 (1990)

Grant details: The trustees' policy is to favour applications from young people between the ages of 17 and 25 who are in need of financial assistance for further education. There is a preference for former pupils of the former Mary Datchelor School and to other girls and young women qualified as above.

Applications procedure: Applications should be made in writing at least three to four months before the start of the applicant's course. Note that it is essential that applicants be under the age of 25 on the date when the course or period of study begins.

Correspondent: C M Mowll, Secretary

Address: The Clothworkers' Foundation, Clothworkers' Hall, Dunster Court, Mincing Lane, London EC3R 7AH (071-623 7041)

Archibald Dawnay Scholarships

Beneficial area: Former ILEA area

Objects: Grants for boys resident in the former ILEA area attending full-time courses of instruction.

Type of beneficiary: Individuals

Grant total: c£2,400 in 1988

Grant details: No recent details available, see 'Other information'.

Correspondent: David Smith, City Educational Officer

Address: Corporation of London, Education Department, PO 270, Guildhall, London EC2P 2EJ (071-260 1750)

Other information: The administration of this fund passed from the London Residuary Body to the Corporation of the City of London in April 1992. Details were not finalised when this book went to press.

The Wayne Davies Memorial Fund

Beneficial area: Greater London

Objects: Relief of sick, disabled or handicapped people

Correspondent: A K Miller

Address: 18 Palmer Close, Heston, Middlesex, TW5 0PU

Other information: This permanently endowed charity was registered in 1984, with a Charity Commission estimate of annual income at £1,500 - £2,000. No accounts are on file, and no further information available.

This entry was not confirmed by the trust.

The Drapers' Consolidated Charity (and Charities General for the Poor)

Beneficial area: Mainly Greater London

Objects: Help for those in need in the following order of priority:

1. freemen of the Company and their widows and dependents

2. people who are or have been engaged in the manufacture or sale of woollen cloth, and their widows and dependents

3. persons who are or have been engaged in any trade or calling in Greater London, and their dependents

4. relief of need generally and individually (but see below).

Type of beneficiary: Individuals in need, both generally and educationally, mainly from the first three categories above

Income: £502,080 (1990/91)

Grant total: £435,303

Grant details: The charity says that "...its funds are almost entirely committed in responding to applications under the first three headings above; regrettably, therefore, it is unlikely that applicants under the fourth priority would receive help." Welfare grants totalling £159,703 were made to individuals in need in 1990/91. Though some recurrent awards are made, there is a preference for one-off awards. Some grants are made to eligible applicants through other organisations such as Counsel and Care for the Elderly (£22,000), the Church Army (£3,500), and Invalids at Home (£2,000).

Applications procedure: To the correspondent, preferably via social worker, medical staff or CAB.

Correspondent: The Clerk

Address: Drapers' Hall, Throgmorton Street, London EC2N 2DQ (071-588 5001/2)

Other information: Some grants under the eligibility requirements above are made from the Company's Charities General for the Poor.

Charles Dixon Pension Fund

Beneficial area: London, Liverpool and Bristol

Objects: Originally for the benefit of needy merchants; grants are now made to married men, widowers or bachelors who are of good character, not less than 60 years of age, members of the Church of England and in reduced circumstances.

Type of beneficiary: Individuals

Grant total: £5,420 (1990)

Grant details: Pensions of about £1,000-£1,500 a year. The fund's resources are at present fully committed.

Applications procedure: To the correspondent.

Correspondent: The Treasurer

Address: The Society of Merchant Venturers, Merchants' Hall, The Promenade, Clifton, Bristol, BS8 3NH (0272 738058)

Other information: No accounts since 1977 are on file at the Charity Commission.

German Society of Benevolence

Beneficial area: Greater London and adjoining counties

Objects: Welfare of people who are or were citizens of the German Federal Republic, German Democratic Republic and Austria, and their dependents

Type of beneficiary: Individuals

Income: £4,000 (1988)

Grant total: £3,000

Grant details: Pensions and small welfare grants can be made for heating, clothing and other need but not for relief of rates and taxes. The society can make no commitment to renew payments.

Applications procedure: Applications considered direct from individuals or from agencies on their behalf.

Correspondent: Mrs L Little

Address: c/o The German Welfare Council, 59 Birkenhead Street, London WC1H 8BB (071-278 6955)

Other information: This society should not be

confused with the German Welfare Council, which is an advisory body only. This entry was not confirmed by the trust.

RL Glasspool Trust

Beneficial area: South East England

Objects: Relief of poor, sick and needy people

Type of beneficiary: Individuals

Income: £21,400 (1986)

Grant total: £21,300

Grant details: No information available.

Applications procedure: Only through social services or recognised welfare agencies.

Correspondent: Mrs F Moore, Secretary

Address: 298 Hoe Street, Walthamstow, London E17 9QD (081-520 4354)

Other information: The trust's resources are fully committed and it does not encourage new applications. This entry was not confirmed by the trust.

Theodore Goddard Trust

Beneficial area: London

Objects: General charitable purposes, including those connected with the law

Type of beneficiary: Organisations

Income: £12,000 (1986/87)

Grant total: £5,350

Grant details: Grants recipients in 1986/87 included the Solicitors' Benevolent Fund (£1,000); Law Society Trustees Ltd, second of four donations for senior research fellowship (£750); Lord Mayor's Trust for Charities (£750); Queen Mary College, Police Foundation, St Bartholomew's Hospital, British Institute of Comparitive Law, Tower Hamlets Trust (£500 each); Newspapers Press Fund (£250); Bromley and District Health Authority Scanner Appeal (£100).

Applications procedure: To the correspondent

Correspondent: Simon Stubbings

Address: Theodore Goddard Solicitors, 16 St Martins-le-Grand, London EC1 (071-606 8855)

Other information: The above information was not confirmed by the correspondent.

The Irish Welfare Bureau

Beneficial area: London

Main grant areas: Welfare of Irish people living in London

Type of beneficiary: Individuals

Grant total: £2,760 (1990)

Grant details: The Irish Welfare Bureau works primarily through its Support and Advice Centre, offering information and support to Irish people newly arrived in London, and to poor Irish people living in the Hammersmith area, especially the isolated and marginalised.

Under normal circumstances the bureau does not make cash grants, although sometimes a grant to a maximum of £20 may be made and in 1990 grants were given for welfare and food. Gifts in kind - food, clothing, footwear, furniture – can be given.

The bureau's other work includes advice about accommodation, employment, rights and entitlements and in 1990 £2,610 was spent on providing accommodation. It also runs Austin House, a short-stay hostel for young adults between 17-23 who have just arrived in London.

Applications procedure: The Irish Support and Advice Centre is open 9.30 am to 5.00 pm on weekdays, closed at lunchtime.

Correspondent: Father Jim Kiely

Address: St Augustine's Priory, 55 Fulham Palace Road, London W6 (081-741 0466)

Other information: This entry was not confirmed by the trust.

Metropolitan Police Civil Staff Welfare Fund

Beneficial area: Unrestricted

Objects: Financial assistance for past and present members of the Metropolitan Police Civil Staff, their families and dependants, who through poverty, hardship or distress are in need

Type of beneficiary: Individuals

Income: About £24,000 per annum

Grant total: No information available

Grant details: Assistance for present members is provided principally by means of loans, together with welfare counselling. Repayment of a loan is by means of regular deduction from pay at source. For former members non-repayable grants may be available.

Applications procedure: In writing to the correspondent

Correspondent: A M J Williams

Address: Room 616, Wellington House, 67-73 Buckingham Gate, London SW1E 6BE (071-230 7168)

Metropolitan Society for the Blind

Beneficial area: The inner 12 boroughs and the City of London

Objects: Relief of blind and partially sighted residents

Type of beneficiary: Individuals

Income: £254,830 (in 1990, about half in the form of a disbursement of funds raised by the Greater London Fund for the Blind, the remainder from investments and legacies)

Grant total: £18,790

Grant details: The society's primary function is as a full-time home-visiting agency on which it spends almost half its income; it also offers a small-scale escort service conducted by volunteer car drivers, normally in the London area. Some general welfare grants are made, and in 1990 £7,820 was allocated. The society can also help with a wide variety of aids and equipment, including radio sets, and it awards a number of pensions, allocating £10,970 towards this end in 1990.

Applications procedure: Any recognised welfare organisation or social services department may apply to the secretary on behalf of a registered blind or partially sighted person in need. The secretary can be contacted between 9.30 am - 4 pm on weekdays.

Correspondent: The Secretary

Address: 4th Floor, Duke House, 6-12 Tabard Street, London SE1 4JT (071-403 6184/6571)

Other information: This entry was not confirmed by the trust.

The Metropolitan Visiting and Relief Association

Beneficial area: The old metropolitan area

Objects: Relief of need

Type of beneficiary: Individuals

Income: £6,000 (1988)

Grant total: £6,000

Grant details: One-off grants usually between £40 and £100 (occasionally to £150) are made for almost every kind of need, just about the only areas that cannot be funded being fines, rent arrears, general or water rates and funeral expenses. The most common requests are for help with fuel bills, children's clothing and holidays, but more unusual needs can also be met: recent beneficiaries have included a family that was unable to afford fire insurance and then had a fire and a woman who was asked to look after a child for a fortnight and was then left with it when the parents never returned and could not be traced.

Applications procedure: On behalf of individuals by a social worker, who can obtain an application form from the correspondent. These forms for the Metropolitan Visiting and Relief Association must then be signed by the vicar of the applicant's parish. Note that beneficiaries do not need to be church-goers or Christians, but that the vicar's signature is essential.

The committee meets about every six weeks.

Correspondent: Mrs Joan Dixon

Address: Family Welfare Association, 501 Kingsland Road, London E8 4AU (071-254 6251)

Other information: The Family Welfare Association administers a wide variety of funds that can potentially meet most cases of individual need nationally. Social workers who are applying on behalf of a client as part of an overall treatment plan can contact the correspondent and give a brief outline of the need. If funds are available an application form will be sent. When this has been returned and processed it is considered by the grants committee whose members include experienced workers from various branches of social work who can also advise on additional statutory benefits to which the client may be entitled. Payment in all cases is through the referring agency or intermediary.

This entry was not confirmed by the trust.

The Middlesex King Edward VII Memorial Fund

Beneficial area: In particular the former County of Middlesex (as constituted in 1912) and north west London; also the Home Counties

Objects: To enable children in need between 6 and 16 years to have a holiday at the seaside or in the country

Type of beneficiary: Individuals

Income: No information available

Grant total: About £5,000 (1991)

Grant details: Grants can be paid to children via headteachers, social workers etc, for school journeys and holidays, including those run by churches, WRVS, the police and other organisations. Note that this charity cannot award grants to older children for educational purposes.

Applications procedure: Written details of proposed holiday, its cost and the circumstances of the children involved should be sent to the correspondent, preferably early in the year.`

Correspondent: A J G Moore

Address: 2nd Floor, 200 Tottenham Court Road, London W1P 9LA (071-580 5191)

Neale's Educational Foundation

Beneficial area: City of London and the London Borough of Westminster

Objects: To help with school, college or university fees or to supplement existing grants and to help towards the cost of education, training, apprenticeship or equipment for those starting work.

Type of beneficiary: Boys having attended school in the beneficial area for at least two years, with a preference for those going into the Royal or Merchant Navy.

Grant total: Usually around £1,000

Grant details: Three or four grants are made each year.

Correspondent: M Farrell, Clerk

Address: St Dunstan's In the West, Fleet Street, London EC4 (071-405 1929)

Other information: This trust is administered with The Charity of John Land for Widows and Children (see separate entry).

The Ogilvie Charities, including the Margaret Champney Rest and Holiday Fund, Ogilvie Charities (Deed No. 2) and The Straitened Circumstances (1961) Fund

For all three charities the following information applies:

Beneficial area: In practice London, Essex and Suffolk

Applications procedure: Only through an official body such as a welfare organisation or social services. A preliminary telephone call can sometimes be useful to establish if an application is worth proceeding with.

Correspondent: I H Gillings, General Manager

Address: The Ogilvie Charities, 2a Church Walk, Colchester, Essex, CO1 1NS (0206 573738)

Margaret Champney Rest and Holiday Fund

Objects: Defraying the costs of providing a quiet opportunity for recuperation

Type of beneficiary: Individuals

Income: £15,150 (1989)

Grant total: £11,850

Grant details: The trustees concentrate their resources on individuals with no other form of help, such as those who care intensively for elderly or handicapped people in their own homes. Grants are only made to adults unless it is in his or her best interest to be accompanied by a dependent child.

Ogilvie Charities (Deed No. 2)

Objects: Assistance to present or former needy governesses or female teachers; country holidays for London children; support of the charity's own almshouses (in Suffolk); support of charitable organisations

Type of beneficiary: Individuals and organisations

Income: £49,440 (1989)

Grant total: £6,800

Grant details: No information available.

Other information: The accounts contained a separate sheet for Mary Ford Smith's Gift and Legacy, which in 1989 had an income of £11,160 and made grants totalling £6,450. It is not known if this legacy shares the same objects as the Ogilvie Charities (Deed No 2) itself.

The Straitened Circumstances (1961) Fund

Objects: Provision of grants to people in straitened circumstances

Type of beneficiary: Individuals

Income: £19,840 (1989)

Grant total: £9,630

Grant details: According to the 1989 annual report, the trustees distributed 29% of grants to individuals living in London boroughs towards the costs of household equipment, clothing, furniture, bedding, travel to hospital, telephones, interior decoration and in exceptional circumstances, rent arrears.

Other information: These entries were not confirmed by the trusts.

H & L Paxton Children's Fund

Beneficial area: The former administrative County of London

Objects: Benefit of poor and necessitous children

Type of beneficiary: Individuals

Grant details: No information available.

Correspondent: W T C Shelford

Address: Moor House, London Wall, EC2

Other information: A schedule shows that in 1964, the last year for which accounts are on file at the Charity Commission, the fund had investments of just over £19,000. We have been advised by the last listed contacts, Withers Nicholl and Manisty, that they forward all correspondence relating to the fund to Mr Shelford. Further information would be welcomed.

This entry was not confirmed by the trust.

Queen Adelaide's Fund

Beneficial area: Greater London and the former County of Middlesex

Objects: Relief of people who are receiving or within the previous five years have received treatment or training in respect of mental disorder

Type of beneficiary: Individuals

Income total: £17,570 (1991)

Grant total: £13,140

Grant details: One-off grants of less than £100 towards needs including clothing, furnishing, telephone installation and holidays. No grants can be made to repay arrears of any kind and every source of statutory funding (i.e. DSS/social services) must have been applied to in vain.

Applications procedure: On application forms via a social worker or other professional worker involved with the applicant.

Correspondent: Ms Jo Lucas

Address: c/o MIND, 22 Harley Street, London W1N 2ED (071-637 0741)

The Royal Scottish Corporation

Beneficial area: 35 mile radius of Charing Cross

Objects: Welfare of Scots resident within the beneficial area

Type of beneficiary: Individuals

Grant total: The trust has a welfare budget of about £360,000 and about £200,000 is given in grants

Grant details: The bulk of the grant total is given in pensions of up to £6 a week to elderly Scottish people. One-off grants may also be made, e.g. £150 for a fridge. The corporation is also able to offer advice and flats and sheltered housing are available for Scottish people with housing needs.

Applications procedures: An applicant for relief must have been born in Scotland or be a child of parents, one of whom was born in Scotland. A widow or widower whose partner was born in Scotland may also be eligible. These requirements have to be strictly applied, so the applicant should include in his/her application details of date and place of birth.

Correspondent: Wing Commander Alan Robertson

Address: 37 King Street, Covent Garden, London WC2E 8JS (071-240 3718)

The Society for the Relief of Distress

Beneficial area: The City of London and City of Westminster, and the London Boroughs of Camden, Islington, Hackney, Tower Hamlets, Greenwich, Southwark, Lambeth, Wandsworth, Hammersmith and Fulham and Kensington and Chelsea only.

Objects: Relief in need.

Type of beneficiary: Individuals

Income: £7,700 (1991)

Grant total: £7,770

Grant details: One-off grants, usually in the £25-£100 range, are made for "any cases of sufficient hardship or distress, whether mental or physical." Grants may help towards essential household items, clothing and sometimes convalescent holidays, funeral expenses and debts.

Applications procedure: Via social workers, a

CAB, registered charities and church organisations.

Correspondent: Mrs D Hughes, Honorary Secretary

Address: 5 Dunsany Road, London W14 OJP

Society for the Relief of Distressed Widows

Beneficial area: Seven mile radius of Charing Cross

Objects: Relief of poor widows resident in the beneficial area

Type of beneficiary: Individuals

Grant total: £2,100 (1991)

Grant details: The society can make small cash grants to help with the initial problems of widowhood. 28 grants were made during the year, 13 to widows with dependent children.

Applications procedure: Applications are welcomed in writing from a social worker or any other responsible person. Note that for applications to be eligible they must be received within four months of widowhood. A meeting will then be arranged with Mrs Idle, the society's visitor.

Correspondent: Mr W N Barr, The Secretary

Address: 175 Tower Bridge Road, London SE1 2AH (071-407 7585)

The Benevolent Society of St Patrick

Beneficial area: London postal area

Objects: To assist poor Irish people irrespective of creed or politics

Type of beneficiary: Individuals

Income: £8,650 (1987)

Grant total: £7,630

Grant details: A total of 366 grants were made for items of clothing, essential household items, fuel bills, convalescence, funeral expenses, visit to families at time of bereavement, and general assistance for hardship caused by illness or unemployment. Some grants have been made to help towards the cost of summer outings for children and for elderly Irish people.

Normal maximum grant is £25 although at the secretary's discretion this may be increased to £40. In exceptional circumstances monthly grants may be paid.

Applications procedure: Only via welfare organisations, charitable institutions or local authorities.

Correspondent: Mrs J Dixon, Grants Officer

Address: The Family Welfare Association, 501-505 Kingsland Road, Dalston, London E8 4AU (071-254 6251)

Other information: This entry was not confirmed by the trust.

Swiss Benevolent Society

Beneficial area: Greater London area

Objects: To assist Swiss citizens, temporarily or permanently resident within the beneficial area, who may be in need.

Type of beneficiary: Individuals

Income: £66,720 (1990)

Grant total: £28,630

Grant details: About a third of the grant total is given in weekly pensions to elderly people or mothers with a young family living on income support. The remainder is given in grants, usually in cash although on certain occasions equipment has been bought. Grants cover many areas including help towards the cost of holidays in Switzerland for both children and adults in need.

Note that the society does not make educational grants.

Applications procedure: In all cases proof of Swiss nationality is required.

Referrals can be made by either letter or telephone. The executive committee meets once a month to process applications, but emergency cases can be dealt with. Wherever possible the society would like to interview the applicant either at its offices or at the applicant's home.

Correspondent: Mrs A R Sharp

Address: 31 Conway Street, Fitzroy Square, London W1P 5HL (071-387 2173)

The Transport Benevolent Fund

Beneficial area: London and adjoining counties

Objects: Welfare of needy or distressed past and present employees of London Transport who were members of the fund, and their dependents

Type of beneficiary: Individuals

Grant total: £94,500 (1989)

Grant details: One-off grants ranging between £50 and £300 (average £100) are made for all types of need, (outside convalescence, osteopathy), the only exclusion being residents of long-term retirement homes.

Applications procedure: Telephone the correspondent for an application form.

Correspondent: R Monk, Chief Executive/Secretary

Address: 10 Melton Street, London NW1 2EJ (071-387 3479)

The Turner Exhibition Fund

Beneficial area: Diocese of London or that part of the diocese of Southwark which lies within the London Boroughs of Greenwich, Lambeth, Lewisham, Southwark and Wandsworth

Object: Educational grants for girls and women who have attended a state-maintained school for at least two years, are members of the Church of England and are now living in the beneficial area.

Type of beneficiary: Individuals

Grant total: £3,000 (1990/91)

Grant details: Small cash grants for school pupils, to help with books, equipment, clothing or travel, and for older students small grants to help with school, college or university fees for which grants are non-mandatory or to supplement existing grants.

Applications procedure: In writing to the correspondent, including the course of education and training which the applicant intends to pursue and availability of other funding. Applications are considered in May/June and September/October.

Correspondent: The Clerk

Address: c/o Tweedie & Prideaux, Solicitors, 5 Lincoln's Inn Fields, London WC2A 3BT (071-242 9231)

Vicar's Relief Fund

Beneficial area: National, with an emphasis on inner city areas

Objects: Welfare of poor and needy people

Type of beneficiary: Individuals

Grant total: £90,000 (1991)

Grant details: One-off grants in the range of £50 to £100 are made to individuals and families. All types of need will be considered including the needs of those in crisis.

Applications procedure: In writing only, and must be through social worker. A SAE is necessary for a reply. Further advice from the correspondent.

Correspondent: Mrs H Mabley, Administrator

Address: St Martin-in-the-Field, 6 St Martin's Place, London WC2N 4JH 071-930 1732 (answering machine message only)

London-wide Companies

British Gas plc, Eastern Region

Beneficial area: Barnet, Borehamwood, Edmonton, Enfield, North Finchley, Southgate, Tottenham and Wood Green.

Grant total: Not known

Grant details: The company is more sympathetic towards local sports and charities but may also support national charities. Donations are decided on merit on a first-come, first-served basis.

Correspondent: Ron Napper, Public Relations Officer

Address: Star House, Mutton Lane, Potters Bar, Hertfordshire EN6 2PD (0707-51151)

Other information: British Gas plc has its own programme of support for national causes.

British Gas plc, North Thames Region

Beneficial area: Most of London north of the Thames.

Grant total: Not known

Correspondent: Mr Derek Dutton, Regional Head of Public Relations

Address: North Thames House, London Road, Staines, Middlesex TW18 4AE (0784 461666)

Other information: British Gas plc has its own programme of support for national causes. This entry was not confirmed.

British Gas plc, South Eastern Region

Beneficial area: Most of London South of the Thames.

Grant total: Not known

Correspondent: Julie Stribbling, Social Policy Adviser

Address: Segas House, Katharine Street, Croydon CR9 1JU (081-688 4466)

Other information: British Gas plc has its own programme of support for national causes.

Capital Radio

Beneficial area: London

Grant total: £81,000 (1990/91) but see below

Grant details: The company directs its donations budget towards the arts in London. Typical beneficiaries include the Wren Orchestra of London, the Actor's Centre, the London Choral Society and the National Youth Orchestra.

Every year Capital commits itself to spending a certain amount (around £7,000 in 1990/91) on advertising space in charity publications. The company prefers to support children's charities whose work is based in the London area. It tries to support the same charities each year, if possible it supports events of relevance to radio and to London.

Each year at Easter, Capital runs 'Help a London Child', an on-air Radiothon to raise money from listeners for the benefit of London Children. In 1990/91 a total of £750,000 was raised. This was distributed by 'Help A London Child' (See separate entry).

The Christmas Toy and Food Appeal raised £250,000 worth of goods in kind. A further £150,000 worth of goods in kind are raised each year for other causes via Helpline broadcasts.

Capital's major sponsorship is the Capital Coca-Cola Music Festival where some 60 music events are sponsored at various venues including the Festival Hall, Wembley Arena, the Crystal Palace Bowl and local clubs. Other sponsorship is in tune with the young, lively image of the station and includes the Children's Film Festival and musical activities, all in London. Capital is a member of ABSA.

Applications procedure: Applications should be addressed to Richard Eyre, Managing Director (for donations and charity advertising); to Tamsin Wheeler, Administrator, Help A London Child Appeal Fund (for donations from HALC); to Peter Turner, Head of Community Affairs (for sponsorship etc.)

Address: Euston Tower, Euston Road, London NW1 3DR (071-608 6080)

Carlton Television plc

Beneficial area: London, Greater London

Grant total: to be decided

Grant details: Carlton Communications is developing the 'Carlton Education Project' aimed at educational and community organisations working with young people in London.

Correspondent: Colin Stanbridge, Controller of Regional Affairs

Address: 101 St Martin's Lane, London WC2N 4AZ (071-240 4000)

Other information: Carlton Television won the franchise bid from Thames Television and started producing programmes for the London area in December 1992.

Co-operative Retail Services Ltd, South Eastern Sector

Beneficial area: London and Home Counties North of the Thames

Grant total: Not known

Policy: There is no set policy and appeals are decided on individual merit. Co-op shops give vouchers randomly to small local groups such as schools, community groups or organisations which look after the elderly.

Correspondent: Mr Wilson, Member Relations Officer

Address: 78-102 The Broadway, Stratford, London E15 1NL (081-534 4201 ext 265)

Other information: The co-operative movement supports various community and youth organisations and through its Member Relations Department seeks to encourage co-operative ways of working. It also runs an annual Community Awards Scheme which gives small grants (maximum £250) to local groups or voluntary associations which are doing a useful job for the community.

Greater London Radio

Beneficial area: Greater London

Charitable support: Charitable support is given through air campaigns and publicity to BBC Children in Need and to occasional ad hoc projects which are relevant to GLR's target audience. These include projects for carers, adult literacy, women returners, BLIND Day, and ethnic minorities.

Correspondent: Gloria Abramoff, Sequence Editor

Address: 35c Marylebone High Street, London W1A 4LG (071-224 2424)

Other information: GLR is the BBC's adult music and talk station for London, serving up to one million 25 to 45 year olds a week.

London Broadcasting Company

Type of beneficiary: Organisations

Total money raised: £1,110,000 (in 1991 through auctions and event association)

Grant details: LBC associates itself closely with a number of carefully selected charitable organisations to boost their fundraising efforts for specific projects.

In 1991 the radio station raised £100,000 for Hammer Cancer Appeal and £10,000 for the Royal National Institute for the Blind through on-air auctions. Air-time and resources were also given to the East End Community Trust for their annual charity walk through London. In addition LBC and Cadbury's contributed to the London Strollerthon and raised £1 million to fund a mobility laboratory for children suffering from cerebral palsy.

In 1992 LBC will continue to work with Cadbury's, and the East End Community Trust to raise funds, and the charity to benefit will be Save the Children. Additionally LBC will continue to support other major charities and discussions were under way at the time of publication.

Correspondent: Anita Hamilton, Director of Marketing

Address: 72 Hammersmith Road, London W14 (071-371 2000)

London Electricity plc

Beneficial area: London

Grant total: £40,000 (1991)

Policy: Support for local charities, particularly those which deal with London-specific issues, and appeals relevant to company business. The LEB is currently targeting its donations on charities working in three areas: homelessness, drug abuse and hearing difficulties. Additional support available from local operating areas in London for specific local needs.

Generally no support for circular appeals, advertising in charity brochures and programmes, purely religious appeals, local appeals not in areas of company presence, large national appeals or overseas projects.

Applications procedure: Contact the correspondent if appeal meets the above criteria.

Correspondent: Derek Salter, Principal Public Relations Officer

Address: (Head office) Templar House, 81-87 High Holborn, London WC1V 6NU (071-331 3844)

London Transport

Policy: LT does not give money to charity as it is a publicly funded organisation. Concessionary rates for the elderly etc. are subsidised by the local authorities.

Correspondent: Ivor Godfey-Davies, Head of Parliamentary and Public Affairs

Address: 55 Broadway, London SW1H OBD (071-222 5600)

L W T Holdings PLC

Beneficial area: The LWT transmission area

Policy: Support of the arts, sciences and local charities.

Type of beneficiary: Organisations

Latest figures: 1990

Grant total: £251,000 (arts and sciences)

£28,000 (charitable donations)

Grant details: The company prefers to support the arts, social welfare, community services and small local charities based within the beneficial area. The charitable donations budget was spent mainly on small-scale support of good-cause activities operating within the immediate vicinity of the London Television Centre (ie the London Boroughs of Lambeth, Southwark and Lewisham). National grants are administered through the ITV Fund. Local grants range from £250 to £5,000.

Proportionally large-scale support is given to the performing arts within LWT's transmission area, including donations to national organisations based in that area, such as the National Theatre. The company has sponsored schemes such as 'LWT plays on Stage', which was launched in 1987.

The company does not support advertising in brochures, large national appeals, small purely local appeals not in areas of company presence, appeals from individuals, fund-raising events or circulars.

Applications procedure: A donations committee meets quarterly. All applications for donations and sponsorship should be directed to Suzy Stoyel, Public Affairs Manager, Corporate Affairs Department

Address: The London Television Centre, Upper Ground, London SE1 9LT (071-620 1620)

Radio Kiss FM

Beneficial area: London

Grant total: not known

Type of beneficiary: Organisations

Grant details: No policy has been developed but individual directors or department heads choose organisations for Kiss to support. These are often larger, well-known charities such as Great Ormond Street. No further information is available.

Other kinds of support given: Free publicity is given to charities on a daily magazine programme called 'The Word' which is presented by Lisa I'Anson and produced by Lorna Clarke. Either of these should be contacted about a charitable appeal.

Correspondent: Gordon McNamee, Managing Director

Address: Kiss House, 80 Holloway Road, London N7 8JG (071-700 6100)

Thames Water plc

Beneficial area: The Thames area

Grant total: £70,000 (1990/91)

Grant details: The company makes in-kind donations from time to time. It is a member of Business in the Community and supports a number of local community, recreational, educational and environmental activities.

Correspondent: Mr Julian Le Patourel, Assistant Secretary.

Address: Nugent House, Vastern Road, Reading RG1 8DB (0734-593757/593690)

Sources of advice

Action Match

105 Barking Road, Canning Town, London E16,
(071-473 2270)

Contact: Veronica Pettifer

Action Match aims to encourage 'social sponsorship', that is the sponsorship by business of social action projects. It has developed from the very successful sponsorship programmes of Community Links, the Newham community centre where it is based.

Action Resource Centre

102 Park Village East, London NW1 3SP
(071-383 2200)

Correspondent: Loren Sherman, Greater London Area Manager

General: Action Resource Centre (ARC) is a national voluntary organisation which enables business and public bodies to provide practical, non-cash support to community organisations.

ARC's Greater London Office seeks to support organisations in London's most disadvantaged inner-city areas, such as groups contributing to the social and economic development of their communities through, for example, employment, environment, recycled resources and community transport projects. ARC's services are:

Secondment brokerage: providing secondees with management skills to carry out short- or long-term projects with community organisations;

Lawyers in the community: for Hackney, Tower Hamlets and Southwark groups, volunteer commercial solicitors who are willing to join management committees;

Business links: goods such as office furniture, donated by business, are sometimes available;

Community accountancy: in Tower Hamlets, training in financial skills for workers and committee members of community organisations.

For more details of ARC's Greater London services, which are free of charge to community organisations meeting ARC's criteria, contact the correspondent above.

Business in the Community

227A City Road, London EC1V 1LX
(071-253 3716)

Contact: Julia Cleverdon, Development Director

BiC promotes local partnerships between voluntary organisations concerned with training and employment and the national network of enterprise agencies. It can publicise examples of joint action between charities and business through its regular publications *BiC Magazine* and *BiC Post*.

The Charity Commission

St Alban's House, 57-60 Haymarket, London
SW1Y 4QX (071-210 3000)

The Charity Commissioners for England and Wales are appointed under the Charities Act 1960 principally to further the work of charities by giving advice and by investigating and checking abuses. In particular the Commissioners make Schemes and Orders to modernise the purposes and administrative machinery of charities and to confer on trustees additional powers, give consent to land transactions by charities and maintain a register of charities.

The Commissioners publish a wide range of advisory leaflets about their functions, the responsibilities of trustees and matters affecting charities. These, and the other services to charity trustees, are free - but requests for leaflets should be accompanied by an SAE not less than 229mm by 162mm.

Directory of Social Change

Radius Works, Back Lane, London NW3 1HL
(071-435 8171)

Contact: Luke FitzHerbert

The Directory of Social Change is an educational charity which provides information and training to the voluntary sector. Its work falls into two main categories. It is a leading publisher of guides and handbooks which give practical information and advice to those working for charities and voluntary organisations. It also organises meetings, seminars and training courses in fundraising, financial management and communications.

Publications include: *A Guide to the Major Trusts*,

48

A Guide to Company Giving, *Major Companies Guide* and *A Guide to Grants for Individuals in Need*, as well as the present volume.

Full details of publications and courses are available upon request.

London Research Centre,

Parliament House, 81 Black Prince Road, London SE1 7SZ (071-735 4250)

The London Research Centre specialises in the provision of London-wide information, research and consultancy across a range of local government and urban affairs.

The Centre can offer a variety of services for any organisation involved in social and public policy formation and implementation: including a specialist research library and a number of major databases concerning, principally, London's demography, transportation, housing and employment. A wide range of publications and bulletins are produced regularly.

Contact: Patricia Brown, Public Relations Officer (071-627 9614)

London Voluntary Service Council (LVSC)

68 Chalton Street, London NW1 1JR (071-388 0241)

Contact: Jacki Reason

The LVSC is the main co-ordinating body for voluntary activity in London. It is an independent, non-profit making agency which aims to support, encourage, develop and defend voluntary activity throughout the capital. It brings together voluntary groups with similar concerns so that they can pool resources, exchange information and plan joint activities. Advice may be sought from the LVSC on a vast range of topics concerning voluntary service.

National Federation of Community Organisations

8/9 Upper Street, London N1 0PA (071-226 0189)

Contact: Diana Hopkins, Information Officer

The NFCO is a federation of over 1,000 community and neighbourhood organisations, offering information, advice and practical help to new community associations and centres and other local community organisations.

Assistance includes an information sheet service, practical handbooks, a quarterly newsletter, advice on legal, constitutional, management and financial matters, and support for local training initiatives among member organisations.

The Volunteer Centre UK

29 Lower King's Road, Berkhamstead, Hertfordshire HP4 2AB (04428-73311)

Contact: The Information Service

The Volunteer Centre supports the work of volunteers, and those who organise them, in all settings: the statutory services, voluntary organisations and local groups.

The Centre offers: an *information service* to enquirers by telephone or letter; *training courses* at venues throughout the UK; *specialist advice* on many issues, including social action broadcasting, voluntary work by unemployed people, links between the business sector and volunteers etc.

Part Two
Local funding sources borough by borough

Introduction

This section is organised borough by borough, alphabetically, with a separate section for each of London's thirty-two boroughs, and one for the City of London.

Each section has the same structure, with the information presented in the following sequence:

Local authority grants and contracts

This describes the grant-making practices of the authority, details of any non-financial help they may be able to give to voluntary organisations and an outline of the use of contracts in their Social Services Department. All London boroughs attempt to support local voluntary organisations, but to markedly different degrees.

Borough spending is usually organised through a number of committees each of which is responsible for the council's expenditure within its area of concern. As many voluntary groups operate across these activity boundaries (attracting, for example, the interest of both the education department and of social services), some boroughs have established a central grants unit to coordinate the overall allocation of grants.

Each entry contains a description of the borough's grant making policies and procedures, as known in early 1992. As well as the council's main funding programme, the entry may also include details of funding through the Urban Programme, City Challenge, Joint Finance and Central Government Specific Grants.

The **Urban Programme** (formerly the Inner Area Programme) is a central government initiative which provides support through local authorities for economic, environmental and social projects to address the problems of inner city areas. 75% of the expenditure is subsidised by the Department of the Environment, with the local borough paying the rest.

Each year UP authorities produce a document (Action Statements) outlining local needs, policies, priorities and the kinds of projects which will be eligible for funding.

The document is agreed by a committee chaired by a Department of Environment Minister. The committee consists of local authority representatives and consults with the local private sector and local voluntary and community groups. There is a formal procedure for making an application, and all applications have to be received by a particular date. Anyone considering applying should get hold of the current policy document and make contact with the relevant authority officer at the earliest possible date.

The programme funds three categories of project: economic, environmental and social. Economic schemes aim to encourage enterprise, development and investment to create jobs. Environmental schemes include landscaping derelict land and the provision and improvement of parks. The social category includes support structures to promote parental involvement in schools and preventative health services.

For further information consult the *Urban Programme Annual Programme Guidance and User Guide* issued by the Department of the Environment.

City Challenge is a new initiative, launched in May 1991 by the Department of the Environment. It aims to bring together the work of existing programmes and concentrate resources on key neighbourhoods over several years. Local authorities develop proposals in partnership with the private sector, local organisations and the local community to find ways of improving and solving the problems of their area. Each authority receives £37.5 million over 5 years (about £7.5 million per annum).

In 1991 15 urban priority areas were invited to bid for resources in 1992/93. Eleven of those areas were selected to work up detailed plans for regeneration and these included Lewisham and Tower Hamlets. In 1992 57 more urban priority areas were invited to submit bids and 20 will be selected for funding.

The aims of City Challenge are:

a) to support strategies that will assist a defined area to attract outside investment, stimulate wealth creation and widen social provision.

b) to promote successful partnerships between local authorities and all those that have a stake in the area, including public bodies, private companies, voluntary sector bodies and local communities.

c) to create a climate of environmental quality and business confidence likely to attract people to live and work in the area.

d) to support the development of locally devised and time-limited plans for the regeneration of disadvantaged areas.

e) to promote effective mechanisms for the delivery of these plans, including effective coordination of the resources available to the area.

f) to develop the capacity within the areas selected for self-sustaining regeneration and self-help which will continue after the period of funding.

Any City Challenge bid should indicate the involvement of voluntary organisations. Voluntary agencies which believe they have a contribution to make to City Challenge should approach their local authorities at an early stage in the preparation of bids.

Further information is available in the Department of the Environment's *City Challenge Bidding Guidance 1993/94, City Challenge Financial Guidance Note No 1* and *Working Partnerships – February 1992.*

The Children Act 1989 brings together most legislation relating to children. It emphasizes parental responsibility, partnership between the authority and the family, support for families and the reduction of active intervention. This means that the provision of a wider range of community based services such as Family Centres and Family Aides will become important.

The Act means that services to children are expected to improve and some extra money will be needed by local authorities. The government has recognised this and extra funding is said to be included in the Revenue Support Grant.

For many local authorities the new legislation was an opportunity to review their own practice and service for children and families.

The **Mental Illness Specific Grant** was made available in 1991 for three years so that local authorities could improve the social care they provide to people with a mental illness. This grant takes the form of a recurrent annual contribution from the Department of Health to local authorities' revenue spending within social services and requires the local authority to contribute 30% to the cost of new services.

The **Alcohol/Drugs Specific Grant** was made available in 1991/92 and 1992/93 so that local authorities could develop the voluntary sector's contribution to improving the adequacy, quality and suitability of social care services for alcohol and drugs misusers. Local authorities must contribute 30% towards the costs of these new services.

The *London Boroughs Grants Scheme* provides funding for cross-boundary and London-wide voluntary organisations. This is a major grants programme, details of which are in Part 1 of this book. It is of course still possible for a project to make separate applications to each of the boroughs where it is providing benefit.

Joint Consultative Committees (joint finance)

Joint finance is money allocated annually to the regional health authorities by the Department of Health, and shared out among the district health authorities for the promotion of schemes in collaboration primarily with local authorities, and also with voluntary organisations. It should not be confused with 'joint funding' which is where both health and local authorities agree to contribute part of their main programme funds to an organisation or project. Joint finance money may not be used to fund services which it is the duty of the health or local authority to provide statutorily.

Joint finance is usually used to start off new projects which are designed to bring social and health provision out of hospitals and into the community. Joint finance money is also used to encourage the development of the 'Care in the Community' and other initiatives. The full running costs can be met for up to three years and support can continue for a further four years on a tapering basis, except in special circumstances where the period of funding can be extended. An example of these special circumstances is the 'Care in the Community' project where the full cost is met for up to ten years and can be paid for thirteen years in all. Sometimes after the joint finance period, funding will be taken up by the local authority, health authority, or other grant-aiding bodies.

The Joint Consultative Committees (JCCs) are responsible for co-ordinating the planning of local services with joint finance money. They usually include several members from the local and health authorities, two from the family health services authority (responsible for GPs) and three members from the voluntary sector. The voluntary sector members are elected every four years and the local community health council usually has observer status. Meetings are open to the general public.

In most boroughs there is a JCC for the borough but this depends on the layout of the health authority. For convenience, the JCCs are entered in the book borough by borough; where they cover parts of more than one borough, the entries are duplicated in each section.

The JCC is supported in its work by an officer's group, usually called the Joint Care Planning Team (JCPT). The job of the JCPT is to co-ordinate the strategies and plans produced by the client-based planning teams (see below) and to prepare plans and proposals for collaborative work between all those involved, including advice on proposals for projects and services to be funded by joint finance. The officers on the JCPT usually attend JCC meetings to advise the members from their authority, and provide them with background information and briefings. Usually, the JCPT does not include a voluntary sector representative but in some areas voluntary organisations have obtained a place.

In most areas there are 'Client Care Planning Teams' (or 'Joint Planning Teams'), composed of officers at practitioner level of health and local authorities. Teams will usually exist for such client groups as 'learning difficulties', 'mental health', 'elderly people', 'children' 'drug and alcohol abuse' and HIV/AIDS. They view applications and review services for their client group. They report to the JCPT, which in turn makes recommendations to the JCC. There is usually some voluntary sector involvement in client care and in planning groups.

Applications for joint finance are usually made from September to November for funding the following financial year. Decisions are usually made between January and March.

Variations occur in all aspects of finance, from borough to borough, and health authority to health authority. Some JCCs produce information leaflets and application forms with guidance notes to help voluntary organisations with joint finance. In all cases, potential applicants are advised to identify and approach at an early stage the voluntary sector representatives on the JCC and JCPT. For up-to-date information on this, if not available from the entry in this book, ring the local Council for Voluntary Service or equivalent, listed under Sources of Advice at the end of the section for the borough concerned.

Other statutory or semi-statutory funding sources

Examples include the Inner City Task Forces, the London Docklands Development Corporation and the local arts councils, where these are grant-making (otherwise the arts councils appear at the end of the section under 'Sources of Advice').

Grant-making Trusts

This is a listing of trusts and of other charitable funding sources operating within the borough. They fall into three main types. First, there are those trusts that can or will only support cases of individual need or distress. Secondly, there are those that can also, or only, consider funding the work of voluntary organisations. Both types will usually derive their income from interest and dividends on their historical endowments, or

56

as rents from properties they own. A third type of grant-making charity consists of those which are actively fund-raising, like most of the Mayors' Funds, though there is a wide range of organisations, new and old. In a number of boroughs 'Community Trusts' are being established to raise money specifically for a wide range of local needs.

Potential applicants are urged to read the entries carefully. In particular, applications that fall outside the objects of the trust, or its beneficial area, waste the time of both applicant and trust. A telephone call in advance of a formal application is usually helpful to both.

Major Local Companies

This is a brief listing of some of the major local employers, with a note, where this is known, of their willingness to consider requests for help from local voluntary groups. Many of them find it easier to give help in kind rather than cash. In many cases more information about policies of the company concerned can be found in the companion *The Major Companies Guide*. Your own knowledge of the local area will suggest more large, local employers. There will also be smaller companies ranging from small businesses to local high street shops which may be prepared to give support in cash or kind for local good causes, if invited to do so, and the managers of many of the high street chainstores can give small donations within limited budgets, or give vouchers or stock items for raffle prizes. Here you should contact the store manager in the first instance.

Sources of Advice

Under this heading can usually be found the local Council of Voluntary Service or equivalent and the local arts council or similar body. Both of these are membership organisations seeking to support and help local groups in the area. Most of them have quite close relations with the main funding bodies in the borough and can give personal advice of a kind that is impossible in a reference book like this. We have included details of the local adult education service but omitted details of local enterprise agencies. These supply advice, information and often training for local enterprise projects, especially business start-up and development. Where a voluntary organisation is seeking advice of this sort, the address of the relevant agency, if one exists in the area, can be obtained from Business in the Community, 227a City Road, London EC1V 1LX (071-253 3716)

Barking and Dagenham

London Borough of Barking and Dagenham

Civic Centre, Dagenham, Essex RM10 7BY
(081-592 4500)

Correspondent: J K Goodwin, Senior Committee Officer, Grants Sub-Committee

Grant totals in 1991/92:
£762,500 in main programme funding

Funding: The Grants Sub-committee (of the General Purposes Committee) gives the following criteria for its grant aid programme:

1. The organisation's activities will be of specific benefit to borough residents (and, generally speaking, the organisation or a branch of the organisation will be based in the borough)

2. It is non-profit-making.

3. It does not engage in party political activities.

4. The organisation's financial position indicates the need for assistance that cannot be met from other means.

5. The organisation is seeking to maximise its income from all sources (provided that this is not at the expense of service delivery and is permitted by the organisation's constitution and rules).

6. Where applicable, the organisation has used past assistance from the council in accordance with the purposes for which it was granted.

In 1991/92 major grants were awarded to the CAB (£150,000) the Council for Racial Equality (£37,500) and a total of £70,000 was given to pre-school playgroups and childcare organisations. Ethnic groups and organisations working with the disadvantaged continued to receive assistance, as well as projects providing community facilities.

Mental Illness Specific Grant: In 1991/92 Barking and Dagenham received £140,000 from central government and funded its own Community Mental Health Team.

Drugs and Alcohol Specific Grant: In 1991/92 a bid for funding from central government was un-successful but Barking and Dagenham are waiting to hear if it will receive funding during 1992/93.

Applications Procedure: Applications are made through a standard form and are usually considered once a year, in December, though there is a contingency fund to deal with emergencies or late applications.

Other support: The council offers discretionary rate relief. It may also be able to help more generally by the provision of advice, and it may be able to give assistance with maintenance and running costs of vehicles.

Contracts and the Community Care Plan

In 1992 the council's funding of voluntary organisations was mainly through grants, administered centrally. But this is beginning to change, 'As part of the development of community care we will be considering the use of planning agreements with the voluntary sector', writes one council official.

The council is considering the introduction of general service agreements. It is also reviewing the possibility of a three year rolling programme of funding. It is in discussion with its local Council for Voluntary Service, with local voluntary groups through the Community Care Forum, and large, national voluntary organisations such as MIND which have a branch in the area.

No contracting out is proposed for social services in 1992/93 but the council is reviewing the idea of the 'contract culture' carefully. It is considering new relationships with outside organisations, 'not least of all because those organisations demand it themselves.'

For further information on the Community Care Plan contact: Lawrence Ashelford, Head of Social Services, (Planning, Resources and Review). (081-595 3758 ext 2328)

Barking, Havering and Brentwood Joint Consultative Committee

Beneficial area: London Boroughs of Barking and Dagenham, the Brentwood district of Essex County Council and Havering.

Objects: To get worthwhile schemes off the ground until they can be supported fully by the parent body. These should be schemes for the benefit of the community in a broad aspect.

Funding practices: Funding is spread across the health district and the authorities involved, dependent on the services approved, and is not apportioned specifically between the three local authority areas.

Joint finance budget: £1,060,000 (1992/93 and fully committed)

£300,000 is available for new schemes in 1993/94 onwards.

Details of voluntary projects funded: Funded voluntary organisations include:

Grief Support Worker for St Francis Hospice (£7,170 in 1991/92)

Crossroads Care Attendant Scheme for Havering (£69,000 in 1992/93 and £66,000 in 1993/94)

Applications procedure: Application forms are available from the correspondents. Voluntary organisations may apply direct or through their representatives on the Joint Consultative Committee (JCC) or through one of the authorities represented. All applications are considered on their merits by a Joint Community Care Committee, one for each local authority area, and recommendations made to the JCC. In April 1992 the applications procedure was under review.

Voluntary organisation representatives: Miss D Bunting (Parkinson's Disease Society), 7 Lime Avenue, Upminster RM14 2HY

Mrs E Hare (Dagenham Parish Church), 24 Osborne Square, Dagenham

Ms U Ebel (Barking and Dagenham Voluntary Services Association), 13 Hall Green Lane, Hutton, Brentwood CM13 2RA

Other information: The JCC meets approximately twice a year and the JCCCs four times a year.

Correspondents: Michael Cox, Contracts Manager, Priority Services or Janet de Bruin, Secretary to the authority

Address: Barking, Havering and Brentwood Health Authority, The Grange, Harold Wood Hospital, Gubbins Lane, Romford RM3 0BE (04023 49511)

The Avenue's Trust Fund

Beneficial area: Rush Green area of Romford

Main grant areas: Annual donations to the Rush Green Daily Centre, and assistance to elderly people by provision of grants

Type of beneficiary: Individuals

Income: £4,000 (1990/91)

Grant total: £1,500

Grant details: £300 to the Rush Green Centre and £1,200 in grants for individual elderly people.

Applications procedure: To the correspondent

Correspondent: M F Booth, Honorary Secretary

Address: Barking and Dagenham Old People's Welfare Association, White House, 884 Green Lane, Dagenham, RM8 1BX (081-592 4500)

Barking General Charities

Beneficial area: Barking area

Objects: Welfare of residents in need

Type of beneficiary: Individuals

Grant total: £1,000-£2,000

Grant details: Small one-off grants can be made for the relief of most types of need.

Applications procedure: To the correspondent, through social services etc. or direct. The trustees meet infrequently.

Correspondent: A K Glenny, Clerk to the Trustees

Address: Messrs Hatten, Asplin, Channer & Glenny, Radial House, 3/5 Ripple Road, Barking, Essex, IG11 7NG (081-591 4131)

Other information: The charities' income can fluctuate as it receives support from other groups as well as from its own investments. This entry was not confirmed by the trust.

Barking and Dagenham Mayor's Fund

Beneficial area: London Borough of Barking and Dagenham.

Objects: General charitable purposes at the discretion of the mayor

Type of beneficiary: Organisations and individuals

Income: Variable

Grant total: £1,200 (1990/91)

Grant details: Donations are given for a variety of causes. Some are given through local welfare agencies and social services departments. Examples of grants given include Christmas gifts for pensioners, travelling expenses in cases of hardship, holiday expenses for children in need, household goods for needy individuals and the payment of debts incurred by people on probation. Grants are usually between £10 and £50 in size.

Applications procedure: Applicants should write to the correspondent.

Correspondent: Ms Phipps, Mayor's Secretary.

Address: London Borough of Barking and Dagenham, Civic Centre, Dagenham, Essex RM10 7BN (081-592 4500 ext 2121)

William Ford and Dagenham United Charities

Beneficial area: Ancient Parish of Dagenham

Objects: Individuals in need

Type of beneficiary: Individuals

Grant total: £1,700 (1990)

Grant details: Grants of £15 were given to 78 individuals and families.

Applications procedure: To the correspondent or via Director of Social Services, Housing Manager, Gingerbread, Barking Voluntary Services Association, and local vicars

Correspondent: Pauline Bonella, Administrative Officer

Address: Civic Centre, Dagenham, Essex, RM10 7BN (081-592 4500 ext. 2117)

Lester Trust Fund – see entry in Tower Hamlets section.

Uphill and Waters Educational Foundation

Beneficial area: London Borough of Barking and Dagenham, and that part of London Borough of Redbridge previously in the Borough of Dagenham

Objects: Financial assistance for educational purposes for those whose parents or who themselves are living in the beneficial area, and who are under 25 years old

Type of beneficiary: Individuals

Grant total: £600 to £1,000

Grant details: There were four beneficiaries. No further information is available.

Applications procedure: On a form available from the correspondent

Correspondent: Sue Hillsden

Address: Education Department, Town Hall, Barking, Essex, IG11 7LU (081-592 4500 ext. 3145)

Major Local Companies

Exide Batteries Ltd, Chequers Avenue, Chequers Lane, Chequers Avenue, Dagenham, Essex RM9 6PX (081-592 4560). Write to Beryl Hardie, at the Personnel Department

Ford Motor Company Ltd, A13 Dagenham Plant, Dagenham, Essex RM9 6SA (081-592 6680) supports local charities and schools in areas of company presence. All appeals, whether local or national should be directed to Maurice Hurrell, Head Office, Eagle Way, Brentwood, Essex CM13 3BW (0277-253000)

Herberts, PO Box 2, Freshwater Road, Dagenham, Essex RM8 1RU (081-590 6030) Mrs Pulham, Secretary to the Finance Director deals with charitable appeals.

Rhône Poulenc, Rinham Road South, Dagenham, Essex RM10 7XS (081-592 3060). Contact Ian Arnold in the PR Department.

Sources of Advice

Voluntary Services Association of Barking & Dagenham, 383 Heathway, Dagenham, Essex RM9 5AG (081 593 7586).

General Secretary: Ursula Ebel
Opening hours: 9.00-5.00

Borough Arts Forum, London Borough of Barking and Dagenham, Arts Development Unit, Eastbury Manor, Eastbury Square, Barking IG11 9FN Contact Denis Fitt, Arts Development Officer (081-507 0119 or 081-592 4500 ext 3666).

Adult College of Barking and Dagenham, Fanshawe Crescent, Dagenham RM9 5QA (081-595 3237)

Barnet

London Borough of Barnet

Town Hall, The Burroughs, Hendon, London NW4 4BG. (081-202 8282)

Correspondent(s): *Grants Unit:* Rob Mills, Grants Unit Manager, Ken Argent, Administration Officer, Angela Corbett, Administration Officer

Grant totals: £1,441,300 in main programme funding (1991/92)

Funding: Barnet's Grants Unit receives and assesses all grant applications from the voluntary sector, which are then determined by the council's Grants Committee. At present the budget is channelled in three ways:

- annual revenue grants for core running costs, now moving towards three year renewable service level agreements for priority services, with regular monitoring and evaluation;
- pump-priming grants for up to 3 years maximum to support new groups and projects, and one-off grants, preferably on a matching funding basis, to help provide smaller capital items;
- small grants below £2,000.

Most funds are allocated to social support services which supplement or complement council provision and form part of the council's strategies for implementing the Care in the Community and the Children Acts. A lesser amount is awarded to youth services, recreation, and arts and general community benefit.

Social Support Services: In 1991/92 almost £750,000 was given in grants to organisations providing community care services. Priority was given to schemes benefiting elderly people, including day centres, lunch clubs, neighbourhood care schemes, advice and assistance, respite care and community transport. Support was also given to organisations working with people with physical or learning disabilities or mental health problems.

£136,000 was used for advice and advocacy about housing and homelessness and to the local women's refuge for their counselling services. Another £124,000 was given for advice services to the general community (e.g. personal finances, consumer issues) and for counselling over bereavement, emotional crisis, marital and relationship problems.

In 1991/92 playschemes for 5 to 11 year olds received a total of £140,000. Priority was given to provision for 'children in need' as defined in the Children Act 1989, and in some cases grants to children's organisations were increased. For example, Barnet Pre-School Playgroups Association's received a much increased grant towards their support services.

£71,000 was given in grants to co-ordinating infrastructure groups such as Barnet Borough Voluntary Service Council.

The largest grants for social support services were awarded to Barnet Citizens' Advice Bureaux (£153,500), Barnet Care Attendant Scheme (£132,750) and Hendon and District Retirement Services (£120,000).

Youth Services: £86,000 was given in grants to youth clubs providing social, educational and recreational activities for children and young people between 11 and 18. The largest grant of £11,900 went to SPEC Jewish Youth and Community Centre.

Arts and Recreation: Less priority was given to arts and sports, which received a total of £90,000 in grants. Most of this was awarded to four professional arts organisations, including one theatre and two groups working with children and adults with disabilities. Thirteen small amateur arts groups shared about £7,000.

Environment: Three local conservation groups received a total of £10,000 for work in the borough.

The Mental Illness Specific Grant: In 1991/92 the Social Services Committee allocated £19,000 out of its MISG allocation from the Department of Health towards voluntary sector provision for the mentally ill. It has applied for a further £67,000 in 1992/93, the bulk of which will, if approved, be directed to local voluntary organisations including MIND in Barnet (£26,000), Barnet Care Attendant Scheme (£20,000), Jewish Care (£19,000) and Alzheimer's Disease Society (£9,000).

Drug and Alcohol Specific Grant: In 1991/92 the council did not apply for this funding because it considered the conditions under which the grant had to be spent too restrictive and they did not accord with its own priorities in the field. The grant has to be awarded to voluntary organisations for projects linked to residential provision for people with alcohol or drug problems.

Grant Eligibility: Barnet's grant-aid criteria are fairly unexceptional. Basically, recipients must 'provide services or undertake activities in the London Borough of Barnet for the benefit of residents of the borough on a strictly non-political and non-profit-sharing basis.' Full details are available from Grants Unit staff.

Applications procedure: Completed application forms for grants of £2,000 or more must be returned to the Grants Unit by early October each year. Applications for small grants below £2,000 may be made at any time.

Other support: The Grants Unit helps local groups in applying for grants. It also funds Barnet Borough Voluntary Service Council to provide advice and training to voluntary organisations on financial and management issues, fundraising, constitutions etc. Council-owned premises are hired to local voluntary groups at a concessionary hourly rate and Barnet's Education Department has a 'pool' of equipment for local youth and community groups to use.

Contracts and The Community Care Plan
In March 1992 Barnet Council's funding of voluntary organisations was mainly through grants but in future grant-aid will be substantially replaced by contracts. There were only three contracts within Community Services: with MIND to provide meals on wheels to people who are mentally ill; with MENCAP to provide respite care; and with Shree Aden Adepala to provide meals on wheels for Asians.

There has been no decision yet as to what services would be contracted out under the Community Care Plan but the council was discussing possible contracts with MIND, MENCAP and CAB. No other departments besides community services use contracts as yet.

Discussions were taking place as to what kind of contracts should be used. People generally rejected the idea of tightly drawn-up, 'legalistic' contracts in favour of flexible agreements where 'innovation is not stifled.' The council is considering making agreements lasting three years as this would allow a voluntary organisation the greatest planning benefits.

Whilst preparing its Community Care Plan Community Services and the Grants Unit consulted their local voluntary service council and had 15 meetings with users, carers, and voluntary organisations. In addition users' and carers' meetings were held in day-care residential settings.

For further information on contracting contact: Rob Mills, Grants Unit Manager

Barnet Joint Consultative Committee

Beneficial area: London Borough of Barnet

Objects: The Joint Consultative Committee (JCC) determines the allocation of Joint Finance funds for schemes or projects to care for people in the community. Schemes must be consistent with needs identified in the Community Care Plan for the borough.

Funding practices: The committee considers issues of joint interest for care groups such as mental illness, learning difficulties, elderly people, people with physical disabilities. Funding is now given on a one-off basis, and although this may be introduced over a number of years, applicants must consider how they will find funding in future years. For this reason, applications from short term and capital projects are particularly suitable.

Latest figures: 1991/92

Total expenditure: c£926,000 but see below

Expenditure on new schemes: £200,000 was available for new schemes of which £85,000 was used to fund voluntary organisations.

Details of Projects: Several voluntary organisations were funded with funds for new schemes. MIND was the principal beneficiary.

Applications procedure: Applications should be made on the Joint Finance Funding Proposal Form, available from the health and local authorities. Completed forms should be forwarded to the JCC through the relevant Implementation Group for the care group identified in the proposal (see Other information).

Correspondent: Mrs Marion Tucker, Committee Administrator

Address: District Offices, Colindale Hospital, Colindale Avenue, London NW9 5HG (081-200 1555)

Other information: The committee meets about twice a year. Proposals are usually considered at the spring meeting.

The names and addresses of the people administering the Implementation Groups mentioned above are as follows:

Elderly Persons: Ms Christine Halloran, Finchley Memorial Hospital, Granville Road, North Finchley, London N12 0JE

Mental Health and Addictions: Mr Russell Cleaver, Barnet Community Healthcare Trust, Horizon Centre, PO Box 165, London Colney, Near St Albans, Herts AL2 1XD

Learning Disabilities: Ms Jo Jolley, London Borough of Barnet, Ivy House, 1331 High Road, Whetstone N20

Services for Children: Mr Andrew Robinson, Family Health Services Authority, 313 Ballards Lane, Finchley N12 8QN

Physical and Sensory Disability: Ms Margaret Gallagher, Barnet Wellhouse Trust, Edgware General Hospital, Burnt Oak Broadway, Edgware, Middlesex HA8 0AD.

Elizabeth Allen Trust

Beneficial area: London Borough of Barnet

Objects: To assist school-children and students under the age of 25 living in or studying in the beneficial area

Annual Grant total: £20 to £25,000

Grant details: Grants are given to students towards books, equipment, fees and maintenance. Help towards the cost of travel abroad as part of an approved study trip will be considered. Grants are also given to school-children for essentials. Private college fees will not be paid.

Applications Procedure: On a form available from the correspondent

Correspondent: Anthony W Fincken, Clerk to the Trustees

Address: 42 Bells Hill, Barnet, Hertfordshire EN5 2RY

Milly Apthorp Charitable Trust

Beneficial area: London Borough of Barnet

Objects: Charitable purposes for the benefit of residents

Type of beneficiary: Organisations and sponsored individuals

Income: £500,000 per annum

Grant total: £500,000 per annum

Grant details: Awards are made in five categories: young people; sports; illness/disability and health; elderly people; general community benefit. In 1990/91, 113 grants ranging from £100 to £30,000 were made to organisations, and to projects of up to three years duration.

Applications procedure: In writing to the correspondent

Correspondent: Grants Unit, Chief Executive's Department

Address: London Borough of Barnet, Town Hall, The Burroughs, Hendon, London NW4 4BG (081-202 8282 extensions 2020, 2092, 2081)

Barnet Borough Lottery Fund

Beneficial area: London Borough of Barnet

Objects: Assistance for social, recreational, cultural and environmental projects

Type of beneficiary: Organisations

Income: About £15,000 (1990/91)

Grant total: About £15,000

Grant details: Grants are made for one-off items or as pump-priming for up to 3 years and tend to be given to organisations which cannot benefit from the **Edward Harvist Charity** (see separate entry). In 1990/91 eleven grants were made ranging from £575 for the refurbishment of Alyth Youth and Community Centre to £3,500 for a reception for participants in a European sports championship hosted by Shaftesbury Barnet Harriers.

Applications procedure: In writing to the correspondent.

Correspondent: Grants Unit, Chief Executive's Department

Address: London Borough of Barnet, Town Hall, The Burroughs, Hendon, London NW4 4BG (081-202 8282 exts 2020, 2092, 2081).

Barnet Community Trust

Beneficial area: Barnet and surrounding area

Objects: To build up an endowment fund for the long term benefit of the area and simultaneously give some support to local charities and groups

Grant details: Two large grants were distributed to local carers' groups in 1991/92. Currently only small grants from £100 to £500 are considered.

Correspondent: Mrs Frances Slowe

Address: c/o Barnet Voluntary Service Council, Hertford Lodge, East End Road, London N3 3QE (081-346 9723/8644)

Mrs Burgess Fund For Children

Beneficial area: The Hendon area

Objects: Welfare of children, mothers and expectant mothers

Type of beneficiary: Individuals and organisations

Grant details: The last accounts on file at the Charity Commission are for 1942.

Correspondent: Cllr Poole

Address: c/o Town Hall, The Burroughs, Hendon, London NW4 4BG

The Finchley Charities

Beneficial area: The former borough of Finchley (as it was before 1st April 1965), now in the London Borough of Barnet

Main grant areas: Relief of need and distress and housing of the elderly

Type of beneficiary: Individuals and organisations

Income: £176,950 (1991)

Grant total: £20,000

Grant details: Grants vary from £120 to £4,000 in the case of Finchley Old People's Welfare Committee. All grants are made on a one-off basis, but beneficiaries are entitled to submit subsequent applications. The trust also provides over 174 flatlets for the benefit of elderly people in the area.

Applications procedure: Direct to the Honorary Clerk

Correspondent: F H Jex, Honorary Clerk

Address: 3 Caddington Road, London NW2 1RP (081-452 7598)

Edward Harvist Charity Trust

Beneficial area: London Borough of Barnet

Objects: Relief of poverty, distress and sickness; any charitable purpose for the benefit of the residents

Type of beneficiary: Organisations and individuals

Income: £65,000 (1990/91)

Grant total: £65,000

Grant details: Grants are made to local organisations for one-off items or as pump-priming for up to three years. In 1990/91 a broad range of organisations were funded including groups which worked with dance, disability and children. £10,000 was allocated to a separate fund for individuals in need, eligibility for which is confined to the clients of the Social Services Directorate.

Correspondent: Grants Unit, Chief Executive's Office

Address: The London Borough of Barnet, Town Hall, The Burroughs, Hendon, London NW4 4BG (081-202 8282 ext. 2020, 2092, 2081)

William Jackson Trust

Beneficial area: East Barnet

Main grant areas: Benefit of poor widows, resident in East Barnet for 20 years

Type of beneficiary: Individuals

Income: £1,500 (1990)

Grant total: £1,750

Grant details: An annual grant is given rather than a fixed pension. In 1990 the grant was £150, but this may vary according to the number of applicants.

Applications procedure: Direct to the correspondent.

Correspondent: The Rector

Address: The Rectory, Church Hill Road, East Barnet, Herts, EN4 8XD (081-368 3840)

The Douglas Martin Trust

Beneficial area: In practice Surrey and the Barnet area

Objects: Any charitable purpose

Type of beneficiary: Individuals

Income: £40,760 (1990)

Grant total: £25,775

Grant details: The trust made a large number of one-off grants to individuals (average £100) for a wide variety of purposes, especially for or towards the cost of convalescent holidays and essential household equipment and furniture. Two grants were also made to organisations: The North London Rescue Commando received £50 and the Merrow Environmental Fund received £150.

Applications procedure: Through social services only

Correspondent: Mr Lorenz, Administrator

Address: Douglas Martin & Partners Estate Agents, 18 Central Circus, London NW4 3AS (081-202 6333)

Other information: The trust did not wish to be included in this guide.

The Mayor of Barnet Benevolent Fund

Beneficial area: London Borough of Barnet

Objects: Relief of local residents in need

Type of beneficiary: Individuals and organisations

Grant details: This fund makes one-off grants to individuals in need and considers every case on its merits. It includes a Christmas Fund which distributes £5 provisions vouchers to elderly residents.

Applications procedure: In writing to the correspondent.

Correspondent: The Worshipful the Mayor of Barnet

Address: Mayor's Parlour, Town Hall, Hendon, London NW4 4BG (081-202 8282 ext 2010)

Eleanor Palmer's Charity

Beneficial area: The former Urban Districts of Barnet and East Barnet

Main grant areas: The provision of almshouses, a residential home for the elderly and the relief of poverty.

Type of beneficiary: Organisations and individuals

Income: £119,920 (1990)

Grant total: £6,840 (excluding money to almshouses)

Grant details: The trust concentrates on joint housing projects and running its own almhouses. At present grants are made to local charitable organisations engaged in the relief of poverty, and to individuals.

Applications procedure: To the correspondent

Correspondent: J M Pavey, Clerk to the Trustees

Address: 106B Wood Street, Barnet, Herts EN5 4BY (081-441 3222)

The Valentine Poole Charity

Beneficial area: The ancient Parish of Chipping Barnet

Main grant areas: Relief of need

Type of beneficiary: Organisations and individuals

Grant total: £16,280 (1990)

Grant details: £5,410 was given in pensions, and £10,870 in grants. No further information available.

Applications procedure: To the correspondent

Correspondent: Mrs M G Lee

Address: The Forum Room, Ewen Hall, Wood Street, Barnet, EN5 4BW (081-441 6893)

Other information: This trust did not want to be included in the guide.

The Poors' Allotment

Beneficial area: The ancient Parishes of Chipping Barnet and East Barnet

Objects: Purchase of fuel for the needy.

Type of beneficiary: Individuals

Income: c£230 (see other information)

Grant total: c£230

Grant details: Electricity stamps are distributed. In recent years other charities have made donations to allow a wider and larger distribution of electricity stamps to be made.

Applications procedure: Through the clergy (of any denomination) in the above parishes, through social services or to the correspondent in writing

Correspondent: Mr L Whiteley, Clerk to the Trustees

Address: 35 Elmbank Avenue, Barnet EN5 3DU (081-441 4388)

Other information: No accounts are on file at the Charity Commission for the Poors' Allotment. In 1934 this charity sold its property in Chipping Barnet and its income of between £200 and £230 per annum comes from the interest on the sum raised from the sale.

West Hendon and Colindale Relief in Sickness Charity

Beneficial area: West Hendon and Colindale Wards

Objects: Relief of need

Type of beneficiary: Individuals

Income: £600 (1988)

Grant total: £400

Grant details: Grants between £25 and £50 are made where there is no appropriate payment from statutory sources. The trust is empowered to provide help with nursing care for non-carcinogenic terminal illnesses, assistance to people needing holidays to alleviate extreme stress, material goods in an emergency, transport not covered by statutory or other sources, items of specialized nursing equipment which cannot be provided by any other means.

Applications procedure: By phone or in writing to the correspondent. When a written application is made on behalf of a person or family it would be appreciated if full details could be included.

Correspondent: Miss Diana Hopwood, Secretary

Address: 4 Flower Lane, Mill Hill, London NW7 2JB (081-959 1563)

Major Local Companies

Dixons Ltd (electronic goods retailers), Dixon House, 28-24 High Street, Edgware, Middlesex HA8 7EG. Through its head office Dixons gives gift vouchers to local charities. Write to Nicola Marsden, Head of Corporate Affairs Officer at the Corporate Affairs Department, 29 Farmers Street London W1X 7RD (071-499 3494).

John Laing plc (builders), Page Street, Mill Hill, London NW7 2ER (081-959 3636) supports charities in the vicinity. All appeals should be addressed to Mr Derek Featherstone, Secretary of the Laing's Charitable Trust.

Northern Telecom, Oakleigh Road South, New Southgate, London N11 1HB (081-945 4000) supports local charities. Write to Susan Edwards, Director of Human Resources.

Sources of Advice

Barnet Voluntary Service Council, Hertford Lodge, East End Road, London N3 3QE (081-346 9723/081-346 8644)

Director: Sue Nyfield
Opening hours: 9.00-2.00 (appointments by arrangement)

Barnet Arts Department, Ravenfield House, The Burroughs, Hendon, London NW4 4BE (081-202 5625) Contact Joanne Hawley, Arts Officer.

Barnet Arts Council, 9 Rosslyn Ave, East Barnet, Herts (081-368 8654) Contact Pam Edwards, Honorary Secretary.

Barnet College of Further Education, Wood Street, Barnet EN5 4AZ (081-440 6321)

Hendon College of Further Education, Corner Mead , Grahame Park NW9 5RA (081-200 8300)

Bexley

London Borough of Bexley

Bexley Civic Offices, Broadway, Bexleyheath, Kent DA6 7LB (081-303 7777)

Correspondent: Alan Twyman, Committee Clerk, Management Secretariat

Grant totals 1990/91:
£445,360 in main programme funding

Funding: Bexley's main programme funding of local voluntary organisations operates on a decentralised basis. All applications for help are now considered by the department most involved in an organisation's area of activity. In the first instance, however, would-be applicants should contact the correspondent, as above.

Grants in 1990/91 can be broken down as follows:

Housing and Personal Services	£370,360
Education	£40,000
Public Works	£16,000
Policy and Resources	£19,000
TOTAL	£445,360

Housing and Personal Services Committee: This funds a variety of welfare and advisory organisations, ranging from the local Citizen's Advice Bureau to children's groups and disabled people's projects. Typical grants are of only a few hundred pounds; larger grants (of £20,000 to £107,000) are awarded to seven major, staffed organisations which receive a three year funding guarantee.

The Children Act 1989: No information was available.

Education Committee: This committee funds groups categorised under two headings:

Schools: Grants of between £140 and £810 were paid to eight school or school-based educational projects in 1990/91. Activities supported ranged from music and sports associations to a play centre.

Further education: Most money is spent in this category. Almost £19,000 was spent on youth and community service grants to local youth organisations; the other two beneficiaries were a local students' union and the Workers' Educational Association.

Arts: Over £13,000 was awarded to the local arts council for funding arts activities in the borough.

Public Works Committee: Contrary to what its name suggests, this committee supports sporting clubs and community centres. Grants are small, ranging £50 to £3,000 and in 1990/91 grants amounting to £16,000 were made.

Policy and Resources Committee: This committee picks up projects not funded by the other committees. In 1990/91 one grant of £19,000 was made to a single outside agency.

Mental Illness Specific Grant: In 1991/92 the council received funding and spent it developing its own daycare facilities for the mentally ill.

Drug and Alcohol Specific Grant: In 1991/92 the council supported Greenwich and Bexley Council for Alcoholism with a grant of £3,125.

Applications Procedure: Different committees have different deadlines for the return of completed application forms. For up-to-date information on this most important point, potential applicants should contact the department concerned.

Other support: Bexley's Social Services Department offers general advice and information about funding to local voluntary organisations and also gives limited places on in-house courses. In addition, the council provides free premises to several organisations.

Contracting and the Community Care Plan
In 1992 Bexley was holding monthly meetings with a Voluntary Sector Liaison Group, public meetings for formal consultation of the draft plans and attending discussions organised by their local council for voluntary service. A gradual shift from grant-aid to contracts was anticipated.

In most cases the council proposed to use three-year contracts in Social Services in which each part of the service to be provided was specified. In 1992/93 the following services will probably be contracted out:

Service to be provided	Budget
Residential services for people with learning disabilities (joint service with Bexley Health Authority)	£3.3 million

Residential services for elderly people	Not known
Residential services for people with mental health problems	Not known
Resource centre for people with hearing impairment	£20,000
Relief for Carers Scheme	£20,000

For further information contact: Andrew Cresswell, Service Development Officer (081-303 7777 ext 2666)

Bexley District Joint Consultative Committee

Beneficial area: London Borough of Bexley

Objects: The Joint Consultative Committee (JCC) invites submissions for joint finance from both voluntary and statutory authorities. Submissions are considered on their ability to meet the criteria for joint finance. In addition a recent policy document issued by the Regional Health Authority indicated that 35% of joint finance expenditure should be on mental health schemes. From time to time underspends within the existing programme may occur. It is possible to spend this money on non-recurring items of expenditure such as equipment, but not on revenue items such as staff costs. Applications can be submitted at the same time as those for new projects.

Funding practices: Each bid is considered on its merits. Schemes are not normally approved unless they are time-limited or have already secured funding for the period after joint finance expires.

Latest figures: 1991/92

Total expenditure: £450,000

Expenditure on voluntary organisations: c£80,000

Details of projects: In 1991/92 Crossroads Care Attendant Scheme (£40,000) and MIND, Bexley, (£25,000) were among the voluntary organisations funded.

Applications procedure: Applications are not normally invited unless it is clear that funds are available. Applicants are recommended to read the Community Care Plan for Bexley which indicates areas where development bids are likely to be given. For advice contact the correspondent.

Correspondents: Andrew Cresswell, Service

Development Officer and Joanna Newman, Joint Planning Officer

Address: London Borough of Bexley, Bexley Civic Offices, Broadway, Bexleyheath DA6 7LB (081-303 7777)

Other information: For further advice on applications contact Kathleen Boyle, General Secretary at Bexley Voluntary Service Council, 41a Broadway, Bexleyheath, Kent DA9 7JT (081-304 0911)

Bexley Mayor's Fund

Beneficial area: London Borough of Bexley

Objects: The relief of hardship (at the discretion of the Mayor)

Type of beneficiary: Organisations and individuals

Income: £7,000-£8,000 (1990)

Grant total: £7,000-£8,000.

Grant details: Grants can be made to needy individual residents of the borough and to voluntary organisations operating within the borough. Payments are made for a variety of purposes, such as a grant towards an electric wheelchair for a severely disabled man and the purchase of new clothes for an elderly person whose home had been damaged in a fire. Grants to voluntary organisations can be for the purchase of equipment or to help with running costs. The Mayor has sole discretion as to who benefits and can make grants instantly in emergency cases.

Applications procedure: Applications should be made in writing to the Mayor. In practice, many applications are referred by the council's Social Services Department and all applications from individuals are vetted by this department.

Correspondent: The Mayor

Address: London Borough of Bexley, Civic Offices, Broadway, Bexleyheath, Kent DA6 7LB (081-303 7777)

Bexley United Charities

Beneficial area: Ancient Parish of Bexley

Main grant areas: Relief in need of pensioners and almspersons; education and training of young people under 25

Type of beneficiary: Individuals

Grant total: £500 (1991)

Grant details: Bexley United Charities are principally concerned with almshouses in Bexley and sometimes make Christmas gifts to their almpersons. However, the Reverend Thomas Smoult Charity and the J E Mason Charity are administered as part of the United Charities and one or two grants are made annually, usually involving musical instruments.

Applications procedure: To the correspondent

Correspondent: Mrs J Avey, Clerk to the Trustees

Address: 32 Knoll Road, Bexley, Kent DA5 1BB (0322 522814)

The Samuel Edward Cook Charity for the Poor

Beneficial area: Bexley Heath

Main grant areas: Relief of need

Type of beneficiary: Individuals

Grant total: £1,500 (1988)

Grant details: About 20 one-off grants are made each year to individuals and families.

Applications procedure: Direct or through a welfare agency. Allocation of funds is at the discretion of the Minister of Trinity Baptist Church.

Correspondent: Rev D G Barter

Address: 75 Standard Road, Bexley Heath, Kent (081-303 5858)

Other information: This entry was not confirmed by the trust.

The Charities of Sir Culling Eardley and George Henry Martin

Beneficial area: **London** Borough of Bexley, especially the former Metropolitan Borough of Erith

Objects: Educational grants for residents under the age of 25

Type of beneficiary: Individuals

Income: £1,970 (1990/91)

Grant details: £250

Grant details: Usually one-off grants to a maximum of £50 for general educational purposes where assistance cannot be obtained from another source. Over recent years calls on the charities' resources have declined and the trustees are anxious to encourage applications.

Applications procedure: Application form obtainable from the correspondent.

Correspondent: Jackie Woods, Principal Committee Clerk, Committee Section

Address: Directorate of Education, Hill View, Hill View Drive, Welling, Kent DA16 3RY (081-303 7777 ext. 4319)

John Payne's Charity

Beneficial area: Ancient Parish of East Wickham

Objects: Welfare of elderly people

Type of beneficiary: Individuals

Grant total: £500 (1991)

Grant details: Grants cover fuel bills and essential needs e.g. gas fire installation. Two pensions of £2 per week are paid and summer and Christmas bonuses; there may be one or two vacancies for others. Support is also given to the local Age Concern and to a home for mentally handicapped people.

Applications procedure: To the correspondent, direct or through Age Concern or similar.

Correspondent: The Headmistress, Clerk to the Trustees

Address: Foster's Primary School, Upper Wickham Lane, Welling, Kent (081-854 1092)

Other information: The trust's income of about £500 per annum varies little from year to year.

Sidcup and District Charitable Association

Beneficial area: Sidcup and District

Main grant areas: Relief of need

Type of beneficiary: Organisations

Income: £95 (In 1989, from the charity's own fund-raising efforts)

Grant total: £370

Grant details: Grants ranging between £40 and £100 were made to local organisations, including St John's Ambulance, the Social Club for the Blind, the Dansonette Royales, the London Borough of Bexley and the Mayor's Benevolent Fund.

Correspondent: R V Plant

Address: 8 High Street, Sidcup, Kent

Other information: This information was not confirmed by the association.

Major Local Companies

BICC plc, Erith Works, Church Manorway, Erith, Kent DA8 1HS (081-311 2222) supports local organisations and charities, such as the scouts, local schools, the Association of Friends of Erith Hospital and the Royal British Legion. Donations range between £20 and £100. Contact Mr Barnet, Head of Personnel.

Coca Cola and Schweppes Beverages Ltd, Cray Road, Sidcup, Kent DA14 5DF (081-302 2600) supports local groups through donations of products and raffle prizes. Each application is assessed on its merits. Contact Sharon Hunt, Consumer Services.

ADM Ltd, (part of Unilever plc) Church Manorway, Erith, Kent DA8 1DL (03224-36966) supports local charities. Contact Mr P L Bates, Trading Manager.

Woolwich Building Society, 45 High Street, Bexley, Kent DA5 1AB (0322 525534) supports local charities. Contact Mr Tipping, Manager of Customer Services.

Sources of Advice

Bexley Voluntary Service Council, 41a Broadway, Bexleyheath, Kent DA9 7JT (081-304 0911)

General Secretary: Kathleen Boyle
Opening hours: 9.30-1.00/2.00-5.00

Bexley Arts Council, Hall Place, Bourne Road, Bexley, Kent DA5 1PQ (0322-526574 ext 203/204) Contact Mr G K Barnett, Secretary.

Bexley Adult Education Office, Sidcup Arts Adult Education Centre, Alma Road, Sidcup, Kent DA14 4ED (081-309 5570).

Brent

London Borough of Brent

Brent House Annexe, 356-368 High Road, Wembley, Middlesex HA9 6BX (081-904 1244)

Correspondents:

Education, Arts, Libraries and Housing Committee: Ramesh Patel, Head of Grants and Evaluation Unit, (081-900 5615/6)

Social Services Committee, Shenaz Hayatoolah, Divisional Manager, Contract Management, Room 319, 349/357 High Road, Wembley, (081-900 5267)

Brent Regeneration Agency: Sylvan Golden, 10th Floor, York House, Empire Way, Wembley, Middlesex HA9 OPA (081-903 8368)

Urban Programme: Apu Alam, Urban Programme Administrator, for grants made via the Central Policy Unit, The Town Hall, Forty Lane, Wembley, HA9 9HX (081-908 7082),

Grant totals in 1992/93:

£5,886,200 in main programme funding (inclusive of debt charges)

Grants made in the period 1992/93 can be broken down as follows:

Education, Arts, Libraries	£1,909,000
Housing	£1,083,300
Social Services Committee	£2,236,900
Brent Regeneration Agency and Urban Programme	£657,000
TOTAL	£5,886,200

Funding practices: In November 1991 Brent council amalgamated its departments and reorganised its grant-making committees. A central Grants Sub-committee was established which reports directly to the Policy and Resources Committee and decides on all grants across the council, including housing, education, and social services. The membership includes the chairpeople of all major departmental committees.

Education, Arts, Libraries and Housing Committee: This committee now deals with grants for the voluntary sector under the following categories:

Employment Training: the promotion of Employment Training must be as laid down by the Employment Training (ET) and Youth Training Scheme (YTS) and also be in line with future changes in government funding criteria.

Education: the courses offered must lead to qualifications or an award of a certificate.

Legal, Welfare and General Advice Provision: the organisation should provide advice and information to the residents of this borough on matters relating to Legal Rights, Welfare Rights and/or other general advice.

Housing: Accommodation or assistance for accommodating homeless people should be provided.

Youth: the organisation must cater for the needs of the age group 12-21 years.

Sports Provision: sports facilities and competition should be complement services provided by the council.

Culture: the organisation must promote national cultures which include lessons in language, food, clothing, and literature, music, social arts, painting and performance.

Leisure: grants are available for artistic or entertainment events or for workshops leading to their performance.

Feasibility Studies: Grants for feasibility studies should relate to employment and/or training and/or other new initiatives.

Religious activities: Religious organisations will not receive grants for promoting religion but if they provide any of the previously listed activities for residents in Brent, they are eligible for funding.

Social Services Committee: For the first time since 1988 new initiatives as well as those already supported were considered for funding during 1992/93. Existing organisations generally retained their funding whilst only five new groups received support out of a total of 44 funded. New groups applying are more likely to be successful if they have a track record.

Examples of organisations funded include: Kensal Green Under fives, (£77,890), Brent Crossroads (£122,650), Brent MIND (£129,690), Brent Family Service Unit (£122,570), Brent Community Transport (£157,200).

Brent Regeneration Agency: As part of the Urban Programme the Brent Regeneration Agency makes grants to promote local economic development initiatives and enhance buildings and town centres. It is currently putting together a bid for City Challenge funding.

Urban Programme, Policy and Resources Committee: considers applications from small businesses and voluntary organisations before these are submitted to the DoE.

A proposed project must deal with employment, economic, environmental and social issues and must be based in one of the following key target areas:

The area around Stonebridge, Harlesden, Roundwood, St Raphaels and the Park Royal Industrial Estate; the Kilburn and Carlton area around the council's housing estates; St Andrews, incorporating the Chalkhill Estate and the Wembley Industrial and Business Complex; Willesden High Road extending into Church End Shopping Centre; Wembley High Road and Ealing Road.

Mental Illness Specific Grant: In 1991/92 Brent received approximately £190,000 in funding and with it developed new services of its own for people who are mentally ill. It has not applied for additional funding to cover new projects in the next few years.

Drug and Alcohol Specific Grant: Brent applied for funding for 1992/93 for a joint health and social services outreach team managed by the voluntary sector and was waiting to hear if it had been successful.

Applications procedure: Potential applicants are recommended to make careful preliminary enquiries to one of the above correspondents before submitting a formal application.

Contracting and the Community Care Plan
In 1991/92 Social Services made grants totalling £2.2 million which mostly funded services for the elderly, Under Fives, and people with special needs. It was introducing contracts which initially will be generally framed and vary between one and two years. Specifications, terms and conditions will be tailored to each voluntary group.

Other departments within the council were ceasing to use grants.

In 1992/93 The Education, Arts and Libraries Department aims to make contracts with arts and community organisations totalling £500,000 and the Housing Department intends to enter into contracts totalling £1 million with advice groups and women's refuge organisations.

For further information contact: Shenaz Hayatoolah, Divisional Manager, Contract Management, Room 319, 349/357 High Road, Wembley, (081-900 5267)

Brent Joint Consultative Committee

Beneficial area: London Borough of Brent

Objects: Joint Finance funding is available to voluntary groups proposing schemes in line with the local authority and health authority objectives, particularly in areas of elderly services, learning difficulties, mental health, physical disability, children and HIV/AIDS.

Total expenditure: £750,000 (1992/93), £500,000 was available for funding new projects.

Funding practices: Revenue funding is usually given for a three year period and capital grants are also considered. Schemes funded to date reflect local needs and provide complementary services to the statutory sector, with grants ranging from £5,000 to £100,000. Funds available depend on year-on-year revenue commitments.

Details of projects: Voluntary groups funded include: Age Concern, an early discharge scheme (£100,000), Paddington Churches Housing Association (£5,000).

Applications procedure: The Joint Finance process is initiated in the autumn and decisions are made early in the new calendar year for schemes to start on 1 April.

Correspondent: David Panter, Deputy Director of Purchasing and Secretary to the JCC

Address: Parkside Health Authority, Bays 6 and 7, 16 South Wharf Road, London W2 1PS (071-725 6479)

Brent Mayor's Charity

Type of beneficiary: Mainly charities within the borough

Objects: To raise money for general charitable purposes

Grant details: Each year the Mayor decides which charity should be supported and raises money for it.

Correspondent: The Mayor

Address: Town Hall, Forty Lane, Wembley HA9 9EZ (081-904 1244)

Edward Harvist Charity

Beneficial area: London Borough of Brent

Objects: Relief of poverty, distress and sickness; provision and support of recreational and educational facilities; any charitable purposes for the benefit of residents.

Type of beneficiary: Organisations

Grant total: £143,260 (1990/91)

Grant details: Grants to a maximum of £1,500 are made to organisations but this could be exceeded where members decide otherwise.

Applications procedure: Application forms are available from the correspondent

Correspondent: Miss Tolani

Address: Finance Dept, London Borough of Brent, 5th Floor, Lakeside House, Lakeside Way, Wembley, Middlesex HA9 0LA (081-862 3325)

The Kingsbury Charity

Beneficial area: Ancient Parish of Kingsbury

Objects: Provision and maintenance of almshouses; general relief of poverty

Grant total: £3,000 (1990/91)

Grant details: Most of the charity's expenditure was on almshouses but several grants were made: £300 to the Bonanza Gateway Club (Brent MENCAP), £100 towards a trip to Lourdes for a terminally ill woman, £1,000 to the Wednesday Club, the Mall, Kenton, £1,500 to St Luke's Hospice, £250 to Delarue College to purchase a 'Light Talker', £100 to help a family with a six year old child suffering from leukaemia.

Applications procedure: Applications would normally be made through social services.

Correspondent: Mr J B Jordan, Honorary Secretary,

Address: 55 Grove Crescent, Kingsbury, London NW9 0LS (081-205 2101)

The Wembley Charitable Foundation (formerly the Michael Jackson Trust Fund)

Beneficial area: London Borough of Brent

Objects: To support training for young people between the ages of 16 and 25 when funding is not available from other sources

Type of beneficiary: Individuals and organisations

Income: c£16,000 per annum

Grant total: c£16,000

Grant details: Successful applicants are expected to match the grant given by the same amount. In 1992 several people, including dancers and musicians, received grants to advance their careers. Applications were particularly favoured when people's vocational training would benefit the local community. Grants ranged between £250 and £1,500 and a few were recurrent.

Applications procedure: Applications are sometimes invited through the local press. An application form is available from the correspondent.

Correspondent: Sid Franks, Community Relations Manager

Address: Wembley Stadium, Community Relations Department, Wembley, Middlesex HA9 0DW (081-902 8833, ext. 3387)

Other information: Wembley Charitable Foundation was set up in 1988 with a joint donation by Wembley Stadium and Michael Jackson. Since then various artists, including the Rolling Stones and Madonna, have contributed to its funds.

The Wembley Samaritan Fund

Beneficial area: Former urban district of Wembley

Objects: Benefit of poor sick persons

Income: £4,000 (1990)

Grant total: £3,000

Grant details: Much of the grant total was spent on providing holidays for handicapped people. Grants were also made for items such as heaters and bedding for sick or elderly people.

Applications procedure: By 'phone or in writing to the correspondent. A visit to the applicant by two trustees will be arranged.

Correspondent: Miss J Hancock

Address: 31 Lily Gardens, Alperton, Wembley, Middx (081-998 3488)

Wembley Stadium Market Traders Charities Organisation

Beneficial area: London Borough of Brent, and elsewhere

Objects: The promotion of charitable purposes by making donations to charitable organisations

Type of beneficiary: Individuals and organisations

Income: £12,500 (1980)

Grant total: £8,200

Grant details: In 1980 the charity made donations to the following local and national causes: cancer research, mental handicap, Jewish welfare, spastics, Sue Ryder homes and others, as well as £3,700 to the Mayor's Appeal. £750 was also used to provide food hampers for the elderly.

Applications procedure: To the correspondent

Correspondent: Mr H Berg, Chairman of the Committee

Address: 6 Linkside, Chigwell, Essex (telephone number is ex-directory)

Other information: No information for this charity is available at the Charity Commission after 1980. This entry was not confirmed by the trust.

Major Local Companies

McDermott (Engineering) London, McDermott House, 140 Wembley Park Drive, Middlesex HA9 8JD (081-903 1333) supports local charities. Contact Mr Ray Bettiss, Director of Personnel.

Unisys Ltd (UK Headquarters), 31 Brentfield, Stonebridge Park, London NW10 8LS (081-965 0511/3666) supports local appeals such as those from hospitals and educational institutions. Contact Mr Chris Cherkas, Director of Human Resources.

Hart and Freedman, Park Royal Road, London NW10 7LY. (081-961 5171). Contact Dr Laurence Swan, Brand Development Manager at the parent company, Fyffes Group Ltd, 12 York Gate, Regents Park, London NW1 4QJ (071-487 4472). Projects receive support which promote employment in disadvantaged areas or are recommended by local staff.

Sources of Advice

Brent Arts Council, c/o The Stables, Dollis Hill Lane, London NW2 (081 452 8655). Contact Caroline Jenkinson, Arts Officer. (Hours: Thursdays and Fridays 11-5.00)

Brent Adult and Community Education Service, The Old Library, Willesden Green Library Complex, High Road, Willesden Green, London NW10 2SD (081-908 7473)

Bromley

London Borough of Bromley

Bromley Civic Centre, Stockwell Close, Bromley, Kent BR1 3UH. (081-464 3333)

Correspondent(s):
Social Services Committee: W Ford, Administration and Finance Manager, Jim Graham, Director of Field Work, (mental illness specific grant)
Education Committee: M Shipp, Budget and Resources Officer
General Purposes Committee: Lynn Hill, Senior Committee Administrator
Leisure Services Committee: Mrs Lilian Harris, Finance Officer
Housing Committee: A Long, Principal Administrative Officer
Technical Services Committee: R Harrison, Senior Committee Administrator.

Grant totals 1991/92:
£1,563,305 in main programme funding;

Funding: Grant applications from the voluntary sector are usually considered individually by the service committee concerned. These can be broken down in 1991/92 as follows:

Social Services	£827,510
Education	£162,550
General Purposes	£63,530
Leisure	£464,815
Housing	£43,900
Technical Services	£1,000
TOTAL	£1,563,305

Social Services Committee: The committee with greatest grant-aid resources in 1991/92 was Social Services, which divided a total of £827,510 between 39 welfare organisations. Its grants budget is subdivided into the following categories of activity:

- general services (assisting groups such as Bromley Women's Aid, Bromley Centre for Voluntary Service and Bromley Victims Support Scheme);
- children's services through supporting organisations such as Bromley Mencap, Bromley Welcare, Bromley Pre-School Playgroups Association;

- services for the elderly (with groups supported such as Age Concern);
- services for mentally ill adults. In 1991/92 support was given for new services provided by Bromley Carers' Information and Support Service and Bromley Care Support Services.

Education Committee: The Education Committee is an important grant-maker. The majority of beneficiaries are youth groups with grants totalling £67,000 in 1991/92; many grants are in the form of 'lettings' (£71,120), or assistance with rent payable on educational premises.

General Purposes Committee: The General Purposes Committee's 1991/92 budget of £63,530 was divided between diverse organisations, ranging from the Greater London Home Safety Council to the London Boroughs' Association.

Leisure Services Committee: The Leisure Services Committee is Bromley's second largest grantmaker, with the Churchill Theatre Trust being the major beneficiary. Significant amounts are also given to Bromley Arts Council and Chislehurst and St Paul Crag Conservators.

Housing Committee: The Housing Committee awarded grants to three organisations in 1991/92: Bromley Council for Voluntary Service, the Federation of Housing Associations and the Federation of Council Tenants.

Technical Services Committee: The Technical Services Committee is a small grant-making committee essentially concerned with highways in Bromley. In 1991/92 it gave one grant of £1,000 to Environment Bromley to help with the upkeep and promotion of country walks within the borough.

Mental Illness Specific Grant: In 1991/92 the council was successful in its bid for central government funding and supported three voluntary organisations: Springpark project organised by MIND (£8,500); Advocacy Project run by the Bromley Mental Health Forum (£25,000); and Bromley Council for Voluntary Service (£16,500), a coordinator to run volunteers for people with mental health problems and their carers.

Drugs and Alcohol Specific Grant: Bromley Council did not receive any central government funding for alcohol/drugs services in 1991/92.

Eligibility: Bromley's grant-making policy is un-exceptional: basically, to be eligible for a grant voluntary organisations must work with and for local communities and must be non-profit-making and non-political. Each service committee carries out this policy according to its own individual priorities.

Applications procedure: Main programme funding is dealt with annually, and completed application forms should be returned to the council by mid-September each year. Occasional one-off applications from groups with a very urgent need may be referred to a service committee for approval after this deadline has been passed.

Other support: Bromley gives occasional support in the form of goods in kind, particularly sports equipment. Discretionary rate relief is offered to some voluntary organisations including sports clubs. Council staff are happy to give advice regarding funding and management issues when required. In addition, vehicle maintenance and petrol are offered to Age Concern to help with its meals-on-wheels service.

Contracting and the Community Care Plan
In 1992 the London Borough of Bromley entered into contracts with voluntary organisations for high cost services via its Social Services and Housing departments. In 1992/93 contracts will be made for day care for the elderly. (£145,000) for HIV/AIDS advice and training, (£13,600) and for services for the blind (£67,800). Most contracts in Social Services last for two years.

The voluntary sector was involved in developing Bromley's Community Care Plan with Bromley Centre for Voluntary Services coordinating the suggestions, plans and ideas put forward by local voluntary organisations.

For further information contact: Charles Ogden, Chief Social Services Officer

Bromley Joint Commissioning Strategy Group (this replaced the
Bromley Joint Consultative Committee)

Beneficial area: London Borough of Bromley

Objects: To provide the strategic direction for Joint Commissioning of Care Services in Bromley.

Funding practices: The Joint Commissioning Strategy Group (JCSG) is currently considering its future funding practices in areas including joint finance and how its activities might relate to the functions of individual agency support-funding mechanisms.

Total expenditure in 1992/93: c£763,300, £90,000 was available for new schemes, of which £63,000 was awarded to voluntary sector projects.

Details of projects: Not available when the book went to press.

Applications procedure: Under review. Contact one of the correspondents.

Correspondents: Rachel Wood, Administrator, or Robin Lorimer, Project Manager

Address: Family Health Services Authority, Global House, 10 Station Approach, Hayes, Kent BR2 7E8 (tel 081-462 2211) (fax 081-462 6767)

Other information: In October 1991 The Bromley Joint Commissioning Strategy Group was formed, with representatives from Bromley Health Authority, Bromley Family Health Authority, London Borough of Bromley and the local voluntary sector. It replaced the Bromley Joint Consultative Committee and was reviewing joint finance arrangements in March 1992.

Bromley Arts Council

Beneficial area: London Borough of Bromley

Objects: See below

Type of beneficiary: Organisations

Grant details: The council is primarily a source of advice and support for arts organisations in the borough. It does however also have a small budget for grant-aiding of affiliated amateur groups.

Correspondent: Mrs Jean Dyne, Secretary

Address: Ripley Arts Centre, 24 Sundridge Avenue, Bromley, BR1 2PX (081-464 5816)

Other information: This entry was not confirmed by the trust.

Bromley Benevolent Association

Beneficial area: London Borough of Bromley

Objects: Affording assistance to the aged and infirm, the sick and other distressed persons

Type of beneficiary: Individuals

Income: £1,450 (1988)

Grant total: £1,450

Grant details: One-off grants are made, and a few small recurrent grants to elderly people for heating.

Applications procedure: To the correspondent, preferably through a social worker.

Correspondent: Miss J C Farrer

Address: 30 Cedar Road, Bromley, BR1 3BZ (081-460 8228)

Other information: This trust is currently in the throes of joining forces with Bromley Relief in Need, a local charity with very similar aims. (see separate entry)

Bromley Relief in Need Charity

Beneficial area: Ancient Parish of Bromley

Objects: Relief of hardship and distress

Type of beneficiary: Individuals

Income: About £1,000 a year

Grant details: Grants usually in the range of £50 to £100 are made for the relief of hardship; this may include help with debt and fuel bills. In recent years the charity has been receiving too few applications to dispose of its income and a surplus of several thousand pounds has accumulated.

Applications procedure: Only through social services or welfare agency, CAB, GP, headteacher etc.

Correspondent: J Holt

Address: 51 Hope Park, Bromley, Kent BR1 3RG (081-464 0205)

Other information: This entry was not confirmed by the trust.

The Chislehurst Charities

Beneficial area: Former parish of Chislehurst (most of the Chislehurst postal area and a small part of Sidcup)

Objects: Relief of need and assistance of young people embarking on a career

Type of beneficiary: Individuals

Income: £600 (1990)

Grant total: £200

Grant details: Two charities are administered separately under the heading of the Chislehurst Charities.

The Chislehurst Relief in Need Charity made grants of £8 to 24 elderly people, and a grant of £10 to a family in 1990.

The Lund and Warwick Charity makes grants to young people under the age of 25 who are embarking on a career. Its last grant (£1,750) was made in 1987.

Applications procedure: Direct to the correspondent

Correspondent: Dr J W Fox

Address: Marlow House, 3 Camden Park Road, Chislehurst, Kent, BR7 5HE (081-467 3011)

Major Local Companies

Wallis Ltd (head office), 47 Homesdale Road, Bromley BR2 9TN (081-464 3377) makes one or two local grants yearly. Contact the Managing Director.

Muirhead Vactric Components Ltd, Oakfield Road, Penge, London SE20 8EW (081-659 9090), supports charities in the locality which are related to the engineering business. Write to the Personnel Office.

Marks & Spencer, 123 High Street, Bromley BR1 1JL (081-460 9131) makes donations to local charities. Contact Carol Luffman.

Sources of Advice

Bromley Council for Voluntary Service, 28a Beckenham Road, Beckenham BR3 4LS (081-663 3773)

Contact: Gregory Beaman
Opening hours: 9.00-5.00

Bromley Arts Council, see entry on pg 76

Bromley Adult Education Centre, Princes Plain, Church Lane, Bromley, Kent BR2 8LD (081-462 9184)

Camden

London Borough of Camden

Town Hall, Euston Road, London NW1 2RU (071-278 4444)

Correspondent(s):
Voluntary Sector Unit: Sue Wilby, Head of Unit (071-860 5791);

Economic Development Unit: Naomi Kingsley, Head of Unit (071-860 5966)

Social Services Dept: Simon White, Director of Social Services; Vijay Sawmy, Development Officer for mental illness and drug/alcohol specific grants (071-413 6648 ext 2830)

Libraries and Arts Committee: Dan Shaw, Senior Arts Officer (071-860 5831)

Grant totals 1991/92:
£11,316,351 in main programme funding

Funding: Most of Camden's grant-making is carried out via the Voluntary Sector Unit though other units do have a degree of grant-making autonomy. The total budget for 1991/92 can be broken down as follows:

Policy and Resources (Grants) Sub-Committee	£9,395,294
Planning, Transport and Employment Committee	£1,312,770
Social Services Committee	£586,287
Libraries and Arts Committee	
festivals	£14,000
arts	£8,000
TOTAL	£11,316,351

Camden's various grant-making committees give priority to the following:

1. organisations providing direct services to those most in need and most vulnerable (the income of those most benefiting from the service should be taken into account, and the service should seek to offset the worst effect of government policies on low-income groups);

2. organisations with a strong Camden connection which provide services to Camden residents;

3. organisations which are 'service effective' in terms of the number of people benefiting;

4. organisations demonstrating financial and management competence;

5. organisations which attempt to combat racism/sexism, which are managed by the communities that they serve, and which work with disadvantaged and disabled people, ethnic minorities, women, lesbians and gay men.

The main condition of grant-aid is that every applicant organisation must submit copies of its constitution, standing orders, rules and regulations. No grant-making committee will consider an application before these papers have been both submitted and approved. However, in 1991/92 and for the foreseeable future Camden was unable to fund any new applications due to financial constraints.

Social Services: The Children Act 1989: In March 1992 this legislation had not greatly affected Camden's grant-making policy towards organisations working with children. The then imminent review of children's services for under eights may have implications for future funding strategies.

Mental Illness Specific Grant: In 1991/92 Camden was successful in its bid for funding from the Department of Health and awarded £40,000 to Crossroads, £4,000 to Camden Consortium, a user group, and £5,000 to Camden Carers' Forum.

Drug and Alcohol Specific Grant: In 1991/92 Camden Council received funding from the DoH and made grants to CASA (Camden Alcoholics Support Association) and Rugby House Project.

Applications procedure: The deadline for submission of application forms is normally at the end of September.

Other support: Camden gives free advice and consultancy and occasionally allows local voluntary groups the use of premises on a cheap or rent-free basis. It also gives discretionary rate relief to local charities.

Contracting and the Community Care Plan
In February 1992 Camden was restructuring the whole of its Social Services department and this

delayed the development of its Community Care Plan. Social Services was the only department set to use contracts in 1992/93. The duration and nature of the contracts were still under consideration.

Discussions about community care took place with Voluntary Action Camden, local voluntary organisations, local branches of national agencies and liaison groups with different service users.

For further information contact: Simon White, Director of Social Services (071-278 4444)

Camden Joint Consultative Committee

Beneficial area: London Borough of Camden

Objects: Promoting community care and collaboration between statutory and non-statutory agencies particularly focusing on services for elderly people, children, the mentally ill, the physically disabled, people with learning difficulties, people with drug/alcohol related problems, the homeless, AIDS/HIV patients, and ethnic groups.

Funding practices: Joint finance is for supporting selected personal social services provided by local authorities, voluntary organisations or health authorities, and helps finance projects which support people in their own homes or in residential homes. Grants are for a limited time, normally three years, after which tapering arrangements or alternative funding must be available. Grants cannot be used to fund services which it is the statutory duty of the health or local authority to provide.

Expenditure in 1990/91: c£610,000 (see below)

Details of projects: Amongst voluntary organisations funded were Camden Carers for the post of Coordinator (£14,150) and Health Action Camden for the salary of a Development Worker (£9,640)

Applications procedure: Apply to the council or health authority or directly to the JCC Secretariat.

Correspondent: Diane Stacy, Committee Administrator

Address: Camden JCC, c/o Camden and Islington Family Health Services Authority (FHSA), Hobson House, 155 Gower Street, London WC1E 6BH (071-383 4155 ext 250)

Other information: The committee meets at least three times a year and is supported by a Joint Care Planning Team which comprises officers from the constituent health authorities, the local authority and the voluntary sector.

The Bloomsbury Dispensary

Beneficial area: Bloomsbury

Objects: Relief of sickness and illness

Type of beneficiary: Individuals

Income: £4,000 (1987)

Grant total: £3,450

Grant details: One-off grants, from about £10 to an average value of £100, are made for the relief of sickness and illness; note that this does not include pregnancy. The trustees are not empowered to offer assistance for debts incurred.

Applications procedure: Initial application can be made directly to the Secretary

Correspondent: Mrs J Rustage, Secretary

Address: 17a Macklin Street, Drury Lane, London WC2V 5NR (071-405 1878)

Other information: See also William Shelton's Educational Foundation and the Dibdin Brand Charity. This entry was not confirmed by the trust.

Dibdin Brand Charity

Beneficial area: The former Metropolitan Borough of Holborn and elsewhere

Objects: Provision of pensions for the indigent classes

Type of beneficiary: Individuals

Income: £2,600 (1974/75)

Grant total: £900

Grant details: Pensions were paid to 12 individuals in the Holborn area. The most recent accounts on file at the Charity Commission are for 1974/75; since then it is not thought that the trust's income has increased.

Applications procedure: To the correspondent

Correspondent: Mrs Joan Rustage, Secretary

Address: 17a Macklin Street, Drury Lane, London WC2V 5NR (071-404 3166)

Other information: See also William Shelton's Educational Foundation and The Bloomsbury Dispensary. This entry was not confirmed by the trust.

The Fitzdale Trust

Beneficial area: London Borough of Camden

Objects: Welfare of young people

Type of beneficiary: Organisations

Income: £7,860 (1990)

Grant total: £5,650

Grant details: Grants are made to organisations only, and specifically those concerned with the social or moral welfare of young people in London. Grants of about £200 can be made to youth clubs (church or otherwise), and support is given to school voluntary committees, the Church Army and to local hostels for young women who may be single parents, homeless or newly-arrived in London. Grants are one-off and usually for about £200. Renewed applications may be considered.

Applications procedure: In writing to the correspondent. Applications are considered twice-yearly in March and October.

Correspondent: Mrs Anne MacGeorge

Address: 6 Stanhope Gardens, London N6 5TS

The Hampstead Wells and Campden Trust

Beneficial area: Individuals must be resident in the former Metropolitan Borough of Hampstead; organisations from a wider area may apply if their work benefits Hampstead residents among others.

Main grant areas: Relief of individual need, hardship, distress, disablement, infirmity or sickness; provision of assistance to organisations active in these areas.

Type of beneficiary: Individuals and organisations

Income: £271,000 (1986/87)

Grant total: £225,700

Grant details: During the year pensions totalling £51,500 were paid to 165 individuals. In addition 400 one-off grants amounting to £38,000 were made for the relief of individual need, covering such areas as clothing, furniture, fuel and heating, holidays, removals and travel expenses, television and telephones, and a few grants for education and help with debts.

Grants were made to 36 organisations, all but one between £500 and £11,000.

Applications procedure: Applications should normally be sponsored by a statutory or voluntary organisation, or by a person familiar with the circumstances of the case, e.g. social worker, doctor, clergyman etc. To apply for a weekly pension, the sponsoring person or body should outline the case and complete an application form. Office hours are between 10-1 Mon, Wed, Fri and 10-4 Tues, Th.

Correspondent: C M Regan, Clerk to the Trustees

Address: 62 Rosslyn Hill, London NW3 1ND (071-435 1570)

Other information: The original Wells Charity was established in 1698 with a gift of land. In 1971 a Scheme amalgamated a number of charities into the Hampstead Relief in Sickness Fund and the Hampstead Relief in Need Fund which are administered together as the Hampstead Wells and Campden Trust. This entry was not confirmed by the trust.

Edward Harvist Charity

Beneficial area: London Borough of Camden

Other information: The charity is administered as part of the totality of Camden Council's support of voluntary organisations. There is no separate applications procedure. See entry for the council.

The Mayor of Camden's Charity Trust Fund

Beneficial area: London Borough of Camden or immediate neighbourhood

Objects: Relief of need

Type of beneficiary: Individuals and organisations

Income: £33,000 (1987)

Grant total: £15,200

Grant details: £6,500 in charitable payments and £8,700 in other payments.

Applications procedure: To the correspondent, in the case of individuals either directly or through social workers.

Correspondent: The Mayor's Secretary

Address: Mayor's Parlour, Town Hall, Euston Road, London NW1 2RU (071-278 4444 ext 5130)

Other information: This entry was not confirmed by the trust.

Philological Foundation

Beneficial area: London Borough of Camden and the City of Westminster

Objects:

1. Educational grants for children and young people who are or have been pupils at any secondary school in the beneficial area

2. Assistance of county and voluntary schools within the beneficial area, and especially in the former of borough of St Marylebone

Type of beneficiary: Individuals and organisations

Income: £66,000 (1990/91)

Grant total: c£47,000

Grant details: Grants are made to enable young people to pursue higher or further education or to travel abroad for educational purposes. The trustees are required to pay particular regard to the needs of former pupils of the St Marylebone Grammar School. Grants are available for outfits, clothing, tools, instruments, or books to assist children and young persons to prepare for or enter a profession, trade, occupation or service on leaving school, university or other educational establishment.

In 1990/91 nine educational grants to individuals totalled £6,000 and were given to help young people participate in Operation Raleigh and similar projects, to undertake further drama, dance training, educational studies and research.

However, the trust primarily gives grants to schools for playground improvements, (including equipment, safety materials, and gardens) and for books, computers, musical instruments and library equipment. In 1990/91 about £41,000 was given in grants to schools.

Applications procedure: Applications from schools should contain full details of the project and costs; a visit to the school will often be arranged. Individuals should contact the correspondent for an application form.

Correspondent: Miss E E Amos, Clerk to the Trustees

Address: Flat 2, 8 Camden Crescent, Bath, Avon, BA1 5HY (0225) 335536

Other information: Established after the closure of St Marylebone Grammar School in 1981, the foundation now publicises itself to all schools in the beneficial area. Its programme of educational grants for eligible individuals (see above) is perhaps less known.

The Eva Reckitt Trust

Beneficial area: Camden, Islington; national and overseas

Objects: General charitable purposes

Type of beneficiary: Organisations

Income: £50,000 (1989)

Expenditure: £47,000

Grant details: The trust has an extensive programme of grants which it makes under the headings of overseas, housing projects, medical, educational, relief of hardship, prisoners/ex-offenders, arts, Ireland, community projects, victims support, disabled and the environment. Eva Reckitt, the founder of the trust, lived in the NW3 area and the trust, when it makes grants to specifically London groups, tends to make them in that area. Recent beneficiaries have included Hampstead Old People's Housing, Camden Family Service Unit, Voluntary Action Camden, Kentish Town Project, Islington Girl's Project, Islington Play Lorry Project, Camden Society for the Mentally Handicapped, Disabled in Camden, Camden Help for Victims of Crime and Highgate Counselling Centre. Grants to these groups ranged between £100 and £750.

Applications procedure: In writing to the correspondent. The trustees meet every two months.

Correspondent: George Bunney

Address: 24 Mitchell Walk, Amersham, Bucks (0494 725146)

Other information: This entry was not confirmed by the trust.

The St Pancras Welfare Trust

Beneficial area: The old Metropolitan Borough of St Pancras (NW1, NW5, small parts of WC1 and NW3)

Objects: Individuals in need; payment of fuel bills; grants to voluntary organisations

Type of beneficiary: Individuals and organisations

Income: £32,000 (1988)

Grant total: £30,000

Grant details: One-off grants to both individuals and organisations, the majority between £50 and £200.

Applications procedure: Through social workers, hospitals, voluntary organisations etc. Applications are considered quarterly, but emergencies for sums up to £100 can be considered on an ad hoc basis by the Chair.

Correspondent: Pam Warren, Clerk to the Trustees

Address: 38a Belsize Grove, London NW3 4T (071-483 4493)

Other information: This entry was not confirmed by the trust.

Stafford's Charity

Beneficial area: Parishes of St Andrew Holborn and St George the Martyr, roughly the area between Russell Square and Farringdon station.

Objects: Following a recent consultation with the Charity Commission the trust broadened its objects. It still provides pensions to persons of good character who have lived in the beneficial area for three years but can also make one-off grants to individuals in need and organisations assisting people in need.

Type of beneficiary: Individuals and organisations

Income: c£75,000 (1991/92)

Grant total: c£50,000

Grant details: Quarterly pensions totalling £300 are paid to about 150 pensioners and in 1991 these accounted for about £44,000 of the grant total. The pensions are paid unequally with higher sums paid during the winter months. Usually only persons in receipt of supplementary benefits or rate/rent rebates will be considered; particular regard will be paid to the health of the applicant. Grants amounting to £6,000 were paid out to or on behalf of individuals.

It is likely that the pension level will remain unchanged or possibly reduce during the next year or so.

Applications procedure: Application form available from the correspondent. A meeting will be arranged after the form has been completed.

Correspondent: Mr Tahourdin, Secretary

Address: Simmonds Church Smiles & Co, 13 Bedford Row, London WC1R 4BU (071-242 9971)

Other information: The correspondent says that there are currently vacancies for pensions.

Matthew Wistrich Trust

Beneficial area: Camden (previously Greater London)

Objects: Children and young people up to the age of 25 who are physically disabled or have learning difficulties, and their families

Type of beneficiary: Individuals

Income: £5,150 (1991)

Grant total: £3,220

Grant details: Grants for clothing, travel, holidays and equipment. The trust also recently contributed towards the cost of playground equipment at a school for children with hearing impairments.

Applications procedure: By referral from social workers.

Correspondent: Bob Goldsmith, Honorary Secretary to the trust

Address: Room 210, Town Hall, Euston Road, London NW1 2RU (071-278 4444)

Local Major Companies

Cable and Wireless plc, New Mercury House, 26 Red Lion Square, London WC1R 4UQ (071-315 4126) occasionally supports charities in the Camden area. It is currently funding Camden ITEC which provides information technology training for the disadvantaged. Contact Aubrey Davidson, Community Affairs Manager.

Cable London (television cable network), Centro House, 20-23 Mandela Street, London NW1 ODU (071-911 0555) makes donations to local organisations. Contact David Edwards, Managing Director. Grapevine, its local television channel, sometimes promotes charitable events and services. Contact Carol Enahoro, Programming Coordinator.

Hillsdown Holdings plc, Hillsdown House, 32 Hampstead High Street, London NW3 1QD (071-794 0677) Write to Mr Harry Solomon, Chairman.

NCR Ltd, 206 Marylebone Road, London NW1 6LY (071-723 7070) sometimes supports local charities and organisations where its members are active. Contact Patrick Stroudley, Charities Committee.

Sources of Advice

Voluntary Action Camden, 1st Floor, Instrument House, 207/215 Kings Cross, London WC1X 9DB (071-837 5544)

Director: Rosemary Nicholson
Opening hours: 9.30-5.00

Camden Youth Office, 6 Camden High St, London NW1 0JH (071-388 2011).

Camden Adult Education Institute, Longford Street, London NW1 3HB (071-388 7106)

City of London

Corporation of the City of London

Guildhall, London EC2P 2EJ (071-606 3030)

Correspondent: The first point of contact for any organisation wishing to apply for a grant is Kevin Lee, Town Clerk's Department.

Grant totals in 1991/92: Approximately £750,000

Funding: The City of London gives grants to voluntary organisations through two main committees (a few other committees make very minor grants). These can be broken down approximately as follows:

Port and City of London Health and Social Services Committee	£350,000
Finance Committee	£400,000
TOTAL	£750,000

Finance Committee: Grants are made to a broad range of organisations and generally range from several hundred pounds to £25,000. An application must meet the following criteria in order to be successful:

They must have some link with the City OR

They must be part of some special nationwide activity

Preference will be given to supporting one-off needs rather than salaries

Grants are not usually given to individuals

Grants are not considered if the organisation has been a recipient of a grant within the last five years

Grants are not normally given to organisations funded by the London Boroughs Grants Scheme.

The Port and City of London Health and Social Services Committee: This committee provides assistance to charitable organisations based in or around the City area which provide assistance or benefit to residents or workers in the City.

In 1991/92 the corporation did not receive a Mental Illness Specific Grant or a Drug and Alcohol Specific Grant.

Applications procedure: The Finance Committee considers applications in the spring and in autumn. Applications to the Port and City of London Health and Social Services Committee are considered annually, and forms should normally be returned by the end of the year. Would-be applicants are advised to contact the correspondent in the first instance.

Contracting and The Community Care Plan: In March 1992 the Social Services Department was funding voluntary organisations through grants and was not making any significant changes. In specific instances Service Level Agreements were being considered.

The corporation has discussed its Community Care Plan with local voluntary organisations.

For further information contact: Miss E Crowther, Director of Social Services

City and Hackney Joint Consultative Committee

Beneficial area: City of London and London Borough of Hackney

Objects: Care in the Community. The committee wishes to target its aims more and an information pack is available outlining these aims.

Funding practices: In 1991/92 £400,000 was available for new schemes. If a bid is successful funding will not always be guaranteed after the first three years and therefore time-limited schemes are welcomed.

Total expenditure: c£600,000 (1991/92) but see below

Details of voluntary projects funded: The following voluntary organisations were amongst those funded:

Off Centre Counselling For Sexually Abused Survivors (£7,800)

Age Concern, towards a pensioners' handbook (£3,200)

Living Space, which provides residential care homes for people with mental health problems (£3,000)

Hackney Independent Living Team to fund a development worker for their residential homes for people with learning difficulties (£17,000)

Applications procedure: The committee meets four times a year in January, April, July and October. Bids should be in August to September for projects starting in the following year.

Correspondent: Mr Shun Au, Coordinator for the Joint Planning Unit

Address: Saint Leonard's Hospital, Nuttall Street, Kingsland Road, London N1 5LZ (071-739 8484 ext 4204)

Other information: Ras Mark-I, the Voluntary Sector Development Worker for Joint Planning, has been appointed to coordinate and encourage voluntary sector applications. He is based at Hackney Community Action, 90 de Beauvoir Road, London N1 (071-923 1962).

There are six Joint Executive Teams: Public Health and Primary Care, Learning Difficulties, Mental Health, Children and Young People, Disabilities, and the Elderly. Voluntary organisations usually have more success if they liaise with the planning group from the start as each has its own priorities.

Aldgate Freedom Foundation

Beneficial area: The freedom part of the Parish of St Botolph, Aldgate

Objects: Pensions to old people in need; support of charities working for poor homeless and other needy people in the beneficial area; the relief of people in need resident or employed in the beneficial area; the upkeep of the churchyard of the parish church of St Botolph.

Type of beneficiary: Organisations and individuals in need

Income: £33,120 (1990)

Grant total: £33,660

Grant details: The foundation still gives a substantial part of its income in pensions, one-off donations and Christmas gifts of £25 to aged needy people. However, support is also given to organisations serving those in need. In 1990 grants can be broken down as follows: £6,183 in the form of pensions and £1,175 in Christmas presents for pensioners; £250 on relief for the sick; £2,300 in regular subscriptions to charitable institutions and hospitals; £750 to the Portsoken Ward Club. By far the largest grant was for £23,300, awarded to the St Botolph Rehabilitation Centre.

Applications procedure: To the correspondent

Correspondent: Michael Sparks, Clerk to the Governors

Address: 31 Jewry Street, London EC3N 2EY (071-480 5884)

Thomas Carpenter's Trust

Beneficial area: The Bread Street and adjoining wards in the City of London.

Objects: To help in the education of residents of the beneficial area, or those whose parents have worked for three years in the area. Applicants should be under the age of 25.

Type of beneficiary: Individuals

Grant total: Approximately £12,000 per year

Grant details: Grants are made to those at school, college or university, to those who need to travel abroad to pursue their education, towards the costs of studying music or the other arts and towards the cost of education, training, apprenticeship or equipment for those starting work.

Correspondent: Thomas Ackland, Secretary

Address: 287 Green Lanes, Palmers Green, London N13 4XS (081-882 9520)

Castle Baynard Educational Foundation

Beneficial area: City of London, in particular the Ward of Castle Baynard

Objects: Educational grants tenable at any place of learning

Type of beneficiary: Individuals

Grant total: c£2,000 per annum

Grant details: Educational grants are made to individuals in need whose parents live or work in the City of London. In view of the trust's limited funds, the trustees prefer applicants to have a connection with the Ward of Castle Baynard.

Applications procedure: To the correspondent

Correspondent: The Clerk

Address: c/o Messrs Ellis Wood, Langdales, New Garden House, 78 Hatton Garden, London EC1N 8JR (071-242 1194)

The City Chapter and Percy Trentham Charity

Beneficial area: City of London including Glasshouse Yard

Objects: Pensions and grants for elderly people in need

Type of beneficiary: Individuals

Income: £5,000 (1988)

Grant total: £4,000

Grant details: Assistance is limited to people not less than 60 years old who are or have been resident or employed in the beneficial area. Cash grants are made to a maximum of £400. About 26 regular grants are made to people over 80 years old who are in poor health.

Applications procedure: Only through social worker, welfare officer or clergyman. Applications for regular grants are processed twice a year; all other applications are dealt with as they are received.

Correspondent: Mrs F Meek, Honorary Secretary

Address: 56 Venner Road, London SE26 5EL (081-778 4639)

Other information: The similar but smaller Hammond Pension Charity is administered with the above. Its beneficial area is the ancient Parish of St Andrew Holborn. This entry was not confirmed by the trust.

The Cordwainer and Bread Street Wards' Foundation

Beneficial area: The Cordwainer and Bread Street Wards, and adjoining wards, and the parish of St Vedust, Foster Lane, all in the City of London

Objects: Educational grants for residents

Type of beneficiary: Individuals

Grant total: £1,400 (1986)

Grant details: Four grants were awarded to residents in the beneficial area – grants for school pupils, to help with books, equipment, clothing and travel or for students for college or university fees or to supplement existing grants.

Applications procedure: To the correspondent

Correspondent: Thomas Ackland, Secretary

Address: 287 Green Lane, Palmers Green, London N13 4XS (081-882 9520)

The Farringdon within Ward Trust

Beneficial area: The Ward of Farringdon in the City of London

Objects: Financial assistance towards education for young people in need

Type of beneficiary: Residents of the beneficial area under the age of 25.

Grant total: £5,500 (1990/91)

Grant details: People under the age of 25 and in need of financial assistance can receive grants if they fulfil one of the following categories. They are listed in order of priority:

(a) People whose parents or one of whose parents are resident or work in the Ward of Farringdon Within;

(b) People who are resident or attend schools or other educational establishments in the City of London;

(c) People whose parents or one of whose parents work in the City of London.

Grants are made 'To promote the education (including the social and physical training) of persons eligible by awarding scholarships, exhibitions, bursaries, grants and maintenance allowances tenable at schools, colleges of education or other institutions of further (including professional and technical) education approved by the trustees.' In practice, most grants are made by way of contributions to school fees.

Applications procedure: Applications must usually be submitted by mid-April for the ensuing academic year. Prospective applicants or their parents should write in the first instance to the correspondent.

Correspondent: Mr C W Stunt

Address: Orchard House, Leigh, Sherborne, Dorset DT9 6HL (0935 872959)

The Charity of John Land for Widows and Children (Apprenticing Branch)

Beneficial area: The City of London

Objects: To help towards the cost of education, training, apprenticeship or equipment for those starting work.

Type of beneficiary: Poor children of freemen

resident in the beneficial area or with some other residential connection with the City.

Grant total: About £1,000 per annum

Grant details: Three to four grants are made each year.

Correspondent: M Farrell, Clerk

Address: St Dunstan's in the West, Fleet Street, London EC4 (071-405 1929)

The Ada Lewis Winter Distress Fund

Objects: The relief in need of poor and distressed people living or working - or who have formerly lived or worked - in the City of London area, and their dependants.

Income: £4,000 (1988/89)

Grant total: £3,000

Grant details: Annual grants of £75 are made to individuals in need.

Applications procedure: Usually through the welfare officers of the Corporation of the City of London.

Correspondent: Alan Page, Assistant Town Clerk

Address: The Town Clerk's Office, Corporation of the City of London, PO Box 270, Guildhall, London EC2P 2EJ (071-606 3030)

The Mitchell City of London Charity

Beneficial area: The City of London and elsewhere

Objects: Provision of pensions and grants for necessitous people who live or work, or have lived or worked, in the City of London, and the widows and children of such persons

Type of beneficiary: Individuals

Latest figures: 1990/91

Income: £59,500

Grant total: £20,500

Grant details: £8,600 was given in grants and £11,900 in pensions. £36,550 was transferred to the Educational Foundation.

Correspondent: P A Guilford, Clerk

Address: 6th Floor, 24-30 Holborn, London EC1N 2JB (071-242 0581)

Other information: The most recent accounts on file at the Charity Commission are for 1990/91.

The Mitchell City of London Educational Foundation

Beneficial area: Great Britain, with particular reference to the City of London

Objects:
To assist individuals financially who are under 25 and who have, or whose parents have lived or worked in the City of London for at least five years. Grants are made in the following categories:

1. For further education where no local education authority funding is available.
2. For sixth form school fees where university entrance is probable
3. Up to GCSE Level for children of one-parent families.
4. For further education where no local authority funding is available and the student has been educated at a City School. (In this case parents or student do not need to have lived in the City of London for five years).

Type of beneficiary: Individuals

Income: £60,170 (1990/91)

Grant total: £56,000

Grant details: Grants for people at school, college or university for whom no local education authority award is available ie. 16 to 18 year olds studying for A-levels needed for university and post graduates, but not first degree students. Grants range from £500 to £1,100 and are usually recurrent, occasionally one-off.

Grants are given towards fees for school-children, but very rarely for books, maintenance or educational outings. Awards to students are for fees/living expenses and books, but not for study/travel abroad. Preference is given to school-children with serious family difficulties so the child has to be educated away from home.

Applications procedure: On a form available from the correspondent. Two referees and details of parental income are always required. Applications should be made by the individual or parent, or through the individual's school for sixth form awards.

Correspondent: P A Guilford, Clerk

Address: 6th Floor, 24-30 Holborn, London EC1N 2JB (071-242 0581)

Stafford's Charity

See entry in the Camden section

Samuel Montagu Charitable Trust (formerly the Montagu Drayton Charitable Trust)

Beneficial area: National but particularly the City of London and the East End of London

Objects: General charitable purposes

Type of beneficiary: Organisations only

Income: See below

Grant total: £47,000 (1990)

Grant details: Great Ormond Street Hospital received £5,000 as the last of four payments, with the Tony Lorenz Memorial Trust receiving £1,000 . Other small grants were made to the Life Anew Trust, the Samuel Montagu Boys Club 25 years Appeal, the Tate Gallery, Crisis, RNLI and the European Educational Research Trust.

Correspondent: The Secretary

Address: Samuel Montagu & Co. Limited, 10 Lower Thames Street, London EC3R 6AE

Other information: The trust receives £34,000 gross under deed of covenant from Samuel Montagu & Co. Limited each year.

Croydon

London Borough of Croydon

Taberner House, Park Lane, Croydon CR9 3JS
(081-686 4433 ext 2922)

Correspondent: David Freeman, Policy Adviser (Voluntary Organisations), Chief Executive's Office

Each service department administers its own grants and contracts. Enquiries should be addressed to the above correspondent who will then refer them on as appropriate (a detailed list of contact officers is available on request).

Grant totals 1990/91: £2,367,540 in main programme funding;

Funding: Croydon allocates money to local voluntary organisations via a number of committees. Grants in 1990/91 can be broken down as follows:

Voluntary Sector	£764,570
Social Services	£955,170
Education	£356,760
Libraries, Museum and Arts	£144,320
Housing	£127,510
Parks and Recreation	£19,110
Highways and Public Works	£100
TOTAL	£2,367,540

Voluntary Sector Sub-committee: The Voluntary Sector Sub-Committee provides support for voluntary organisations considered to be of strategic importance in the borough, ethnic minority groups, advice agencies, employment and training groups, community centres and other organisations which do not fall within the remit of any other funding committee of the Council. From 1991/92 it will also administer a small budget (£5,000) for grants to ecology groups.

In 1990/91 the largest grant was made to the CAB, amounting to £278,000. Other organisations funded include: the Bangladesh Welfare Association of Croydon (£37,000) to provide a general welfare advice service and to fund a women's worker; Edgecoombe Community Centre Association (£4,000) to operate a small community centre; and the Croydon and District Small Bore Rifle League (£25) to enter a regional competition.

The Sub-Committee also manages the council's Lottery Fund which exists to provide for 'improvements in the environment and the provision of social and leisure facilities'.

The council's capital allocation for the voluntary sector support is managed by the sub-committee together with a revenue allocation for the repair and maintenance of council owned buildings leased to voluntary groups.

Social Services Committee: The Social Services Committee provides support to voluntary organisations whose activities complement the work carried out by the Social Services Department. These are grouped loosely into five categories.

1. Children and families
2. Community Groups
3. Counselling organisations
4. Groups providing services to elderly people
5. Organisations concerned with health and disability

In 1990/91 the largest single grant was made to WELCARE for a social work service for young single parents. Approximately 110 organisations were funded, the majority with grants under £2,000.

Voluntary organisations have also had a significant input in the chapter on children in the Croydon Community Care Plan.

Education Committee: The Education Committee provides grants to voluntary organisations which provide services to augment and complement the statutory duties it carries out in securing educational services to the borough.

The majority of grant-aided organisations are youth groups. In 1991/92 about 12 youth centres were grant aided for general running costs with grants ranging from £19,000 to £2,500. Summer Schemes and After School schemes were supported through Play Plus (the Play Council) which administered grants amounting to £65,000.

Libraries Museum and Arts Committee: The Libraries Museum and Arts Committee supports arts in the borough by providing revenue grants for major arts organisations on an annual basis, and by giving one-off project grants for arts activities in the borough. The Committee's current funding policy is to support:

1. Arts projects that will enable a wider audience to experience the arts, especially those who would not normally be associated with such activities, or for whom there is little provision;

2. Arts projects and activities that seek to broaden audiences;

3. Arts projects that encourage co-operation between different groups, particularly those that are not usually associated with the arts.

In 1990/91 one major arts venue, the Warehouse Theatre was supported with a grant of £110,000. Most other grants were for one-off projects and were for less than £2,000. This committee is seeking to assist new groups with revenue funding in the region of £5,000 to £10,000 from 1991/92.

A new scheme for local and community heritage projects is being introduced in 1991/92.

The Heritage Grants Scheme aims:

1. To help people understand, appreciate or celebrate Croydon's different communities, their cultures and histories

2. To help people understand and appreciate the Croydon area, its history and its environment.

Housing Committee: This committee supports a number of groups within the borough which provide advice and assistance on housing related matters, particularly to homeless people in the borough who have no 'priority need' under the housing legislation. The services provided range from the provision of advice through to the management of hostel accommodation.

In 1990/91 the largest single grant of £33,000 was made to Croydon Association for Young Single Homeless towards the cost of a hostel. Most grants are in the range of £10,000 to £20,000.

Parks and Recreation Committee: The Parks and Recreation Committee supports carnival associations, conservation and nature groups and sports organisations. About £3,500 is provided to each of two carnivals annually. Other grants are one-off, usually under £2,000.

Highway and Public Works Committee: This makes very minor grants.

Mental Illness Specific Grant: The council received DoH funding for about £143,000, exclusive of the borough's contribution. It was used to fund a furniture project and a welfare benefits service, both run by MIND.

Drugs and Alcohol Specific Grant: Through its funding from the DoH Croydon provided about £10,500 to one voluntary group. Its bid on behalf of another voluntary group was unsuccessful.

Applications procedure: The major grant-making committees have specific closing dates for grant applications, normally the end of October. However, applications may also be considered outside the normal cycle. Details of closing dates and departmental contacts are available on request.

Other support: Croydon gives some non-financial assistance to local voluntary groups in the form of practical advice for people proposing new projects and the occasional use of council-owned premises at a reduced rent. The council will also consider giving discretionary rate relief to non-profit organisations.

Contracting and the Community Care Plan
This authority wants to retain a strong element of grant-aid in its support for voluntary groups. Social Services will be introducing service agreements for a limited number of services and in March 1992 this was in the early stages of discussion. No other departments were funding voluntary organisations through contracts.

The council took part in a thorough consultation process for its Community Care Plan. Croydon Voluntary Action facilitated a Voluntary Sector Care Forum which had a direct input into Croydon's planning process and local voluntary organisations, both small and large, were consulted.

For further information contact: David Freeman, Policy Adviser (Voluntary Organisations)

Croydon Joint Consultative Committee

Beneficial area: London Borough of Croydon

Objects: To fund jointly planned projects, especially those which are compatible with the Community Care Plan

Funding practices: Both capital and revenue grants are made which are sometimes one-off. Some tapering grants are made to statutory authorities.

Total expenditure: £697,000 revenue funding, £133,000 capital funding (1990/91)

Expenditure on voluntary organisations: £287,300 revenue, £33,500 capital (1990/91)

Details of projects funded: Examples of voluntary organisations funded in 1990/91 include Drug Concern, Croydon, (£51,500), Age Concern (£31,100), MIND (£47,400), MENCAP (£82,600), Crossroads Care Attendant Scheme, (£35,700), ACE (£16,000), and Hyde Housing Association (£13,700), all of which received revenue funding. In addition MIND received a capital grant (£33,500).

Applications procedure: Applications should normally be sent in before November for projects starting in the following year.

Correspondent: Jenny Finch, Joint Planning Officer.

Address: Room 6.09, Chief Executive's Office, Taberner House, Park Lane, Croydon CR9 3JS (081-686 4433 ext 4924)

Other information: The committee meets four times per year. Its membership has been reviewed in the light of a new Joint Planning structure.

Church Tenements Charity

Beneficial area: London Borough of Croydon

Objects: Educational grants for residents under the age of 25

Type of beneficiary: Individuals and organisations

Income: £51,700 (1990/91)

Grant total: £46,200

Grant details: The trustees have a limited amount of funds at their disposal. They are therefore inclined to apply the trust income to exceptional or extraordinary cases of hardship or circumstance. They will generally favour an application below £5,000 where a grant has not been given previously by the local education authority. Grants are wide-ranging but mainly cover primary, secondary or post-school education, training, and apprenticeships. Grants may also be given towards the cost of uniforms, equipment, musical instruments, etc. Grants range from £150 to £500.

Grants can also be made to organisations such as Scouts, Boys Brigades, Guides etc.

Whilst no preference is given to any type of application the trustees will be encouraged to give grants if the applicant has made some effort to raise some finance him/herself.

Applications procedure: On a form available from the correspondent. Applications may be made throughout the year, to be considered by the trustees at quarterly meetings.

Correspondent: Ray Simpson, Committee Administrator

Address: Taberner House, Park Lane, Croydon, CR9 3JS (081-686 4433 ext. 2326)

Coulsdon Parochial Charities

Beneficial area: Ancient Parishes of Coulsdon, Sanderstead, Chelsham and Warlingham

Main grant areas: Relief of elderly people

Type of beneficiary: Organisations and individuals

Income: c£500 (1990/91)

Grant total: c£500

Grant details: Grants are made to elderly people in need and to welfare organisations working for the elderly

Applications procedure: To the correspondent

Correspondent: Rev J Wiltshire, Chairman of the trustees

Address: The Rectory, Coulsdon Road, CR5 1ED (07375 52152)

The Croydon Benevolent Association

Beneficial area: London Borough of Croydon

Objects: Holidays for elderly people

Type of beneficiary: Individuals

Grant details: No grants are given directly. Each year group holidays are organised for elderly residents of Croydon. The trust is administered by Age Concern and the holidays organised from the address below. In 1975, the last year for which accounts are on file at the Charity Commission, the association spent £3,400 on providing holidays.

Correspondent: Hilda Vincent

Address: Joyce Grant Centre, Davidson Lodge, Freemasons Road, Croydon CR0 6PO (081-654 7726)

Other information: This entry was not confirmed by the trust.

Croydon and District Children's Aid in Sickness Fund

Beneficial area: Croydon and neighbourhood

Objects: Benefit of needy children who are or have been sick

Type of beneficiary: Individuals

Income: £410 (1985/86)

Grant total: £400

Grant details: 15 grants were made to a maximum of £50 to cover a wide range of need, including payment towards the cost of a holiday and full payment for small household furnishings, a pram, telephone installation, wheelchair cover, window locks, mattress and heating.

Applications procedure: To the correspondent.

Correspondent: Patrick Martin, Team Manager

Address: Mayday Acute Unit Social Work Department, Mayday Road, Thornton Heath, CR4 7YE (081-684 6999 ext. 3226)

Croydon Lottery Fund

Beneficial area: London Borough of Croydon

Objects: Improvements to the local environment and the provision of social and leisure facilities

Income: Diminishing; see 'Other information'.

Grant details: The lottery fund can make grants to assist with repairs to buildings, the replacement and renewal of equipment, events and one-off activities and contingencies for emergencies. Grants are always one-off; groups are expected to raise a proportion of the required funds from other sources.

Applications procedure: Application forms and guidance leaflets are available from the correspondent

Correspondent: John Rowden, Principal Financial Services Assistant

Address: London Borough of Croydon, Taberner House, Park Lane, Croydon CR9 3JS (081-686 4433 ext 2750)

Other information: This is a reducing fund and is unlikely to remain in existence for many more years. Its income comes from investment interest; the trustees are, however, empowered to use as much of the capital as they wish, and could, in theory, distribute what remains of the fund in one fell swoop.

Croydon Mayor's Fund

Beneficial area: London Borough of Croydon

Objects: To raise money for general charitable purposes in the borough.

Grant details: The Mayor decides which charity or charities should be supported. In 1991/92 money was raised for MIND in Croydon through various activities including a charity ball and a coffee morning.

Correspondent: The Mayor's Secretary

Address: Mayor's Parlour, Town Hall, Katharine Street, Croydon CR9 1XW (081-686 4433)

Croydon MENCAP (Croydon Society for the Mentally Handicapped)

Beneficial area: Croydon and districts

Objects: Relief of need among people with learning disabilities/their families and carers

Type of beneficiary: Individuals and organisations

Income: £27,600 (1990)

Grant total: £300

Grant details: Small grants are available for individuals and welfare organisations working with people with learning disabilities. In the past donations have been awarded towards playschemes, toy libraries, mini-buses and sports centres. The society, itself a grant-seeking organisation, has seen its income drop at the same time as the call on its services has risen. Now its resources can only stretch to small discretionary grants.

Correspondent: The Director

Address: Peter Sylvester Centre, 11 Bramley Hill, South Croydon, CR2 6LX (081-688 3121)

The Frank Denning Memorial Foundation

Beneficial area: London Borough of Croydon

Objects: Travelling scholarships for full-time students at colleges of further education who are between the ages of 19 and 25 and who live, or whose parents/guardians live, in the beneficial area, and who have every intention of returning to the UK at the end of their travel abroad.

Type of beneficiary: Individuals

Grant total: c£7,000 (1990/91)

Grant details: Travelling scholarships of up to £800 each for travel abroad in the summer vacation. Projects must have specific educational objectives. Preference is given to students of mechanical sciences.

Applications procedure: On the application form available from the correspondent after 1 September. Note that these must be returned by 1 March, and that it is to this date that the age qualification noted above refers. A handout is sent to all Croydon students giving information on the foundation.

Correspondent: John Whittington, Assistant Honorary Secretary

Address: Taberner House, Park Lane, Croydon , CR9 3JS (081-686 4433 ext. 3873).

King Edward VII Children's Convalescent Trust Fund

Beneficial area: London Borough of Croydon and the County of Surrey

Main grant areas: Provision of convalescent holidays for women and children in need

Type of beneficiary: Organisations

Income: £25,460 (1989/90)

Grant total: £37,000

Grant details: Three grants were made to organisations which are assisted on a regular basis: Tadworth Court Children's Hospital (£12,500), Invalid Children's Aid Association (£5,000) and Cherry Trees - The Peter Pierrepont Bursary Fund (£20,000).

Correspondent: See below

Address: Messrs Gregory Rowcliffe & Milners, Bedford Row, London WC1R 4BZ (071-242 0631)

Other information: The previous correspondent at Messrs Gregory Rowcliffe & Milners has died and I was unable to find out who was now administering the trust. Further information would be welcomed.

See also the entry for the Princess Mary Memorial Trust Fund. Another trust, the Victoria Convalescent Trust Fund, is also administered. This trust was established to assist organisations providing recuperative holidays in an unrestricted beneficial area. £31,800 of its 1987 income of £43,000 was given, as in previous years, to homes, hospices and hospitals in the south of England.

Annie Jane Knowles and Edward George Bates Pension Fund For The Blind

Beneficial area: London Borough of Croydon

Objects: Provision of pensions for blind people

Type of beneficiary: Individuals

Income: About £1,200 (1990)

Grant total: About £1,000

Grant details: 16 pensions are currently being awarded.

Applications procedure: To the correspondent via Croydon Voluntary Association for the Blind

Correspondent: Bruce Middlemiss, Borough Secretary

Address: Taberner House, Park Lane, Croydon, CR9 3JS (081-686 4433 ext. 4959)

The Lavender Trust

Beneficial area: Primarily, but not restricted to, the London Borough of Croydon

Objects: General charitable purposes

Type of beneficiary: Organisations and individuals.

Income: £8,800 (1990/91)

Grant total: £8,020

Grant details: Grants ranging from £25 to £2080 were made to charities, churches, Christian groups, arts groups and children's organisations, in particular, The Crusaders' Union.

Applications procedure: In writing to the correspondents

Correspondent: C D Leck and Mrs E J Leck

Address: 50 Hartley Down, Purley, Surrey, CR8 4EA

The Rosetti Foundation

Beneficial area: London Borough of Croydon

Main grant areas: Relief of need

Type of beneficiary: Organisations

Income: £4,020 (1990/91)

Grant total: £2,850

Grant details: Grants up to £500 were made to youth clubs, hospices, hospital appeals, churches, counselling and advice groups.

Applications procedure: In writing to the correspondent

Correspondent: Mr R Stiby, Chairman of the Trustees

Address: Croudace House, 97 Godstone Road, Caterham, Surrey CR3 6XQ (Tel: 0883 341517 Fax: 0883 341729)

St John the Baptist Charitable Fund

Beneficial area: Parish of St John the Baptist, Purley

Objects: Relief of poverty and sickness among residents of the beneficial area

Type of beneficiary: Individuals

Income: £2,350 (1991)

Grant total: £2,510

Grant details: Grants are made primarily to individuals, but organisations may also be considered when they are local to the parish. Nine grants were made in the year including £530 for a Lourdes visit for parishioners, £500 towards a special bed for a sufferer of muscular dystrophy, £250 for the special needs of the wife of a severely disabled man, £260 for a holiday for severely disabled man and his family, and £100 for the local branch of the Handicapped Pilgrimage Trust.

Applications procedure: Direct to the correspondent or through the parish priest of St John the Baptist Church. Applications are considered by the trustees on an ad-hoc basis.

Correspondent: P Bunce

Address: 4 Highclere Close, Kenley, Surrey, CR8 5JU (081-660 7301)

The Mary Hannah Taylor Trust

Beneficial area: West Croydon

Objects: Relief of need, especially among people over 60

Type of beneficiary: Individuals and organisations

Income: £910 (1989/90)

Grant total: £910

Grant details: Grants ranging between £100 and £200 are made to the local Age Concern and to London City Mission for their work with local people in need, especially to help with such items as fuel bills.

Applications procedure: Direct to correspondent. The trust meets twice yearly in spring and autumn

Correspondent: Rev C K Meachin

Address: 80 Croham Road, South Croydon, CR2 7HA (081-680 4705)

Major Local Companies

The Nestlé Company Ltd (head office), St Georges House, Park Lane, Croydon, Surrey CR9 1NR (081-686 3333). Contact Pam Hards, Secretary to the Nestle Charitable Trust.

Philips Industrial Electronics, City House, PO Box 298, 420-430 London Road, Croydon, Surrey CR9 3QR (081-689 2166). Contact Mr N Rigler, Public Relations Manager, Philips UK, 188 Tottenham Court Road, London W1P 9LE (071-436 4044).

Crown House Engineering plc, 320 Purley Way, Croydon, CR9 2DE (081-686 2411) occasionally supports local charities through its parent company, Tarmac Construction Group Ltd, Construction House, Birch Street, Wolverhampton WV1 (0902 22431). However, appeals on a national basis are favoured. Contact John Baxter, Director of Services.

Bank of America, 25 Cannon Street, London EC4 (071-634 4000) supports recognised charities in areas of operation ie Hackney, Croydon and Bromley. Contact the Public Relations Department.

Sources of Advice

Croydon Voluntary Action, Eldon House, 78 Thornton Road, Thornton Heath, Surrey CR4 6BA (081-684 3862/5)

Director: John Knightly
Opening hours: 9.00-5.00

Continuing Education and Training Services, London Borough of Croydon, Taberner House, Park Lane, Croydon CR9 1TP (071-760 5461)

Ealing

London Borough of Ealing

Percival House, 14/16 Uxbridge Road, London W5 2HL. (081-579 2424)

Any initial or general enquiry should be made to the *Grants Unit:* Nigel Fogg, Acting Head of Grants Unit and Mark Aung, Grants Officer.

Further enquiries should be made to the following:

Social Services Department: Sue Brooks, Voluntary Services Officer, ext 52409, Peter Mawson, (mental illness specific grant) ext 52706

Leisure Services: Philip Britton, Assistant Chief Officer, ext 52364

Housing Department: Pat Nicholas, Special Project and Monitoring Officer, ext 55113

HIV/AIDS Unit: Philip Sharpe, AIDS/HIV Coordinator, (081-992 5566 ext 36652)

Under eights: Jenny Benwell, Advisor/ Coordinator, ext 53584

Education Department: Betty Moss or Barry Pollock, (ext 54146 and ext 52607 respectively)

Arts: Gillian Daire, ext 55086

Unified Community Action (UCA): see below

Environmental Services: Mick Aldridge , Chief Environmental Health Officer ext 52326

Health and Administration: Laura Fisher, Animal Welfare Officer ext 55039

Grant totals 1992/93:
Main programme funding   £3,050,680

Funding: The grant-giving process was centralised in 1990/91 so that the Grants Unit is now responsible for the administration of all grants and the Finance (Grants) Sub-Committee decides on all grants. The grants budget is broken down into: welfare (health, housing and social services); education; leisure (cultural activities, arts, community projects, sport and youth); miscellaneous (environmental services, employment, transport, community advice, multidisciplinary projects).

In 1992/93 it is estimated that the grants budget will be allocated as follows:

Welfare:

Housing	£260,350
Social services	£1,424,186
Education	£10,828
Miscellaneous:	
Environment	£2,100
Employment and transport	£321,297
Community advice	£342,250
Multidisciplinary projects	£298,802

Leisure:

Culture and arts	£97,970
Youth and Community	£117,800
Sport and physical recreation	£1,800
Horticulture/environment	£4,437
TOTAL	£2,881,820

There is also a rolling grants scheme whereby funds are allocated throughout the financial year, as opposed to the other grants which are awarded before the beginning of the financial year. In 1992/93 the funds for this scheme can be broken down as follows:

Community Youth and Schools	£43,000
Community Centres	£10,000
Entertainment	£3,500
Arts	£2,000
Holiday Projects:	£23,000
Under eights groups:	£23,100
Youth:	£9,500
Sport	£9,500
TOTAL	£123,600

The Children Act 1989: It is clear that the new legislation will entail increased costs for voluntary groups working with children but as yet Ealing has not set aside additional funds.

Unified Community Action (UCA)
UCA was set up by the council to act as a link between the council and local voluntary organisations. The UCA network can give initial advice about council grant-aid and covers four areas of the borough, with four area offices and one central contact:

Jerusha Castley, UCA Manager, Ealing Town Hall, New Broadway, W5 ext 45389

Ian Mark, UCA Acton, Acton Hall, Winchester Street W3 6NE (081-992 5566 ext 2225)

Carol Smith, UCA Greenford/Northolt/Perivale, Stanhope First School, Mansell Road, Greenford, Middlesex UB6 9EG (081-578 9323 ext 2420).

Dina Berlin, UCA Ealing/Hanwell, Hanwell Library, Cherington Road, Hanwell, London W7 3HL (081-567 9438).

Lynn Purcell, UCA Southall, 12 The Green, Southall, Middlesex (081-574 2466).

Mental Illness Specific Grant: In 1991/92 the council received a grant of £190,000 from the DoH and contributed £81,500 itself so that a total of £271,500 was available to fund services for the mentally ill. Contracts were made with two voluntary organisations: £66,414 to Age Concern's relative support scheme which provides weekend respite for demented elderly and their carers; and £33,000 to St Mungo's as a contribution towards permanent residential care for adults who mentally ill. The council has put in a bid for £283,200 of funding from central government in 1992/93 and its total expenditure will probably be £404,700.

Drugs and Alcohol Specific Grant: The council was unsuccessful in its application for this funding in 1991/92 but is putting in a new bid for 1992/93.

Eligibility: Generally, organisations applying to Ealing Council must operate for the benefit of local people, should be well-run and have matching funding amongst other fairly standard criteria, details of which are obtainable from the council itself.

Applications procedure: Grant applications must be submitted to the Central Grants Unit in early September and are dealt with annually. Decisions are made in the period from December to February. All grant applications are considered by the Finance/Grants Sub Committee.

There is also a rolling grants programme which enables other units to make smaller grants more frequently.

Contracting and the Community Care Plan
Ealing Social Services instigated and assessed a number of 'trial' contracts with voluntary organisations in 1992/92. The success of these contracts will be reviewed in early 1993 and future policy developed accordingly.

In the longer term Ealing proposes that large groups, providing major services will have full, legally binding contracts with the council, which will probably run for more than one year. Small groups would still receive grants and possible intermediate groups would have some form of service level agreement which would be less complex than the full legal contract but would define services 'more vigorously' than at present.

For further information contact: D Ewart, Chief Officer, Establishment and Admin, ext 42432 or Alan Clark, Acting Assistant Director, Admin and Development, ext 52414

Ealing Joint Consultative Committee

Beneficial area: The London Borough of Ealing.

Objects: To stimulate innovative community-based services which promote joint planning and collaboration with other providers.

Total expenditure: £732,000 (1991/92), with £110,000 being allocated to new schemes

Expenditure on voluntary organisations: £146,000 (1991/92)

Details of projects: Voluntary organisations supported have included: Mencap for the provision of a home for people with learning difficulties (£25,000); Age Concern for a support scheme for the carers of old people (£22,500); Ealing Voluntary Service Council for the post of a Joint Planning Officer; Turning Point for alcohol advice sessions (£10,800); MIND for a one-to-one counselling service (£6,200).

Applications procedure: Joint finance monies are allocated on a yearly basis from April to March. Submissions can be made at any time but no later than September if the request is for funds from the following April. Applications should address inequalities in health, enable increased participation by the community, develop collaboration between statutory and voluntary organisations and promote community care and support. Any submissions requiring financial support from the local authority, in addition to an allocation from joint finance, should be sent to the appropriate head of department in the first instance.

Correspondent: Clare O'Riordan, Joint Planning Officer

Address: Ealing Health Authority, Priority Services, St Bernard's Wing, Uxbridge Road, Southall, Middlesex UB1 3EU, (081-574 2444)

Other information: The committee meets quarterly.

Acton (Middlesex) Relief in Need Charity

Beneficial area: Former Parish and Borough of Acton

Objects: Relief of need

Type of beneficiary: Individuals and organisations

Income: £2,730 (1990, from many charities)

Grant total: £1,950

Grant details: Payments are made mostly to individuals and to a few organisations for services and facilities for those in distress or need.

Applications procedure: Referral from clergy, doctors, social services, professional people in general

Correspondent: Dr T Harper-Smith

Address: 48 Perryn Road, London W3 7NA (081-743 3476)

Other information: The correspondent notes that although this trust's beneficial area is only the former parish and borough of Acton, requests are received from all over the British Isles!

See also **Edwin Bridger Athawes Scholarship Fund**

Edwin Bridger Athawes Scholarship Fund

Beneficial area: Former parish and borough of Acton. (This does not coincide with the current Acton postal district)

Objects: Educational grants

Type of beneficiary: Individuals

Grant total: £3,500 (1990)

Grant details: Grants are made to postgraduate students and to pupils and students in maintained institutions.

Applications procedure: On a form available from the correspondent

Correspondent: Dr T Harper Smith, Clerk

Address: 48 Perryn Road, London W3 7NA (081-743 3476)

Other information: Dr Harper Smith is also the correspondent for the Acton (Middlesex) Charities

Education Fund. At present, its grantmaking capacity is under £100 a year, but this is growing through reinvestment.

Francis Courtney Educational Foundation

Beneficial area: Southall in the London Borough of Ealing

Objects: Educational grants for young people under 25 in need who are living or being educated in the beneficial area

Type of beneficiary: Individuals

Grant total: £3,500 (1990)

Grant details: Generally beneficiaries are under 18 and in full-time continuous education; grants are rarely given to applicants approaching the age of 25.

One-off grants are made towards the cost of books, equipment, travel etc. for those at secondary school, college or university. No grants are made for fees.

Applications procedure: On a form available from the correspondent. The applicant's place of study will have to approve the completed form.

Correspondent: E Vickers, Clerk to the Trustees

Address: 1 Vine Cottage, Tentelow Lane, Southall, Middx UB2 4LU (081-574 3973)

Other information: An almshouse charity, the Norwood (Middlesex) Charities, is administered alongside the educational foundation.

Ealing Aid in Sickness Trust

Beneficial area: Borough of Ealing

Objects: Relief of persons in need who are sick, disabled, infirm or convalescent

Type of beneficiary: Individuals

Income: £2,010 (1990, from investments)

Grant total: £2,660

Grant details: Grants are made at the trustees' discretion.

Applications procedure: Application forms are available from the correspondent.

Correspondent: Mr K C Fox, Trustee and Coordinator,

Address: 118 Church Road, Hanwell, London W7 3BE (081-567 5748)

See also the **Charity of William Hobbayne**.

Ealing Consolidated Charities

Beneficial area: London Borough of Ealing

Objects: Maintenance of almshouses and relief in need both generally and individually of elderly people living in the beneficial area

Income: £170,860 (1990)

Grant details: £127,880 was spent on the charity's almshouses during the year, but there was no expenditure on the wider welfare side provided for under the trust instrument, as outlined above.

Applications procedure: To the correspondent.

Correspondent: R H Hetherington

Address: 129 Ealing Village, Hanger Lane, Ealing W5 2LZ (081-997 5553)

Other information: This trust did not wish to appear in the guide.

Ealing Philanthropic Institution

Beneficial area: Ealing W5 and W13 postal districts

Objects: Benefit of old, sick or needy residents

Type of beneficiary: Individuals

Income total: £5,040 (1990/1991)

Grant total: £4,020

Grant details: Over half the charity's expenditure was devoted to outings for 150 elderly people and a Christmas outing to the pantomime for about 50. Christmas gifts to old people amounted to £820 and £790 was given in one-off relief grants to individuals.

From time to time grants ranging between £50 and £100 are made to local charities providing services for elderly or handicapped people. In 1990/91 the Ealing Philanthropic Old Folk's Club, West London Women's Aid and the Log Cabin Adventure Playground for Handicapped Children were among the groups supported.

Applications procedure: Directly or through an intermediary

Correspondent: P F Jacobsen, Honorary Secretary

Address: 137 Coldershaw Road, West Ealing, London W13 9DU (081-567 7482)

The Hanwell Philanthropic Institution

Beneficial area: The London W7 postal area

Objects: Relief of need

Type of beneficiary: Individuals

Grant total: About £5,000 (1986)

Grant details: The institution tends to concentrate on socially based activities such as visits, outings, Christmas parties and Christmas boxes, but can help if cases of individual need arise.

Applications procedure: To the correspondent

Correspondent: Mr David Lane, Honorary Secretary

Address: 18 Cromwell Court, Bishop's Road, Hanwell, London W7 (081-567 7753)

Other information: The grants coordinator for the Ealing Aid in Sickness Trust is also president and trustee for the Hanwell Philanthropic Institution. This entry was not confirmed by the trust.

The Educational Foundation of William Hobbayne

Beneficial area: Hanwell (W7 area) in the London Borough of Ealing

Objects: Educational grants

Type of beneficiary: Individuals

Grant total: £2,500 per annum

Grant details: Grants are probably made to help with the cost of books, clothing and other essentials of those at school. Grants may also be available for people at college and university.

Applications procedure: On a form available from the correspondent. Applications must be supported by a sponsor (presumably a welfare agency, vicar or other professional).

Correspondent: K C Fox, Grants Coordinator

Address: 118 Church Road, Hanwell, London W7 3BE (081-567 5748)

William Hobbayne Charity

Beneficial area: The Hanwell, London W7 area

Objects: Relief of residents who are in need, hardship and distress

Type of beneficiary: Organisations and individuals

Income: £57,320 (1990)

Grant total: £21,900 (but varies from year to year according to the applications received)

Grant details: Grants are made at the trustees' discretion. The 1990 accounts show the grant total to have been divided between education (£2,500), general charitable purposes (£10,190) and organisations such as Hanwell Neighbourly Care Scheme (£3,500), Age Concern (£680), and St Mary's Church Bell Fund (£5,030). Many grants to organisations are recurrent.

Applications procedure: Local sponsoring bodies apply on an application form which has to be completed by the sponsor and sent in the first instance to the correspondent.

Correspondent: Mr K C Fox, Trustee and Grants Coordinator

Address: 118 Church Road, Hanwell W7 3BE (081-567 0705)

Other information: See also the **Ealing Aid in Sickness Trust.**

The Mayor's Christmas Fund

Beneficial area: London Borough of Ealing

Objects: The relief in need of people over 70 years old in the beneficial area

Type of beneficiary: Individuals and organisations

Grant details: At Christmas individuals are given gifts of money - in 1990 this was £10 each, or £20 for applicants who were over 100 years old. Due to a shortage of funds individual payments at Christmas will probably have to be reduced.

Grants to organisations depend on how much money remains in the fund at the end of the financial year. No money was paid to organisations in March 1991. Generally, donations are in the region of £75. Beneficiaries are organisations such as Age Concern and homes for the elderly.

Applications procedure: Applications are processed at Christmas for individual gifts, and in March for grants to organisations. In emergency cases of exceptional hardship, applications can be considered when they are received.

Correspondent: Mrs A V Snow, Mayoral Officer and Secretary.

Address: Mayor's Parlour, The Town Hall, New Broadway, Ealing, London W5 2BY (081-579 2424 ext 42234/6)

The Pocklington Apprenticeship Trust for the Parish of Acton

Beneficial area: London Boroughs of Acton and Hammersmith

Objects: To help towards the cost of individuals obtaining education and training which will help them to obtain employment in the future.

Type of beneficiary: Boys and girls born in the beneficial area or with one or both parents residents in the area for the last ten years. There is a preference for fatherless (including illegitimate) children.

Grant total: Over £1,200 (1984)

Grant details: Nine grants were made for equipment, tools, and educational expenses in 1984.

Correspondent: Trevor Charles

Address: The London Borough of Hammersmith and Fulham, The Town Hall, London W6 9JU (081-748 3020 ext. 3533).

Major Local Companies

Glaxo Pharmaceuticals Ltd, Stockley Park West, Uxbridge, Middlesex UB11 1BT (081-990 9000) gives to local charities. Contact Mrs Elizabeth Browne, Community Affairs Manager.

Glaxochem Ltd, Stockley Park West, Uxbridge, Middlesex UB11 (081-990 9200) makes donations to local groups. Contact Jackie Gillespie, Communications Manager.

Glaxo Group Research, 891-995 Greenford Road, makes donations to local groups (081-422 3434). Contact Julie-Anne Baker, Community Support.

Lyons and Tetley Ltd, 344-347 Oldfield Lane North, Greenford, Middlesex UB6 OA2 (081-578 2345) supports local charities. Contact Mrs Jay, Consumer Relations Manager.

Quaker Oats Ltd (head office), Bridge Road, Southall, Middlesex UB2 4AG (081-574 2388).

Appeals should be directed at Ms P Massey, Secretary to the Managing Director.

Taylor Woodrow plc, 345 Ruislip Road, Southall, Middlesex UB1 2XQ (081-578 2366) makes donations to local organisations. Contact Ruth Barber, External Events Manager, Taylor Woodrow Plc, Group Head Quarters, World Trade Centre, 1 St Katherine's Way, London E1 9TW (071-488 0555).

Sources of Advice

Ealing Voluntary Service Council, 79 Uxbridge Road, Hanwell, W7 3ST (081- 579 6273)

General Secretary: Mike Phillips
Opening hours: 9.30-5.30 (Fridays 9.30-5.00)

Ealing Arts Council, 110 Argyle Road, Ealing, London W13 8EL (071-323 4831). Contact John Ross, Publicity Officer.

Acton Area: Adult Education Office, Acton High School, Gunnersbury Lane, Acton, London W3 8EQ (081-993 2975)

Southall Adult Education Office, Community Education Team Building, Haverlock Road, Southall UB2 4QD (081-574 2333)

Central Ealing and Hanwell Adult Education Office, Ealing Education Centre, Westlea Road, Hanwell, London W7 2AD (081-840 2221)

Greenford Northolt and Perivale Adult Education Office, Stanhope Site, Mansell Road, Greenford, UB6 9EG (081-575 6635 ext 134)

Enfield

London Borough of Enfield

Civic Centre, Silver Street, Enfield, Middlesex EN1 3ES (081-366 6565)

In the first instance voluntary organisations wishing to apply for funding should contact: Dan Smith, Professional Advisor, Community and Voluntary Organisations, Social Services Department (081-967 9105).

For further information contact:

Policy Committee: John Austin

Education Department: Avril Hunter, Youth and Community Manager

Housing Services: Ian Stratford, Executive Director

Leisure Services (parks, recreation, libraries): Keith Stevens, Executive Director

Social Services: Phil Howes, Professional Adviser, Mental Health, (Mental Illness Specific Grant) (081-967 9103)

Grant totals in 1990/91:

£650,000 in main programme funding
£70,000 in joint finance

Funding: "Within the limits of its legal powers, and financial resources, the London Borough of Enfield may offer assistance to a voluntary organisation which is able to demonstrate that:

- it carries out its activities otherwise than for profit;
- its activities/operations will benefit either the residents of the London Borough of Enfield generally or a particular area or group of residents where there is a specific need;
- there is a need for the service proposed which is not otherwise provided for or is not better catered for by other means; and
- it is prepared to co-operate with any other grant-aided organisation or department of the Council providing similar services."

Policy Committee: The council's Policy Committee considers grant applications which do not fall within the remit of other committees and awards grants to the larger organisations such as the Citizen's Advice Bureaux.

Social Services Committee: The majority of grants awarded by the Social Services Grant Panel in 1990/91 range from £50 to £116,000. Examples of grant recipients are:

Crossroads Care Attendant Scheme (£116,000), Enfield Voluntary Service Council (£70,000) and Enfield Disablement Association (£20,000).

Education Committee: Grants made in the education sector are generally in the realm of £250 and are awarded primarily to youth groups such as scouts.

Leisure Services Committee, For the present, any grants made will be minimal.

Housing Committee, Grants are made to housing associations for specific schemes targeting homeless families. A £4 million housing association programme is planned for 1992/93.

Mental Illness Specific Grant: In 1991/92 Enfield received funding from the DoH and used to fund in-house seven day a week day care services and an in-house outreach team. These services were arranged in conjunction with the local voluntary sector.

Drugs and Alcohol Specific Grant: Enfield did not apply for any funding in 1991/92.

Applications Procedure: Applications are considered throughout the year, however deadlines vary depending on the particular directorate and the nature of each application.

Other Support: Enfield Council can also provide: material and equipment in kind; transport maintenance and petrol; and, discretionary rate relief. Occasionally rental charges can be offset against grant aid.

Contracting and the Community Care Plan
During 1992 Enfield Social Services mostly funded voluntary organisations through grants but will be considering contracts for up to three years with voluntary organisations currently in receipt of a grant over £5,000.

In March 1992 no decisions had been made as to what services would be funded through contracts to voluntary organisations in the following year but users were allowed to purchase individual care and the agency chosen then invoiced the council. In all cases users chose their Crossroads group.

Contracts for sums over £5,000 will probably be operational during 1993 to 1994 and will largely be based on the previously established grant conditions. Any new conditions will be negotiated but not imposed.

The local voluntary sector was closely involved in Enfield's Community Care Plan. Enfield Council for Voluntary Service and the local Race Equality Council ran the Voluntary Sector Community Care Group which held discussions amongst local organisations and council officials. The council consulted small organisations and large agencies including MENCAP and MIND.

In 1992 Social Services was the only department at Enfield which was introducing contracts and it is developing strategies which may well be adopted by others in the council.

For further information contact: Dan Smith, Professional Adviser, Community and Voluntary Organisations (081-967 9105)

Enfield Joint Consultative Committee

Beneficial area: London Borough of Enfield

Objects: The development of plans for all the main care groups which are the concern of the London Borough of Enfield and Enfield Health Authority.

Expenditure on voluntary organisations: £163,400 (1991/92)

Funding practices: Requests for funding are initially considered by a care group team which includes local authority and health authority representatives. There are local Joint Care Planning Teams for the elderly; for people with learning difficulties; for people who are mentally ill; the physically disabled; and for children. Planning team recommendations are considered and decisions taken by members of both statutory bodies. Funding is agreed at the beginning of each financial year.

Details of projects: The following voluntary organisations were supported: Crossroads received £27,000 towards its Care Attendant Scheme; Age Concern was awarded a total of £107,300 for core funding, hospital discharge services, an EMI Day Centre and Day/Hospital Support; Enfield Disablement Association received £6,900 towards its information and advice services; Mencap was awarded

a total of £22,200 for the post of a Development Officer and £15,000 for their Enfield Link Support Initiative.

Applications procedure: An application form is available from the correspondent.

Correspondent: Mrs Fiona Wise

Address: Highlands Hospital, Winchmore Hill, London N21 1PN (081-366 6600 ext 6580)

Haringey Health Authority/ London Boroughs of Haringey and Enfield/Enfield & Haringey Family Health Services Authority Joint Consultative Committee

Beneficial area: London Borough of Haringey plus the Edmonton area of the London Borough of Enfield

Objects: To promote Care in the Community with schemes jointly managed by the health or local authorities and voluntary organisations, or schemes managed by single agencies where support for joint working is demonstrated.

Funding practices: Support for a variety of schemes to provide information and support to carers and to direct care schemes including grants to housing and group homes run by voluntary and statutory organisations for people with mental illness or mental handicap or for elderly people.

One-off grants are made for furniture, fittings, equipment and publications including translation of materials into community languages.

Expenditure on voluntary organisations: £126,000 (1991/92)

Details of projects: An example of a voluntary group which received funding was TULIP. It was awarded a grant to produce a mental health directory (£12,000).

Applications procedure: An applications guide is available from the correspondent.

Correspondent: Janet Miles, Secretary to the JCC

Address: Haringey Health Authority, 85 Tanners End Lane, Edmonton, London N18 1SB (081-803 1444 ext 5216)

Other information: The committee meets quarterly, on the morning of the last Wednesday in the month, commencing January.

The Belling Educational Foundation

Beneficial area: The London Borough of Enfield

Objects: Educational grants for young residents, probably under 25

Type of beneficiary: Individuals

Latest figures: 1975

Grant details: In 1975, the last year for which accounts are on file at the Charity Commission, the trust's income was £3,225 but it did not seem to have made any grants.

Applications procedure: To the correspondent

Correspondent: P Dyster, Director of Education

Address: Civic Centre, Silver Street, Enfield, EN1 3XA (081-366 6565 ext 3445)

Edmonton Aid in Sickness and Nursing Fund

Beneficial area: Edmonton

Main grant areas: Relief of sickness and poverty

Type of beneficiary: Individuals

Income: £3,900 (1990)

Grant total: £3,400

Grant details: 74 one-off grants were made to individuals, over half for fuel and heating costs, the remainder for clothing, convalescence and furniture. The trustees are not empowered to provide periodic or recurrent benefits.

Applications procedure: Through social services, nurses, health visitors, hospitals, GPs. Applications are received at any time and are dealt with immediately and without formality of any kind. Grants over £50 are considered at a trustees' meeting.

Correspondent: David Firth, Honorary Secretary

Address: 178 Wellington Road, Enfield, Middx EN1 2RT (081-360 3659)

The Enfield Church Trust for Girls

Beneficial area: Ancient Parish of Enfield

Objects: To help girls and young women under the age of 25 who are living, studying or working in the beneficial area, to lead full lives by assisting in the areas of social welfare, recreation, leisure and education.

Type of beneficiary: Individuals

Income: £4,800 (1990)

Grant total: £2,600

Grant details: Grants tend to be one-off and made in response to an immediate need. The trustees bought a radio-linked hearing aid to enable a 12 year old girl to continue normal schooling. It has also made educational grants towards course fees when local education authority grants are not available and gives grants to students for books and study or travel abroad. The trust has also given grants for child-care and other child costs to single-parent women who are studying, training or early in their careers and will consider grants for books, equipment and clothing for women starting work. The trustees are particularly concerned to help disadvantaged young women and girls.

Applications procedure: Applications can be submitted directly by the individual or school or educational welfare agency. They must be in writing and state the purpose of the application, the amount of grant sought, the applicant's personal financial situation and family circumstances. If possible, the applicant should provide a day-time telephone number. Applications are considered all year.

Correspondent: Stephen Addison, Committee Administrator

Address: PO Box 50, Civic Centre, Silver Street, Enfield, EN1 3XA (081-982 7262)

The Enfield Parochial Charity

Beneficial area: Ancient Parish of Enfield

Objects: Relief of need; educational grants for residents under 25

Type of beneficiary: Individuals

Income: £250,000 (1990/91)

Grant total: £90,000

Grant details: Grants are distributed either direct to individuals or through a welfare agency or through a suitable third party. The first priority of the charity is relief of need, on which £75,000 was spent. £15,000 was given in educational grants.

While putting no obligation on successful applicants for educational grants, the trustees hope that when they are qualified and earning they will consider repaying part of the grant to enable the trust to continue its work.

Applications procedure: In writing to the correspondent for an application form, either direct or through social services, probation service, hospitals, clinics, clergy. A visit will be arranged to those applicants who write in directly. Applicants for education grants will be invited to an interview with the education committee.

Correspondent: Mrs N D Forkgen, Clerk to the Trustees

Address: 10a Church Street, Enfield, EN2 6BE (081-367 8941)

Other information: This charity derives the major part of its income from the rental of stalls in Enfield market, and a large part of the income is in turn used for maintenance of the market.

The Chairman of the trustees has written a History of the Charity which was published in 1989.

This charity is administered in conjunction with The Hundred Acres Charity and the Enfield Church Trust for Girls.

The Hundred Acres Charity

Beneficial area: Ancient Parish of Enfield

Objects: Relief of poverty, distress and sickness; provision of facilities for recreation; the advancement of education

Type of beneficiary: Individuals and organisations

Income: £54,640 (1990)

Grant total: £69,740

Grant details: Grants are made to school pupils to help with books, equipment, clothing, travel or educational school journeys; to students to help with school, college or university fees or (in exceptional circumstances) to supplement existing grants. Financial assistance is also given towards the cost of education, training, apprenticeship or equipment of those starting work and to mature students for books, travel, and fees. Preference is given to people with special education needs. The charity is pleased to assist those in need, but will not give grants to clear debts. It is particularly pleased to receive applications from organisations working in the beneficial area.

Applications procedure: An application form is available from the correspondent.

Correspondent: Mr Stephen Addison, Committee Administrator

Address: PO Box 50, Civic Centre, Silver Street, Enfield, EN1 3XA (081-982 7262)

The Priscilla Ingram Trust

Beneficial area: The former boroughs of Wood Green and Southgate

Objects: Educational grants for young people under 21 who are or have been pupils of schools in the beneficial area, and residents of those areas under the age of 21.

Type of beneficiary: Individuals

Grant total: £2,500 per annum

Grant details: Educational grants are made to school children for books, equipment, clothing or travel; to students for college or university fees or to supplement existing grants; to help with study or travel abroad; to help towards education, training, apprenticeship or equipment for those starting work. No grants are given to mature students or for school fees or maintenance, or for student exchanges or to foreign students studying in Britain.

Assistance from the trust is not intended as an alternative to an educational grant, but assistance will be considered where a mandatory grant is not available.

Applications procedure: Applications can be submitted directly by the individual, through a school or educational welfare agency. Applications are considered all year.

Correspondent: Stephen Addison, Committee Administrator

Address: PO Box 50, Civic Centre, Silver Street, Enfield, EN1 3XA (081-982 7262)

Mayor of Enfield's Appeal Fund

Beneficial area: London Borough of Enfield

Objects: Health care; general charitable purposes

Type of beneficiary: Organisations and individuals

Grant total: £32,690 (1990)

Grant details: About 90 donations, usually of around £200, are made, a large proportion to the health care sector. Examples of grants are £1,500 to Enfield & Chestnut League of Hospital Friends; £500 to Enfield Society for Mentally Handicapped Children; £200 to Action Research for the Crippled Child, Arthritis & Rheumatism Council (Enfield Branch), British Polio Fellowship, Enfield Mental Health Association, and Sunshine Club for the Blind.

Applications procedure: To the correspondent

Correspondent: Mrs R Aldridge, Mayor's Secretary

Address: Civic Centre, Silver Street, Enfield, EN1 3XA (081-366 6565)

Other information: This entry was not confirmed by the trust.

Southgate Old People's Welfare Committee

Beneficial area: Southgate in the London Borough of Enfield

Main grant areas: Welfare of the elderly

Type of beneficiary: Individuals

Income: £6,500 (1988)

Grant total: £6,900

Grant details: Money was made available for holidays, general welfare, Christmas and Easter celebrations and gifts. Grants were made to affiliated clubs.

Applications procedure: To the correspondent.

Correspondent: Mrs V Gudge

Address: Ruth Winston House, 190 Green Lanes, London N13 (081-886 5346)

Other information: This entry was not confirmed by the trust.

Western Enfield Samaritan Association

Beneficial area: Former urban district of Enfield

Main grant areas: Alleviation of distress, especially among the elderly, and the support of organisations engaged in charitable work

Income: £1,500 from collections rather than investments (1974)

Grant total: £1,500

Grant details: The association organised Christmas parcels, monthly groceries and seaside outings for the elderly.

Applications procedure: To the correspondent

Correspondent: D J Williamson, Honorary Treasurer

Address: 40 Woodlands Road, Enfield, Middlesex (telephone number is ex-directory)

Other information: This information was taken from the association's 1974 accounts, the most recent on file at the Charity Commission. The correspondent declined to update any of the above.

Major Local Companies

Belling & Co Ltd (head office), Bridge Works, Southbury Road, Enfield, Middlesex EN1 1UF (081-804 1212). Contact Mr Derek Phillips, Company Secretary.

BOC Cryoplants Ltd (part of the BOC Ltd), Angel Road, Edmonton, London N18 3BW (081-803 1300) supports social welfare and community services. Local grants are made for £100. Appeals in writing to the Geoff Dobson, Personnel Manager.

Ford Motor Co Ltd, Wharf Road, Enfield, Middlesex EN3 4TN (081-804 1221). (See under Barking and Dagenham)

BT GLS Repairs, Bilton Way, Enfield, Middlesex EN3 7PD (081-804 2400) supports national charities only. Contact Mr A Carter, Head of Personnel.

Stonehill Holdings plc (head office), Riverside House, Lea Valley Trading Estate, Angel Road, Edmonton, London N18 3LD (081-807 1020). Contact Mr A K Fox, Chief Executive.

Sources of Advice

Enfield Voluntary Service Council, 341A Baker Street, London EN1 OLF (081-342 1898)

Director: Paula Jeffrey
Opening hours: 9.00-5.15 (Fridays 9.00-5.00)

Enfield Arts Council, Central Library, Cecil Road, Enfield, Middx, EN2 6TW (081-366 2244 ext 8310)

Acting Honorary Secretary: Peter Herring

TAC (Training Access Centre), 31 Derby Road, Ponders End, Enfield, EN3 4AJ (081-443 0380)

Greenwich

London Borough of Greenwich

8th Floor, Riverside House, Beresford Street, Woolwich, London SE18 6PW (081-854 8888)

Correspondent(s):

Policy and Resources Unit: Christina O'Halloran, Grants Support Worker ;

Social Services Committee: Ann Rennie Payne, Principal Officer, Voluntary Services, Nelson House, 50 Wellington Street, London SE18 6PY,

Leisure Services Committee: Chris Lea, Voluntary Services Liaison Officer;

Housing Committee: Gill Ackrill, Housing Grants Worker, Housing Dept, HAVOC, Peggy Middleton House, 50 Woolwich New Road, London SE18 6HQ;

Employment and Industry Committee: Chris Bernier, Community Worker; John Hillier, Lead Officer, Urban Programme

Education Dept: Miranda Hyslop, Senior Assistant Education Officer

Women's Unit: Gulten Fedayi, Administrative Officer;

Grant totals 1990/91:

£4,800,000 in main programme funding
£56,000 Urban Programme funding

Funding: Grant-making in 1990/91 can be broken down by committee as follows:

Social Services	£1,270,000
Leisure Services	£607,000
Housing	£552,000
Employment and Industry	£242,000
Policy and Resources contingency	£1,970,000
Education	£327,000
TOTAL	£5,398,000

The Women's Unit can also give small 'starter' grants to new groups.

Policy and Resources Committee: In 1990/91 this committee funded about 23 groups, the majority of which specialised in the needs of ethnic minorities and gave welfare benefits advice. In addition, law centres and CABs are funded to give advice generally. Grants range from £300 to £230,000 and all were recurrent. There is no funding for new projects in the foreseeable future.

Leisure Services Committee: This committee spends the majority of its budget (c£500,000) on maintaining its grant-aid to various recreational and arts projects including Greenwich Play Association and Greenwich Sports Council. Occasionally there is scope for funding new groups though this is rare. £10,000 is set aside for small initiatives, with the maximum grant being £500 per year. Sometimes grants can be made to individuals towards vocational expenses or community arts.

Housing Committee: This committee funds homelessness projects like Stopover and the Coordinated Accommodation Scheme, women's refuges, housing advice, tenants' groups, and projects looking at housing and disability. Generally grant-aid is given to existing schemes and there is little chance of new projects being funded.

Employment and Industry Committee: Employment projects are funded and recent beneficiaries included the Business Innovation Centre, The Greenwich Homeworkers' Project and Greenwich Council for Racial Equality (employment project). For the foreseeable future no funding is available for new groups.

Education Committee: This makes grants for community education

Social Services Committee: This committee funds a wide variety of organisations, particularly those working with the elderly, young children, or providing counselling services. Organisations recently funded include Age Concern, Charlton Toy Library, and London Marriage Guidance.

Urban Programme: Greenwich is an Urban Programme authority and grants are available for a wide variety of projects.

Mental Illness Specific Grant: Greenwich Council received £127,000 from the Department of Health in 1991/92 and funded two voluntary agencies, Age Concern Project on Dementia (£20,510) and Feathers (£18,000), a work-based project for people with mental health problems. The remainder of the grant was used to fund mental health posts within Social Services. Slippage money was given to CRUISE and MIND.

Drug and Alcohol Specific Grant: In 1991/92 Greenwich Council was successful in its bid for funding and supported Greenwich and Bexley Council on Alcohol (£7,857).

Applications procedure: Applications should be submitted in October/November and decisions are made in February/March.

Other support: Discretionary rate relief, general advice on financial management and the use of low-rent or free premises can all be made available by the London Borough of Greenwich.

Contracting and the Community Care Plan
In 1992 Greenwich Council funded voluntary organisations through direct grant aid but proposed to start negotiating contracts for 1992/93. It was holding public meetings and consulting a range of voluntary organisations in order to develop its Community Care Plan. Contracts will probably be fairly general, leaving room for flexibility.

For further details contact: Ann Rennie Payne, Principal Officer, Voluntary Sector

Greenwich Joint Consultative Committee

Beneficial area: London Borough of Greenwich

Objects: To co-ordinate joint planning of health, social services and housing between Greenwich Health Authority, the London Borough of Greenwich, the Greenwich & Bexley Family Health Services Authority and voluntary agencies.

Funding practices: For statutory organisations a 5 year revenue taper applies i.e. 100% - first year, 80% - second year, etc. For voluntary organisations funding is for a maximum of 5 years at 75% of cost of project. The balance has to come from other sources, including a voluntary organisation's own core funding, and must be found before submitting an application.

Expenditure on voluntary organisations: £218,000 (1991/92)

Details of projects: Voluntary organisations recently funded include: The Greenwich Association of Disabled People, an Independent Living Scheme (£18,900); Asian Maternal Health Project (£27,000); Age Concern (£37,040); Greenwich Voluntary Sector Forum (£6,680); and the Race and Health Project

(£15,000).

Applications procedure: The JCC writes to voluntary organisations each year, inviting them to apply. Applications should be submitted by about December of each year for funding the following April. If the application is not successful that year, the project could be resubmitted for funding in a later year.

Correspondent: May Clarke, Secretary to the JCC

Address: Memorial Hospital, Shooters Hill, London SE18 3RZ (081-856 5511)

Sir William Boreman's Foundation

Beneficial area: London Boroughs of Greenwich and Lewisham

Objects: The benefit of poor full or part-time students, under the age of 25, with special consideration for those intending a seafaring career; the assistance of organisations for the education of such students

Grant total: About £30,000

Grant details: The main aim of the foundation is to grant exhibitions to assist students at secondary school and institutions of further and higher education. Preference is given to students who are members of the Church of England or whose parents have served in the armed forces or have followed a seafaring career. The average grant is about £250, and the maximum given is £2,500.

The foundation will only consider giving assistance with private school fees in cases of unexpected and considerable hardship and where it is essential that the child attends a fee-paying school.

Applications procedure: To the correspondent.

Correspondent: The Clerk to the Governors

Address: The Drapers' Company, Drapers' Hall, London EC2N 2DQ (071-588 5001)

Other information: See also the Drapers' Charitable Fund and the Drapers' Consolidated Charity.

The Charity of Sir Martin Bowes

Beneficial area: London Borough of Greenwich

Objects: Relief of residents in need

Type of beneficiary: Individuals

Income total: £6,920 (1989/90)

Grant total: £10,870

Grant details: Both one-off grants and regular allowances are given.

Applications procedure: In writing to the clerk.

Correspondent: The Clerk

Address: Worshipful Company of Goldsmiths, Goldsmiths' Hall, Foster Lane, Cheapside, London EC2V 6BN (071-606 8971)

Eltham United Charities (also known as Sampson's Eltham United Charities)

Beneficial area: Parish of Eltham in the London Borough of Greenwich, as constituted at 9th July 1907

Objects: Almshouses for single persons and married couples, and the provision of pensions for poor people who have lived in the beneficial area for not less than 2 years preceding the donation

Latest figures: 1990

Income: £38,500 (figure does not include sale of investments)

Grant details: This charity is principally concerned with almshouses - the expenditure of £36,500 covered almshouse expenses and payments to almspeople. No payments to poor people of the parish of the sort allowed under the trust deed were made.

Correspondent: Mrs J R Andrews

Address: Fifteenpenny Fields, 8 Blunts Road, Eltham, London SE9 1HT

Godson's Charity

Beneficial area: London Borough of Greenwich; Shinfield (Berkshire); Tenbury Wells (Hereford and Worcester).

Objects: The relief of poverty principally through assistance with emigration

Type of beneficiary: Individuals

Income: £4,400 (1990/91)

Grant total: £3,000

Grant details: Lack of suitable applicants has recently enabled the trustees to make some grants to charitable organisations in the qualifying areas.

Applications procedure: Application forms are available from the correspondent.

Correspondent: R G Godson, Trustee

Address: 13/14 Hanover Street, London W1R 9HG (071-629 7986)

The Greenwich Blue Coat Foundation

Beneficial area: London Borough of Greenwich

Objects: The award of exhibitions to persons under 25 who live or are educated in Greenwich, for higher education or otherwise for their advancement in life

Type of beneficiary: Colleges, schools and individuals

Income: £24,500 (1990, the bulk of it derived from investments, and a little from freehold properties in Greenwich High Road)

Grant total: £15,300

Grant details: 24 individuals received grants ranging from £100 to £1,500 and a number of organisations were supported including the 5th Royal Eltham Scout Group, Thames Polytechnic, the Roan School and Maze Hill School for the Handicapped. The trust's scheme specifies it must assist the Blackheath and Blue Coat Church of England School so each year a grant is made towards this school's building and maintenance costs.

Applications procedure: To the correspondent for an application form

Correspondent: Mr Shrubsall

Address: Alton Batchelor, Solicitors, 40 Stockwell Street, Greenwich SE10 8EY (081-858 6066)

The Greenwich Charity

Beneficial area: Ancient Parish of Greenwich

Objects: Relief of need

Type of beneficiary: Organisations

Income: £450 (1976)

Grant details: In the years to 1976 grants were paid to many organisations in Greenwich, including the District Hospital, Church Lads and Girls' Brigade, a chest clinic, local CAB, youth theatre, town twinning scheme and the Mayor of Greenwich Charity Fund.

Correspondent: See below

Address: See below

Other information: In 1976, the last year for which accounts are on file at the Charity Commission, the impact of the sale in 1975/76 of property in Greenwich Church Street and Thames Street had not yet come through into higher income figures.

The information given at the Charity Commission is that the correspondent is a Mr J M Bowers at McKenna & Co, (Mitre House, 160 Aldersgate St, London EC1A 4DD, 071-606 9000). When contacted by telephone, Mr Bowers said he no longer administered the trust. He also said that he did not know who now administered the trust or who would know. Mr Bowers was unhelpful when editors were preparing the 1989 edition of *The London Grants Guide*.

This entry has not been confirmed by the charity. See also Randall's Charity and the Charity of Charles Soames.

Greenwich Charities for the Blind and Disabled

Beneficial area: London Borough of Greenwich

Objects: Welfare of blind, partially-sighted and disabled people who live or are regularly employed in the beneficial area

Type of beneficiary: Individuals

Income: £10,000 (1988)

Grant total: £10,000

Grant details: Grants were made for wheelchairs. Help may also be given for small items of equipment, clothing etc.

Applications procedure: By application form from the correspondent. Applications are usually made through social workers. The trustees meet quarterly.

Correspondent: Steve Potter, Principal Administrator of Field Work

Address: c/o Greenwich Social Services, Third Floor, Nelson House, 50 Wellington Street, Woolwich (081-854 8888).

Other information: This entry was not confirmed by the trust.

The Mayor of Greenwich's Appeal Fund

Beneficial area: London Borough of Greenwich

Objects: Any charitable purpose

Type of beneficiary: Organisations

Grant details: One charity is nominated by the Mayor and is sole beneficiary during his or her term of office. Exceptionally, small grants may be given to other local charities.

Correspondent: The Mayor

Address: The Mayor's Office, Town Hall, Wellington Street, Woolwich, London SE18 6PW (081-854 8888)

Other information: This entry was not confirmed.

Randall's Charity

Beneficial area: Ancient Parish of Greenwich

Objects: 2/3 income for benefit of the poor, 1/3 for parish church

Latest information: 1968

Grant total: Over £1,000

Grant details: No information available

Applications procedure: To the correspondent

Correspondent: See below

Address: See below

Other information: The information given at the Charity Commission is that the correspondent is a Mr J M Bowers at McKenna & Co, (Mitre House, 160 Aldersgate St, London EC1A 4DD, 071-606 9000). When contacted by telephone, Mr Bowers said he no longer administered the trust. He also said that he did not know who now administered the trust or who would know. Mr Bowers was unhelpful when editors were preparing the 1989 edition of *The London Grants Guide*.

See also Charity of Charles Soames and The Greenwich Charity.

Charity of Charles Soames (also known as the Charles Soames Nursing Fund)

Beneficial area: Ecclesiastical Parish of St Alfrege with St Peter Greenwich Christchurch with St Andrew and St Michael with Holy Trinity with St Paul East Greenwich

Objects: Relief of need and hardship

Type of beneficiary: Organisations and individuals

Latest information: 1975

Income: £700 (Present financial position probably about £9,000)

Grant total: £2,000

Grant details: Beneficiaries included Greenwich Chest Clinic, District Hospital, nursing home, local handicapped groups, and sums of money were given to three vicars for further distribution within the local parishes.

Applications procedure: To the correspondent.

Correspondent: See below

Address: See below

Other information: The information given at the Charity Commission is that the correspondent is a Mr J M Bowers at McKenna & Co, (Mitre House, 160 Aldersgate St, London EC1A 4DD, 071-606 9000). When contacted by telephone, Mr Bowers said he no longer administered the trust. He also said that he did not know who now administered it or who would know. Mr Bowers was unhelpful when editors were preparing the 1989 edition of *The London Grants Guide*.

See also the entries for the Greenwich Charity and Randall's Charity.

The most recent accounts on file for these three permanently endowed charities date from 1976. The only publicly available information on these charities is therefore out-of-date and in all likelihood useless.

Wiseman and Withers Exhibition Foundation

Beneficial area: London Borough of Greenwich and that part of the London Borough of Newham formerly in the Metropolitan Borough of Woolwich

Objects: Provision of educational grants

Type of beneficiary: Individuals

Grant total: About £1,000 per annum

Grant details: Grants between £20 and £200, often to provide essential equipment needed for courses at further education colleges. The only area that cannot be funded, simply because of the trust's financial constraints, is major awards to finance full-time education. Note that applicants must not be older than 26.

Applications procedure: In writing to the correspondent giving full details

Correspondent: D Fisher, Clerk to the Foundation

Address: Thames Polytechnic, Finance Office, Southwood Site, Avery Hill Road, Eltham, London SE9 2HB (081-316 8283)

Woolwich and Plumstead Relief in Sickness Fund

Beneficial area: London Borough of Greenwich with an emphasis on the Woolwich and Plumstead areas

Objects: Relief of sickness and hardship

Type of beneficiary: Individuals

Income: £5,000 (1988)

Grant total: £4,800

Grant details: The charity can make grants up to about £200 to help with a great range of needs; although an element of sickness must be present, this requirement can be interpreted widely. It has recently been giving particular attention to younger families and single mothers where sickness or disability have imposed financial hardship, or where a partner is in prison. It has also supported the local branches of Age Concern and Mind in funding holidays, and is willing to contribute towards holidays for carers of relatives. The charity cannot help with debts, rates or rent.

Applications procedure: In writing, direct or through health visitors, district nurse, social services, welfare agencies. Although most grants applications are bunched around Christmas, they can be dealt with as and when received.

Correspondent: Miss J A Waugh, Secretary

Address: 64 Kidbrooke Park Close, London SE3 0EG (081-856 6012)

Other information: This entry was not confirmed by the trust.

Major Local Companies

FKI Communications Ltd, Tom Cribb Road, London SE28 OBH (081-317 1717) does not support charities as a standard practice. The company does, however, sponsor local events from time to time. Contact David Cairnie, Managing Director.

Morgan Grampian plc (head office), Morgan Grampian House, 30 Calderwood Street, London SE18 6QH (081-855 7777) supports the National Advertising Benevolent Society. Contact Jean Purser, Assistant Company Secretary.

STC Submarine Systems (part of STC plc), Christ Church Way, Greenwich, London SE10 OAG (081-858 3291). Contact Karen Frost, Personnel Manager.

Sources of Advice

Greenwich Arts Council, c/o London Borough of Greenwich, Leisure Services, 147 Powis Street, London SE18 6JL (081-854 8888 ext 2514) Contact Chris Lea, Voluntary Services Liaison Officer.

Greenwich Youth Office, 20 Passey Place, Eltham SE9 5DQ (081-859 4236)

Greenwich Community College of which the three main branches are: Haimo Road Branch, Eltham SE9 6DZ (081-850 3632), Burrage Branch, Burrage Grove, SE18 7LJ (081-854 6908), Greenwich Park School, King George Street, SE10 8PY (081-858 2211)

Hackney

London Borough of Hackney

Town Hall, London E8 1EA (081-986 3123)

Correspondents:

Community Development Unit: Gareth Osborne, Grants and Administration Officer

Education: Tracy Thompson, Grants Officer

Social Services Committee: Ken Boreham, Programme Officer

Leisure: Jit Singh, Grants Officer

Housing Committee: George Cochran/Damion Tissier, Grants Officers

Employment and Economic Development Unit: Glenroy Anderson

Urban Programme: Peter Brimston, Programme Officer

Environmental Services Committee: Soloman Darko,

Transport Committee: Gareth Osborne, Grants and Administration Officer

Women's Committee: Marima Grant, Grants and Administration Officer

Grant totals in 1992/93 (provisional):

£7,775,815 in main programme funding
£4.7 million in Urban Programme funding
(1.2 million revenue and 3.5 million capital)

Funding: Most of Hackney's corporate grant-giving and development work with the voluntary sector is carried out by its Community Development Unit which reports to the Community Services Committee and coordinates the work of other service committees. Provisional amounts given in 1992/93 can be broken down as follows:

Community Development Unit	£1,969,548
Education	£917,920
Social Services	£1,351,719
Leisure	£1,286,833
Housing	£384,236
Economic Development	£666,418
Environmental Services	£182,847
Transport	£136,294
Small Grants Scheme	£160,000
Yet to be allocated	£700,000
TOTAL	£7,775,815

Community Development Unit: Organisations seeking help should approach the Community Development Unit in the first instance. This advises the council on policy and procedures concerning the voluntary sector. It takes a lead in all matters regarding grants and non-financial support for local voluntary groups. It works to develop facilities, and manages and monitors voluntary sector activities, basing its decisions on the recommendations of the service committees (i.e. housing, social services, planning, etc.). Voluntary groups are dealt with by community development officers, who advise on many issues, including starting up and how to apply for council grants, and can also provide information on what else is happening locally.

The Community Development Unit is responsible for grants to a wide range of community advice and information services, such as Citizens' Advice Bureaux and councils for racial equality.

Would-be applicants should note that in 1992/93 Hackney's main programme budget has recently considered new applications for help. Previously all funds were spent on long-term recurrent grants which were already committed.

The Children Act 1989: In March 1992 Hackney council was considering the implications of the Children Act but was not changing its grant-making policy due to a diminishing budget.

Urban Programme: Hackney is an Urban Programme Authority. As with other UP authorities, Department of Environment approval must be obtained before any grants are given as it provides 75% of the money.

Most money in the Urban Programme is spent on capital projects such as building work and the purchase of equipment. Revenue funding for salaries and running costs is seldom given through UP. Would-be applicants should contact the Programme Officer for advice.

New Grant Scheme: It is likely that a number of small grant-aid funds will be established in 1992/93

as part of a review of funding arrangements throughout the borough. For precise details of these grants please contact the correspondents for the various committees listed above.

Mental Illness Specific Grant: In 1991/92 Hackney received funding from the Department of Health and supported the Psychiatric Rehabilitation Association (£183,954).

Drugs and Alcohol Specific Grant: In 1991/92 Hackney was successful in its bid to the Department of Health and funded the Greater London Advisory Service (£43,263).

Applications procedure: Applications for main programme grants should normally be submitted by the end of September. Applications for Urban Programme support are invited each year between July and September; details are advertised in the local press.

Organisations awarded a grant through both the main programme and the Urban Programme are monitored annually.

Other support: In addition to grants, Hackney can provide advice on funding matters and can support beneficiaries in their search for suitable premises.

Contracting and the Community Care Plan
In 1992 Hackney Social Services mostly funded voluntary organisations through grants but it was reviewing this policy in view of the new Community Care legislation. It will be introducing contracts but had not decided on their nature in early 1992.

Local voluntary organisations were involved in Hackney's Community Care Plan with representatives on the Joint Planning Group.

For further information contact: Athea Wilkinson, Planning Officer, (ext. 4740)

City and Hackney Joint Consultative Committee

Beneficial area: City of London and London Borough of Hackney

Objects: Care in the Community. The committee wishes to target its aims more and an information pack is available outlining these aims.

Funding practices: In 1991/92 £400,000 was available for new schemes. If a bid is successful funding will not always be guaranteed after the first three years and therefore time-limited schemes are welcomed.

Total expenditure: c£600,000 (1991/2) but see below

Details of voluntary projects funded: The following voluntary organisations were amongst those funded:

Off Centre Counselling For Sexually Abused Survivors (£7,800)

Age Concern, towards a pensioners' handbook (£3,200)

Living Space, which provides residential care homes for people with mental health problems (£3,000)

Hackney Independent Living Team to fund a development worker for their residential homes for people with learning difficulties (£17,000)

Applications procedure: The committee meets four times a year in January, April, July and October. Bids should be in August to September for projects starting in the following year.

Correspondent: Mr Shun Au, Coordinator for the Joint Planning Unit

Address: Saint Leonard's Hospital, Nuttall Street, Kingsland Road, London N1 5LZ (071-739 8484 ext 4204)

Other information: Ras Mark-I, the Voluntary Sector Development Worker for Joint Planning, has been appointed to coordinate and encourage voluntary sector applications. He is based at Hackney Community Action, 90 de Beauvoir Road, London N1(071-923 1962).

There are six Joint Executive Teams: Public Health and Primary Care, Learning Difficulties, Mental Health, Children and Young People, Disabilities, and the Elderly. Voluntary organisations usually have more success if they liaise with the planning group from the start as each has its own priorities.

Hackney Task Force

Beneficial area: South Hackney (Kingsland Road across to Hackney Wick and Shacklewell Lane through to Hackney Road) and two housing estates, Clapton Park and Trowbridge.

General: The Task Forces, of which there are four in London, have been set up by the government in areas known to be seriously disadvantaged. The main objective is to create a thriving economy. The goals of this initiative are the provision of jobs for local people, the encouragement of local enterprise, the enhancement of the employability of local people, and the improvement of the local environment, especially through crime reduction and increased safety.

Much of the work of the Task Forces is concerned with improving the take-up and the effectiveness of existing government programmes, and in enhancing their co-ordination, but there are also numerous occasions in which Task Forces work through voluntary organisations and community groups in the area.

The Hackney Task Force was established in November 1991 and intends to work closely with all sectors of the local community.

Grant total: about £1,000,000 a year

Correspondents: Susan Angoy, Task Force Leader, Richard Cohen, Deputy Task Force Leader

Address: UNIT 16B, Dalston Cross Shopping Centre, Dalston, London E8 (081-533 1885)

Mr John Baker's Trust (Brewers' Company)

Beneficial area: Parish of Christchurch, Spitalfields, in the London Borough of Hackney

Objects: Payment of pensions to poor widows and unmarried women over 50 and resident in the beneficial area for at least five years.

Type of beneficiary: Individuals

Income: £2,250 (1988)

Grant total: £2,025

Grant details: 19 regular pensions are given.

Applications procedure: To the correspondent

Correspondent: Rear-Admiral M Wemyss, Clerk

Address: Brewers' Hall, Aldermanbury Square, London EC2V 7HR (071-606 1301)

Hackney Mayor's Fund

Beneficial area: London Borough of Hackney

Objects: General charitable purposes in the borough.

Grant details: Around £2,000 is raised each year by the Mayor for the charities of his/her choice. In 1990/91 the money went principally to ethnic groups, pensioners' groups and other local charities.

Correspondent: The Mayor's Secretary or directly to the Mayor.

Address: Town Hall, Mare Street, Hackney, London E8 1EA (081-986 3123)

The Hackney Parochial Charities

Beneficial area: The pre-1970 Metropolitan Borough of Hackney

Main grant areas: Relief of need and sickness

Type of beneficiary: Individuals and organisations

Income: £50,000 (1988)

Grant total: £45,000

Grant details: Grants are made to sick, disabled and elderly people for bedding, clothing, heating appliances, furniture, and towards the cost of aid and treatment (but not when this should be the responsibility of the statutory authorities e.g. provision of wheelchairs for amputees). The cost of fares to visit such long-stay patients can also be met in the case of close relatives.

Other grant areas cover help towards tools, books and exam fees for apprentices and young people not in receipt of a full grant; holidays for widows with small children and single parent families; gifts at Christmas for children in need.

The maximum grant to an individual is £100 and is one-off, although individuals can apply annually. Grants are not made that would defray statutory charges (rent, rates, gas, electricity, telephone charges).

Grants are also made to organisations working in the beneficial area. In the past these have included schools, hospitals, a talking newspaper, old people's centres and the local branches of Disabled Soldiers' and Sailors' Foundation, St John's Ambulance and Abbeyfield Society.

Applications procedure: In writing to the correspondent. The trustees meet in March, June, September and November and as grants cannot be made between meetings it is advisable to make early contact with the correspondent.

Correspondent: A D M Sorrell, Clerk

Address: Lloyds Bank Chambers, 81/83 High Road, London N22 6BE (081-888 0155)

The Hornsey Parochial Charities

Beneficial area: The ancient Parish of Hornsey in Haringey and Hackney which comprises London, N8 and smaller parts of N2, N4, N6, N10 and N16.

Main grant area: Relief of need.

Type of beneficiary: Organisations and individuals

Income: £95,950 (1990, combined income from the 2 charities)

Grant total: £64,460

Grant details: The charity has two funds to which organisations, and people who have lived in the beneficial area for at least one year, are welcome to apply:

1. The Parochial Charity can make grants to meet needs provided funding is not available from statutory or other sources. Organisations which have recently received grants have included clubs for children, young people and the elderly, schools and a local history society.

2. The Educational and Vocational Foundation can make grants to students who are under 25. Help towards fees and grants for books, equipment, clothing and travel may be available.

Applications procedure: Individuals can phone or write for an application form which, on being returned, can usually be dealt with within a month.

Correspondent: John Bailey, Clerk to the Trustees

Address: 47 The Chine, London N10 3PX

The Samuel Montagu Charitable Trust

See entry in the City of London section

The South Hackney Parochial Charity

Beneficial area: The ecclesiastical Parish of South Hackney

Objects: Almshouses; relief of need and distress

Type of beneficiary: Individuals

Grant details: The charity is concerned primarily with almshouses. When it does have surplus income it can consider applications from residents of the beneficial area.

Applications procedure: In writing to the correspondent. The trustees meet quarterly; grants cannot be made between meetings.

Correspondent: A W Baker

Address: 32a Harrowgate Road, South Hackney, London E9 5ED (081-985 2970)

The United Charities of Saint Leonard's, Shoreditch

Beneficial area: Former Parish of St Leonard's, Shoreditch

Objects: Relief of need among people who have lived in the beneficial area for at least three years prior to application

Type of beneficiary: Individuals

Grant total: £2,780 (1988)

Grant details: 49 charities are now united into four funds. The two largest, The General Charity and Lloyd Thomas House, are concerned principally with almshouses, although it is believed that grants for the relief of hardship in the parish generally can also be made from them. In 1988 The smaller Educational Fund spent £500 on 'grants and expenses'; Jackson's Fund had an income of £198 and spent £375 on 'income and expenses'. The General Charity, spent £1,470 on 'new scheme grants' and Lloyd Thomas House had an income of £7,620 made £430 in 'special grants'. It is not clear to what objects these donations were applied.

Applications procedure: To the correspondent

Correspondent: C A James, Clerk

Address: 1 Forest Court, Snaresbrook, London E11 1PL

Other information: This entry has not been confirmed by the trust and any information about its present administration would be gratefully received. The most recent accounts on file at the Charity Commission are for 1988.

Local Major Companies

Brook Bond Foods Ltd (canning factory), Waterdon Road, Hackney, London E13 2EE has a small grants budget to distribute locally (081-986 0941). Contact Mr George Orgill, Factory Manager. A few grants are made centrally. Contact Duncan Bogie, Head of External Affairs at Brooke Bond Foods Ltd, Leon House, High Street, Croydon, Surrey CR9 1JQ (081-686 8899).

Burberry's Ltd (Wholesale & Export), 29-53 Chatham Place, London E9 6LP (081-985 3344) considers all registered charities on their merit. Appeals in writing only to Mrs Kandy Sanders, Administration Coordinator.

Trade Indemnity Co Ltd, Trade Indemnity House, 12-34 Great Eastern Street, London EC2A 3AX (071-739 4311). Contact Mr G Kent, Company Secretary.

Sources of Advice

Hackney Community Action, 90 De Beauvoir Road, London N1 4EN (071-923 1962)

Administrator: Tina Jenkins
Opening hours: 10-5pm

Hackney Arts Forum, c/o Centreprice, 136/138 Kingsland High St, Hackney, London E8 2NS (071-254 9632).

Contact: Neil Barklem, Acting Chairman.

Hackney Youth Office, 23/25 Sutton Place, E9 6EH (081-533 4444)

Hackney Adult Education Institute, Woodberry Down Centre, Woodberry Grove, N4 2SH (081-809 7737)

Hackney Education Advice Service, Urban Studies Centre, 6/8 Lower Clapton Road, E5 ORD (081-986 2272)

Hammersmith and Fulham

London Borough of Hammersmith and Fulham

Town Hall, King St, London W6 (081-748 3020)

In the first instance voluntary organisations seeking a grant should contact Liz Chambers, Coordinator, Support and Grants Unit, Community Liaison, Strategic Services Committee, (081-748 3020 ext 2480). Further enquiries can be made to the following correspondents:

Correspondents:
Strategic Services Committee: Jack Basharan (ext 2484), Michael Hill (ext 2498), (Urban Programme grants), Sasan Abtahi (ext 2486) (Feasibility Studies Fund, Access for People With Disabilities Fund, Fire-fighting Fund, Low Cost Under Fives Fund grants).

Social Services Committee: Ann Kutek (ext 5010), Colleen Williams (ext 5070), (main programme, mental health specific and drugs and alcohol specific grants),

Leisure and Recreation Committee: Mary Brown (ext 3525), Mohit Bakaya (ext 3522) (main programme grants, Urban Programme Corporate Leisure and Recreation Festival Fund grants, Urban Programme Holiday grants)

Housing Services Committee: Liz Tuckwell (ext 4019),

Education Committee: Paula Marsall (ext 3652), Michael Donovan (ext 3781), (main programme grants), Elaine Mattison (081-576 5335/6) (youth organisations)

Environmental Committee: Caroline Forster, Economic Development Services Group (ext 3388) (main programme, training and workforce grants, Community Chest grants), Trevor Harvey, Planning, (ext 3386) (main programme grants, Local Environment Action Fund), Orin Miller, Economic Development Services Group (ext 3355), (Community Business grants)

Grant total 1992/93:
£5,255,864 in main programme funding

Funding: The main programme budget can be broken down into the following committee areas:

Social Services	£1,803,363
Strategic Services	£1,190,203
Leisure and Recreation	£1,157,407
Education Services	£296,000
Environment	£277,862
Housing	£531,029
TOTAL	£5,255,864

Strategic Services Committee: General revenue grant aid is available for constituted voluntary organisations and can include funding for staff, running costs and rent. Organisations with an advice/information and community resource remit account for most grants which range from £100 to over £100,000. In 1992/93 the budget for this was £1,190,203.

The committee also administers:

Coach Voucher Fund: Vouchers are given towards coach hire expenses, chiefly for outings for pensioners' groups. Priority is given to groups which receive council funding below £2,000 or do not receive council support at all. In 1992/93 the budget for this was £23,812 with vouchers worth about £200.

Corporate Maternity Fund: This meets pay for employees already funded by main programme grants and the budget was about £80,000 in 1992/93.

Small grants: One-off seeding grants of £50 are available to voluntary organisations within a total budget of about £850 in 1992/93.

Urban Programme: Capital grants and limited revenue funding are available to voluntary organisations addressing economic, social, environmental or housing objectives.

Feasibility Studies Fund: Grants are made to voluntary organisations to establish the viability of a new project or a new and untried aspect of an existing project. The budget for this was £10,000 in 1992/93.

Access for People with Disabilities Fund: Grants are made to render premises accessible to people with disabilities. In 1992/93 the budget for this was £50,000.

Fire-fighting Fund: Funding is available for emergency repairs to comply with fire regulations. The budget for this was £20,000 in 1992/93.

Low Cost Under Fives Fund: Grants are made for the provision of equipment, toys and furniture for groups working with under fives. The budget for this was £10,000 in 1992/93.

Social Services Committee: General revenue grant-aid is available for voluntary organisations which provide social and health services, including counselling, luncheon clubs, work with children and families and services for the disabled and the elderly. Health related grants are also available. See 'Contracting and the Community Care Plan' which follows.

Leisure and Recreation Committee: This committee mostly makes revenue grants to organisations providing activities related to arts, sports, community gardens, play, recreation and local history.

The committee also administers:

Urban Programme Corporate Leisure and Recreation Fund: This supports local initiatives which bring members of the community together through local festivals. The budget for this was £10,610 in 1992/93.

Urban Programme Holiday Projects Fund: Grants are made to assist with holiday provision in the local community. Projects such as playschemes, holiday trips for young people, under 5s and people with special needs are supported. The budget for this was £81,100 in 1992/93.

Housing Services Committee: General revenue grant-aid is available for voluntary organisations which provide housing services or address homelessness.

Education Committee: Revenue funding is available to voluntary organisations providing learning opportunities which complement mainstream provision. In addition one-off grants of up to £1,000 are made to youth organisations for equipment, materials, holiday projects, visits, specialised curriculum projects, training events and accredited courses. Youth organisations are also eligible for grants of up to £2,000 towards the running costs of their premises. Funding for new applications is limited.

Environment Committee: Revenue grant-aid is available specifically for organisations which provide either employment and training facilities or environmental and planning services.

The committee also administers:

Training and Workforce Support Fund: Grants are made to organisations which set up and run projects for unemployed borough residents to gain skills through employment-related training. Funding is also available for projects providing advice and information on employment and training.

Community Chest Fund: Grants are made of up to £1,000 to community groups which are based in White City and Wood Lane and provide one of the following: employment/training initiatives, educational services, community businesses or one-off events relating to the preceding activities.

Community Businesses Venture: Funding is available for community based projects or to borough residents to set up trading companies in the borough.

Local Environmental Action Fund (LEAF): Grants of up to £10,000 are made to local groups to carry out small scale improvements to the environment.

Mental Illness Specific Grant: In 1991/92 Hammersmith and Fulham received significant funding from the DoH and all of it was used to support voluntary sector projects: Hammersmith & Fulham MIND, Independent Living, (£79,000), Forward Project (£55,000) and the Alzheimer's Disease Society (£135,000). (See Contracting and Community Care Plan)

Drugs and Alcohol Specific Grant: Hammersmith and Fulham received funding from the DoH in 1991/92 and funded Turning Point (£51,000). (See Contracting and the Community Care Plan)

Bids for funding are processed by the appropriate Joint Planning Team and are reported to Social Services. They must have the support of the district and regional health authorities and be submitted to the DoH by January for funding the following year.

Applications Procedure: Community Liaison within the Strategic Services Department acts as a clearing house for all applications. For general revenue funding for all departments apply in September/October.

Applications can be made throughout the year for the following areas: maternity assistance, seeding grants, feasibility studies, access facilities for people with disabilities, fire-fighting facilities, low cost provision for the under fives, training and workforce services, community chest grants and community business ventures

For Urban Programme Holiday funding and coach vouchers apply in February. Applications for general Urban Programme funding are invited in July/August and in June for the Local Environmental Action Fund.

Other support: A training fund is administered

jointly by the voluntary sector and the council for the training of voluntary management committee members. Individual departments give help in kind and officers for each department should be contacted. Community Transport, funded through the council's main programme, can lend and maintain vehicles for the use of local groups. In addition, the following services can be made available to voluntary groups: discretionary rate relief of up to 100%, cheap premises, advice, and reduced rate bookings of the Town Hall for events or meetings.

Contracting and the Community Care Plan

In March 1992 Hammersmith and Fulham Social Services mostly funded voluntary organisations through grants but used Service Level Agreements (SLAs) when dealing with Department of Health funding targeted at specific areas ie the HIV/AIDS grant, the Mental Illness Specific Grant and the Drug/Alcohol Specific Grant.

In 1991/92 SLAs with voluntary organisations for services in HIV/AIDS, mental health and alcohol/drug abuse totalled £290,000, £214,000 and £51,000 respectively. A Service Level Agreement lasts for one year and is tied to Department of Health funding. It has a standard format with two appendices, one for the service specification and the other for the monitoring of services.

The Community Care Plan was sent to 150 voluntary organisations and was also distributed through voluntary sector network groups. Voluntary organisations are members of the eight Joint Planning Teams (JPTs) involved in community care and each JPT has a voluntary sector representative on the Joint Community Care Plan Team.

For further information contact: Ann Kutek, Head of Strategic Planning, (081- 748 3020 ext 5010)

Hammersmith and Fulham Joint Consultative Committee

Beneficial area: The London Borough of Hammersmith and Fulham catchment area.

Objects: To support health and/or social projects which benefit the residents of the borough. In previous years, priority has been given to people with learning difficulties; people with mental illness, the elderly mentally ill; the elderly; the physically disabled; substance misusers; the homeless; children; and ethnic minority groups. Priorities do change from year to year and this is reflected in the bidding criteria which are produced annually at the beginning of the bidding process.

Funding practices: Schemes may be given one-off capital allocations or receive revenue funding for three years. During the second year of funding a health authority officer initiates discussions with appropriate senior officers in the health and local authority so that possibilities of future funding are established.

Expenditure on voluntary organisations: £157,320 (1990/91)

Details of projects: Voluntary organisations supported in 1990/91 included: The Forward Project, a black mental health project; Barons Court Project, a mental health/homelessness scheme; Blakes Wharf Employment, an employment project for people with learning difficulties; Bangladeshi Association for Culture and Education, a project concerned with mental health needs of the Bangladeshi community; Link Employment, an employment project for those with a history of mental health problems.

Applications procedure: Bids are required in November/December and are considered by the Hammersmith and Fulham Joint Consultative Committee in February. Successful schemes are funded from 1 April.

Correspondent: Debra Cottam, Joint Planning Officer

Address: Riverside Health Authority, 5-7 Parsons Green, London SW6 (081-846 6741)

Other information: Due to limited funds, there will be no joint finance available for new schemes in 1992/93.

The Sarah Campbell Gift

Beneficial area: The old Metropolitan Borough of Hammersmith

Objects: Relief of need amongst elderly and homeless people

Type of beneficiary: Organisations

Income: £1,800 (1990)

Grant total: £1,800

Grant details: Small grants are made, especially towards Christmas time.

Applications procedure: To the Church Wardens, preferably through a social worker or welfare agency.

Correspondent: The Church Wardens

Address: Parish Office, St Paul's Church, Queen Caroline Street, London W6 (081-748 3855)

The Daisy Trust

Beneficial area: London Borough of Hammersmith and Fulham

Main grant areas: Any charitable purpose

Type of beneficiary: Organisations

Income total: £12,570 (1989)

Grant total: £11,340

Grant details: Grants ranging from £50 to £200 are made to a wide variety of social welfare organisations operating in the beneficial area. Recent beneficiaries included groups concerned with housing, mental handicap, bereavement, unemployment, the under 5s, disability and addiction.

Applications procedure: Eligible organisations are welcome to apply in writing to the correspondent. Applications are dealt with once a month.

Correspondent: Mrs C Ground

Address: 13 Ranelagh Avenue, London SW6 3PJ (071-736 0131)

Additional information: This trust mostly raises its own funds through mounting events and in 1989 had an increased income because it received £5,820 in donations. This entry was not confirmed by the trust.

Dr Edwards' and Bishop King's Fulham Charity

Beneficial area: The former Metropolitan Borough of Fulham

Objects:

1. Pensions for poor people resident in the beneficial area for at least two years;

2. Assistance for poor people resident in the beneficial area; also assistance for charities working with the poor and needy in the beneficial area.

3. The provision of meeting space and office accommodation for local organisations and charities at the charity's centre.

Type of beneficiary: Organisations and individuals

Income: £283,110 (1991)

Grant total: £110,400

Grant details: Grants were made under three categories:

Pensions: A total of £29,650 was given in pensions.

Donations: A total of £32,650 was given to organi-sations working in the area and many of the grants were recurrent. Grants generally range from about £100 to £3,000 and in 1991 funded organisations included almshouses, groups for children, the eld-erly, the disabled and the Cyrenians.

Relief in need: Grants for individuals and families in need totalled £45,840, of which one third were for less than £200 and the remainder – over 50 grants – mainly less than £500. Grants were paid via the Family Welfare Association, voluntary organisations, the local authority or direct to companies for wheelchairs, holidays and essential household equipment.

The charity also gave £2,270 in pensioners' Christmas vouchers.

Applications procedure: Applications from organisations can be made directly to the correspondent; in the case of individuals, or social welfare agencies applying on behalf on individuals, application forms are available from the correspondent.

Correspondent: Maria Blackmore, Director

Address: Percy Barton House, 33/35 Dawes Road, SW6 7DT (071-386 9387)

The Fulham Philanthropic Society

Beneficial area: Fulham

Objects: Relief of poverty

Type of beneficiary: Individuals

Income: £1,350 (1978)

Grant total: £650

Grant details: The society no longer gives Christmas parcels as it did in 1978. Small one-off grants are made to relieve most types of need. Bills, however, will not be paid under any circumstances.

Applications procedure: Either direct or through social services.

Correspondent: Mrs Channan

Address: 99 Kenyon Street, Fulham, London SW6 (071-385 3286)

Other information: This entry was not confirmed by the trust.

Fulham United Charities

Beneficial area: Parish of Fulham

Objects: Relief of need

Type of beneficiary: Organisations

Income: £1,900 (1983)

Grant total: £725

Grant details: £250 were given in pensions, £350 in grants in aid, and £25 in educational grants.

Applications procedure: To the correspondent

Correspondent: D F A Trewby, Clerk and Treasurer

Address: 130 West Hill, London SW15 2UF (081-874 9300)

Other information: The above information was not confirmed by the correspondent

Hammersmith Relief in Sickness Fund

Beneficial area: Former Borough of Hammersmith

Objects: Relief of sickness

Type of beneficiary: Individuals

Grant total: £3,800 (1988)

Grant details: Grants are made for the relief of sickness, which includes handicap, infirmity and convalescence, where the applicant is also in financial need. Grants can cover heating bills, furnishings and holidays (especially for carers and handicapped children). The help that the fund would like to offer is constrained by its income - maximum grant is £40.

Applications procedure: Only through an intermediary such as CAB, hospitals or social worker. There is an application form. Applications can be dealt with quickly.

Correspondent: Mrs D Wilde

Address: 14 Fitzwarren Gardens, London N19 3TP (071-263 0531)

Other information: This entry was not confirmed by the trust.

Hammersmith United Charities

Beneficial area: The former Metropolitan Borough of Hammersmith

Objects: The benefit of almspeople; the relief in need generally of residents in the beneficial area.

Type of beneficiary: Individuals

Income: £625,000 (1987)

Grant total: (See below)

Grant details: This organisation is registered as a housing association which applies its income to the building, refurbishment and upkeep of almshouses and sheltered accommodation. It is possible that unspent income may be used to make donations for the relief of individual need. It should be remembered that grants are made at the trustees' discretion and that there is always the possibility that a grant could be made in isolation in exceptional circumstances.

Applications procedure: To the correspondent

Correspondent: A Sheppard, Secretary

Address: Sycamore House, Sycamore Gardens, Hammersmith, London W6 0AS. (081-743 0878)

Other information: The Charities are an amalgamation of the following charities: the Hammersmith branch of the charities of Dr Edward and Bishop King (from which the United Charities received £94,000 in 1987); Dr Iles and Waste Lane Almshouse Charity; William Hill Almshouses; Betts Pension Charity; William Hill Almshouses; Betts Pension Charity; William Payne's Charity; Sarah Gouge for the Poor; and the combined charities of John and Peter Brown, Harriet Clancy, Thomas Collop, Sir Nicholas Crispe, John Powell, Henry Webb, and Nathaniel Dauncer for the Poor.

The trust did not confirm this entry and attempts to reach the correspondent by telephone were unsuccessful.

The Mayor of Hammersmith and Fulham's Appeal Fund

Beneficial area: London Borough of Hammersmith and Fulham

Objects: General charitable purposes at the discretion of the mayor

Type of beneficiary: Individuals and organisations

Grant total: £4,000 to £5,000 (1988)

Grant details: This fund gives small grants to needy residents of the borough. These are in the form of Christmas gift vouchers for elderly people and one-parent families in need, or donations to help pay for holidays for single parents or people with disabilities. Donations range in size from £25 to £50.

Correspondent: The Mayor

Address: London Borough of Hammersmith and

Fulham, Mayor's Office, Room 201, Town Hall, King Street, London W6 9JU (081-748 3020 ext 2013/2014)

Major Local Companies

Bechtel GB Ltd, Bechtel House, PO Box 739, 245 Hammersmith Road, London W6 8DP (081-846 5111) supports charities in particular children's organisations in the local borough. Contact John Baynes, Human Resources Department.

Lucas Power Train Systems, Larden Road, Acton, London W3 7RP (081-743 3111) supports local charities. Contact Alan Toogood, Personnel Manager, Lucas Power Train Systems, Acton, London W3 7RP.

George Wimpey plc, 26-28 Hammersmith Grove, London W6 7EN prefers to support local charities but particularly those active in the caring and helping of the underprivileged. Contact Stefan Bort, Secretary to the George Wimpey Charitable Trust.

Next Menswear, 24 King's Mall, 29 King's Street, Hammersmith W6 (081-563 0366). Donations in areas where Next has a store are made from head office, Desford Road, Enderby, Leicester LE9 5AT (0533 866411). Contact Sarah Howard, PA to the Marketing Director.

Sources of Advice

Hammersmith & Fulham Association of Community Organisations, Palingswick House, 241 King Street, London W6 9LP (081-741 5875)

Coordinator: Jeanette Gould
Opening hours: 10.00-6.00

Hammersmith and Fulham Arts and Education Forum, c/o Acava Ltd, 23-29 Faroe Road, London W14 0EL (071-603 3039). Contact Duncan Smith, Chairman.

Hammersmith and Fulham Community Education Headquarters, Cambridge House, Cambridge Grove, W6 (081-576 5335)

Hammersmith and West London College, Gliddon Road, Barons Court, W14 9BL (081-563 0063)

Haringey

London Borough of Haringey

Civic Centre, High Road, Wood Green, London N22 4LE (081-975 9700)

Correspondents:

Social Services Committee: Denise Hadj-Nassar, Grants Manager (081-888 1292 ext 258). Bob Page, Service Manager, for Mental Health Grant and Drug/Alcohol Abuse grant (081-341 1100)

Housing Committee: Mark Lucas, Voluntary Sector Liaison Officer

Education Committee: Mike Bates, Principal Youth and Community Services Officer, and Tony Michael, Principal Adult Education Officer

Environmental Services and the Urban Programme: Frances Dolan, Head of Urban Programme (grants for Environment Services but see below) Sandra Richards, Coordinator of Urban Programme Unit (081-808 1066)

Grant totals: 1991/92:
£2,997,612 in main programme funding
£2,850,000 in Urban Programme funding

Funding: There is no central grants committee. Grants are given through a number of different committees, and can be broken down as follows for 1991/92 (excluding urban programme funding):

Social Services	£2,427,400
Housing	£99,311
Education	£82,801
Environmental Services	£388,100
TOTAL	£2,997,612

Note: In 1991/92 nearly all of Haringey's main programme budget was already committed in recurrent revenue funding. There were no resources for growth or development. Organisations not already funded by the council are therefore very unlikely to receive a grant unless it is through the Urban Programme or a small grants scheme. This situation will continue for the foreseeable future.

Housing Department: In 1991/92, more than 90% of this committee's grants budget was spent on capital projects carried out by local housing associations. The remainder was allocated to housing organisations and projects for the homeless in recurrent revenue grants.

Social Services: This supports local welfare and social service organisations. In 1991/92, all grants were for revenue costs. Part of its budget is used to make small grants of under £2,500, which can be awarded on a year-round basis; the remainder is committed in recurrent grants to organisations which include Haringey Women's Aid and MIND. Three year long-term funding agreements are given to all Haringey groups in receipt of grants above £2,000.

Environmental Services: This department is responsible for funding five ethnic minority centres and the Haringey Arts Council. In 1992 funds were fully committed and no new applications can be considered for the moment.

Urban Programme: Haringey is an Urban Programme authority and in 1991/92, this was the only significant source of new money for local organisations. Three categories of activity are supported: economic, environmental, and social.

The Urban Programme grants are handled primarily by the Urban Programme Division, based in Environmental Services. Local voluntary organisations are contacted in April/May, bids are invited, and the submission document is sent to the Department of the Environment in December. Organisations are notified of the outcome the following April.

Education: This committee gives grants for two types of activity, youth service and adult education which are as follows:

Youth Service: A limited pattern of maintenance grants is given to local youth groups affiliated to Haringey's Youth and Community Services. Typical beneficiaries are the local headquarters of national voluntary organisations such as the Scouts, the Girl Guides, Boys' Brigade, Girls' Brigade and Woodcraft Folk (grants of around £3,500 and under). Two building maintenance grants of £10,000 and £10,440 are provided to support Turkish Youth Association and Muswell Hill Youth & Community Centre respectively.

Since 1987/88 it has not been possible to assist emerging groups due to continuous cut-backs. However, occasional small one-off grants can be given to assist with the costs of training and a pool of equipment is available because of the closure of a number of youth groups.

Adult Education: Grants are not made to voluntary organisations.

Mental Illness Specific Grant: In 1991/92 Haringey council received a central government grant and mostly funded in-house services though the local branch of MIND was supported (£21,000). In 1992/93 Haringey applied for further funding and is waiting to hear.

Drug and Alcohol Specific Grant: Haringey did not apply for funding in 1991/92 but has applied in 1992/93.

Eligibility: Haringey's overall grants procedure operates according to fairly standard conditions of grant-aid, the main ones being: projects must operate within and/or for the benefit of residents of the borough; proper accounting procedures must be followed and annual reports and accounts submitted to the council. Full details are available from the council in the form of a legally binding document which must be signed by any group offered a grant.

Applications procedure: It is very unlikely that main programme grants funding will be available for new projects but applications are dealt with once a year when any new money is available. The small grants schemes administered by the Social Services department are dealt with twice a year. Application forms are available from the correspondents.

Other support: In addition to grants Haringey supports local groups through discretionary rate relief. Its training officers and staff assigned to work with organisations on specific projects regularly give advice on funding and management matters.

Contracting and the Community Care Plan
In 1992 Haringey Social Services mostly funded voluntary organisations through grants but was starting to introduce contracts. Small voluntary groups are sometimes funded through three year 'grants contracts' which are reviewed annually to monitor the service provided and the amount given. Particular work targeted includes information services, nurseries and creches. Larger, well-established organisations such as MENCAP have a contract of variable length with both the health authority and the council. These contracts can be updated twice a year.

In 1992/93 advocacy services and old people's homes will be funded on a contractual basis. Social Services has already entered into a contract for £21,000 with MIND to provide an information service for the mentally ill and will be entering into contracts with old people's homes for substantial sums. In the next few years homecare services might also be funded through contracts.

All voluntary organisations in Haringey were involved in Haringey's Community Care Plan and the consultation period lasted five months.

For further information contact: Henderson Holmes, Assistant Director, Quality Assurance and Training, Haringey Social Services (081-849 5919)

Haringey Health Authority/ London Boroughs of Haringey and Enfield/ Enfield & Haringey Family Health Services Authority Joint Consultative Committee

Beneficial area: London Borough of Haringey plus the Edmonton area of the London Borough of Enfield

Objects: To promote Care in the Community with schemes jointly managed by the health or local authorities and voluntary organisations, or schemes managed by single agencies where support for joint working is demonstrated.

Funding practices: Support for a variety of schemes to provide information and support to carers and to direct care schemes including grants to housing and group homes run by voluntary and statutory organisations for people with mental illness or mental handicap or for elderly people.

One-off grants are made for furniture, fittings, equipment and publications including translation of materials into community languages.

Expenditure on voluntary organisations: £126,000 (1991/92)

Details of projects: An example of a voluntary group which received funding was TULIP. It was awarded a grant to produce a mental health directory (£12,000).

Applications procedure: An applications guide is available from the correspondent.

Correspondent: Janet Miles, Secretary to the JCC

Address: Haringey Health Authority, 85 Tanners End Lane, Edmonton, London N18 1SB (081-803 1444 ext 5216)

Other information: The committee meets quarterly, on the morning of the last Wednesday in the month, commencing January.

Finsbury Park Community Trust Grants' Fund

Beneficial area: Finsbury Park

Objects: To assist community groups with a base in the Finsbury Park area

Type of beneficiary: Organisations

Income: £7,930 (1990/91, from interest the trust receives on its grant funding)

Grant total: £3,580

Grant details: Grants up to a maximum of £400 are made to community groups which are relatively new and receive little or no funding. Recent organisations supported include the Muslim Welfare Mother and Children Community Centre (£250), St Thomas' Playgroup (£400), Single Homeless Black Women's Group (£200) and the Over Sixties Happy Club (£250).

Applications procedure: In writing to the correspondent for an application form. The small grants committee meets four times a year in January, April, July and October.

Correspondent: The Partnership Development Officer,

Address: 2nd Floor, 261 Seven Sisters Road, London N4 2DD (071-263 3138)

Other information: The trust runs projects in partnership with private, statutory and voluntary organisations to develop employment and training, regenerate community enterprises and enhance the environment.

The Mayor's Fund

Beneficial area: London Borough of Haringey

Objects: Relief of sick and needy residents of the borough

Type of beneficiary: Individuals and organisations

Income: £3,100 (1990/91)

Grant total: £4,200

Grant details: The fund exists as an emergency fund to help elderly, sick and distressed people and children in need. It makes one-off grants only, usually for specific items such as kettles or clothing. These payments are usually in the region of £30 and £40, and in 1990 emergency grants totalling £3,560 were made.

Some of the fund is distributed as Christmas gifts to in-patients in the borough's hospitals. These donations are paid directly to the hospitals, and range in size from £80 to £300 depending on the size of the hospital and the number of patients expected over Christmas. In 1990, £600 was given in Christmas gifts and lunches.

Correspondent: The Mayor

Address: Civic Centre, High Road, Wood Green, London N22 4LE (081-975 9700 ext 2962)

Pauncefort Educational Foundation

Beneficial area: Originally centred on Highgate, now covers parts of the London Boroughs of Haringey, Camden, Islington, and Barnet

Objects: Furtherance of education and training of girls and young women under the age of 25 who are in need of financial assistance.

Type of beneficiary: Individuals

Income: £2,400 (1991/92)

Grant total: £1,800

Grant details: Grants tend to be in the region of £100 and £250 and can cover or contribute towards the cost of school uniforms, course books and equipment, field trips, musical instruments and music lessons. Grants may also be given for help with maintenance and fees for school children and students and to help with the cost of books, travel, and fees for mature students (under 25).

Preference for school children with serious family difficulties so the child has to be educated away from home.

Grants are not given for student exchanges or for foreign students studying in Britain. No grants for people starting work.

Applications procedure: In writing stating the applicant's name, address, age, purpose of award, amount required and the names and addresses of two referees (for applicants at school, one should be the head teacher, year head or form teacher). Applications are considered throughout the year.

Correspondent: G C Pether, Awards Clerk

Address: 13 Maxwelton Avenue, London NW7 3NB (081-959 2727)

Tottenham Aid in Sickness Fund

Beneficial area: Former Borough of Tottenham

Objects: Relief of the sick, convalescent, disabled, handicapped or infirm

Type of beneficiary: Individuals and organisations

Income: £3,850 (1988)

Grant total: £1,900

Grant details: One-off grants for the relief of sickness, and occasionally small grants to organisations (for example, a school for handicapped children was recently supported).

Applications procedure: Application form available from the correspondent. Applicants are usually referred through social services or Age Concern.

Correspondent: Carolyn Banks, Principal Committee Secretary,

Address: Chief Executive Service, Civic Centre, Wood Green, London N22 4LE (081-862 2919)

Other information: This entry was not confirmed by the correspondent.

Tottenham District Charity

Beneficial area: Urban District of Tottenham as constituted 28 February 1896

Objects: Pensions for the elderly and assistance for the poor

Type of beneficiary: Individuals

Income: £75,000 (1990/91)

Grant total: £46,000

Grant details: Grants are given to the poor, elderly, sick or handicapped to reduce need, hardship or distress.

Applications procedure: Contact the correspondent for an application form which should be submitted through a third party such as social services or an advice bureau.

Correspondent: Carolyn Banks, Principal Committee Secretary,

Address: Chief Executive Service, Civic Centre, Wood Green, London N22 4LE (081-862 2919)

The Wood Green (Urban District) Charity

Beneficial area: Urban District of Wood Green (as constituted in 1896): roughly the present N22 postal area

Objects: Provision of pensions for pensioners who have lived in the beneficial area for at least seven years, and the relief of poverty among other residents.

Type of beneficiary: Individuals

Income: £13,000 (1991)

Grant total: £9,000

Grant details: Most of the grant budget is used to provide small pensions and these totalled £8,000 in 1991. Any surplus of income is used to increase the strength of the pensions side of the charity. Small grants, totalling £1,000 in 1991, are also given.

Applications procedure: To the correspondent. Applications are considered in January, April, July and October.

Correspondent: Ms Carolyn Banks, Clerk to the trustees

Address: Chief Executive Service, Civic Centre, Wood Green, London N22 4LE (081-862 2919)

Other information: This entry was not confirmed by the trust.

Major Local Companies

Tottenham Hotspur Football and Athletic Company, 748 High Road, London N17 (081-808 6666) gives signed footballs and free tickets etc. to charities for raffle prizes. Apply in writing to the Charity Commission at the above address.

Tesco plc, 222 High Road, Tottenham N15 (081-801 6673). Grants are made to local charities and those relevant to company business. Contact the Community Affairs Department, Delamare Road, Cheshunt, Hertfordshire EN8 9SL (0992 32222).

Jameson's Chocolates Ltd, Willoughby Lane, London N17 (081-807 4417) makes small donations to local schools and charities. Contact R P Sugden, Managing Director.

J Sainsbury plc, Williamson Road, London N17 (081-809 6065). When a customer brings back a carrier bag, he/she is given a penny and this is often then given to charity. Money is collected from customers throughout the year and head office selects a local charity. Contact Customer Services.

Sources of Advice

Haringey Arts Council, Selby Centre, Selby Road, London N17 8JN (081-801 9520)

Co-ordinator: Manoj Ambasna

Haringey, Adult Education Centre, Petherdown, Muswell Hill, London N10 1ND (081-883 9241)

Harrow

London Borough of Harrow

PO Box 21, Civic Centre, Harrow, Middlesex HA1 2HJ (081-863 5611)

Correspondents:
Lorna Pitt, Resources Manager, Corporate Services, Finance and Corporate Services Department (general contact for local authority grants to voluntary organisations)

Ian Eastburn, Assistant Head of Resources, Finance and Administration for Social Services and Housing, (contact for central government specific grants to local authorities, ie mental illness grant, drugs/alcohol grant, HIV/AIDS grants)

Grants total 1991/92: £451,425

Funding: Towards the end of 1990 Harrow centralised its grant-making structure so that all grants were decided by the Grants Sub-committee servicing the Policy and Resources Committee.

Support is given to local voluntary organisations serving the needs of residents of the borough which directly substitute for or supplement the council's own service provision in priority areas. Grants are made for groups working in leisure and recreation, housing, social services and welfare, education and a number of organisations with 'cross-curricular' activities such as the Harrow Council for Racial Equality, the Harrow Citizen's Advice Bureau and the Harrow in Europe Association.

Mental Illness Specific Grant: In 1991/92 Harrow received a grant of £97,000 (70% of costs) and funded in-house services through contracts.

Drugs and Alcohol Specific Grant: Harrow is applying for funding in 1992/93.

Applications Procedure: Applications are considered on an annual basis and should be submitted by the end of August.

Other support: Discretionary rate relief and discounted hire of council premises are given to approved organisations.

Contracting and the Community Care Plan
In 1992 Social Services was funding voluntary organisations through a mixture of contracts and grants. In future most of its funding will probably be through contracts, with some grant-aid maintained to contribute towards headquarter costs and fixed costs of voluntary organisations.

In 1992/93 day care for mental health (£35,000), bed bureau facilities, luncheon clubs (£23,000), home visiting (£4,000), mental health residential services (£250,000) and other 'non-maintained' projects (c£1 million) will be funded through contracts. Contracts within Social Services run for one year and describe the service to be provided in detail.

The local voluntary sector was involved in developing Harrow's Community Care Plan, with the Harrow Association of Voluntary Service coordinating views and responses.

For further information contact: Paul Quayle, Social Services

Harrow Joint Consultative Committee

Beneficial area: London Borough of Harrow/Harrow Health Authority

Total Expenditure: £517,000 (1991/92)

Details of Projects: In 1991/92 MIND received a grant of £20,000 for the salary of a Development Officer, for secretarial support and general office expenses. MENCAP received a grant for a Development Officer, secretarial support and accommodation. A number of capital grants were made to housing associations to purchase, upgrade or modify suitable houses for people with a mental handicap or who are mentally ill. This formed part of the development of local services for these client groups. The housing associations provide mainstream and landlord services and then enter into contracts with other agencies for care and support to residents. There are two mental health and six learning disability schemes from the voluntary sector managed in this way.

Applications procedure: Contact the correspondents below. All bids for joint finance are discussed within the Joint Planning Teams for each care group (e.g. Mental Health, Drug Abusers etc.) and then prioritised at the JCPT (Joint Care Planning Team) and a recommendation put to the JCC. Despite changes to the joint planning system, this arrangement will probably continue when joint finance becomes available again.

Correspondent: Mrs Julie Waldron, Director of Purchasing,

Address: Northwick Park Hospital, District Headquarters, Watford Road, Harrow HA1 3UJ (081-869 2190)

Other information: Advice about applications is also available from Mr T A Parkin, Head of Resources, London Borough of Harrow, Social Services and Housing Department, PO Box 21, Civic Centre, Harrow, Middlesex HA1 2HJ (081-863 5611)

Edward Harvist Trust

Beneficial area: London Borough of Harrow

Objects: General charitable purposes

Type of beneficiary: Organisations

Income: About £25,000 (1988)

Grant details: Grants are made to a wide range of organisations; recent beneficiaries have included a playgroup, a pilot project for mentally handicapped people, and funding towards the salary of a social work assistant.

Applications procedure: To the correspondent

Correspondent: Mr Gowling, Clerk to the Trustees

Address: Director of Law, IT and Contract Services, Civic Centre, Harrow, HA1 2HJ (081-863 5611 ext. 2239)

Mayor of Harrow's Charity Fund

Beneficial area: The London Borough of Harrow

Objects: Any charitable purpose

Type of beneficiary: Individuals

Grant details: Two funds are operated: one is permanent and set up to make small one-off grants to individuals and families in need, the other operates for as long as the mayor's term of office and makes one grant to a charity of his or her choice.

Applications procedure: Individuals and families are usually referred through social services, although applications can be made directly to the correspondent.

Correspondent: The Mayor's Secretary

Address: Civic Centre, Harrow, HA1 2UH (081-863 5611)

Other information: This entry was not confirmed by the trust.

Major Local Companies

A M P GB Ltd (components and manufacturers), Merion Avenue, Stanmore HA7 4RF (081-954 2356), makes money available to each site consultative committee. In practice mainly local charities are supported. Write to Miss Labbett, Personnel and Administration Department, with details of the project.

Iceland Frozen Foods plc, 1 Garland Road, Honeypot Lane, Stanmore HA7 1LE (081-951 1313) supports local charities. Write to Jill McWilliam, Public Relations.

Kodak Ltd, Headstone Drive, Harrow HA1 4TY (081-427 4380) supports children, youth, social welfare, education, environment and heritage in areas of company presence. All appeals should be sent to Mr M R J Richardson, Corporate Communications, PO Box 66, Kodak House, Station Road, Hemel Hempstead, Herts HP1 1JU (0442-61122).

Reckitt & Colman plc (manufacturers of household and toiletry, food and pharmaceutical products etc.), White Friars Avenue, Wealdstone HA3 5RH (081-427 4343) does not have a charitable budget independent of head office. Head office makes donations to registered charities in areas where the company operates and to appeals relevant to the company's business. Contact P D Saltmarsh, Company Secretary, 1 Burlington Lane, London W4 2RW (081-994 6464).

Sources of Advice:

Harrow Association of Voluntary Service, The Lodge, 64 Pinner Road, Harrow, Middlesex HA1 4HZ (081-863 6707)

Administrator: Margaret Nunn
Opening hours: 10.00-4.00

Harrow Arts Council, Harrow Arts Centre, Uxbridge Road, Hatch End, Middlesex HA5 4EA (081-428 0123). Contact Nicola Clench, Arts Development Officer, Phil Ward, Performance Arts Officer.

Adult Education:

Greenhill College, Lowlands Road, Harrow, Middlesex, HA1 3AQ (081-422 2388) **Weald College**, Brookshill, Harrow Weald, Middlesex HA3 6RR (081-954 9571) **Elm Park College**, Elm Park, Stanmore, Middlesex HA7 4BQ (081-954 9481), **Harrow College**, Polytechnic of Central London, Watford Road, Northwick Park, Harrow HA1 3TP (071-911 5000).

Havering

London Borough of Havering

Town Hall, Romford, Essex RM1 3BB (0708-746040)

Correspondent(s):

Education Committee: Mr C Hardy, Director

Policy and Finance Committee: The Chief Executive

Social Services Committee: M S Talbot, Director

Leisure and Recreation Services Committee: Mr C Hardy, Director

Grant total 1990/91: £429,590

Funding practices: A large proportion of grants to voluntary organisations in the Borough of Havering are made through the quite substantial Havering Lottery Fund. Net proceeds of the lottery are allocated by the Lotteries Subcommittee. This is separate from the council's main programme budget and details can be found in the Lottery Schemes section of this book. In 1990/91 the council's main programme budget can be broken down as follows:

Policy and Finance Committee	£73,980
Education Committee	£49,730
Leisure and Recreation (including guarantee against loss for Queen's Theatre)	£217,420
Social Services	£88,460
TOTAL	£429,590

The Borough of Havering has four committees with budgets for grant-making programmes but there is no central grants unit. General enquiries can be directed to Peter Powell, Deputy Head of Secretariat.

Education: Assistance includes grants to primary and secondary school parent teacher association projects, extramural classes, community and youth centres and youth events.

Leisure and Recreation: Support is given to the local Sports Council and self-help improvement grants are awarded to sports clubs. There is substantial funding for the Queen's Theatre, Hornchurch, including a guarantee against loss.

Social Services: Grants are made to local organisations which give support to the elderly and to the physically and mentally handicapped.

Policy and Finance: Assistance is given towards local advice services.

Specific Grants: In 1991/92 the council did not receive a Mental Illness Specific Grant and although it was awarded DoH funding for alcoholism/drug abuse in 1992/93 this was used in-house.

Applications Procedure: Applications are usually considered twice a year in late spring and late autumn.

Contracting and the Community Care Plan

In 1992 Social Services planned to make the funding procedure of voluntary organisations 'more business-like' and in future will probably use contracts rather than grants.

In March 1992 it was in the process of setting up service specifications and was looking at various kinds of contracts.

The local voluntary sector was involved in developing Havering's Community Care Plan and the council was planning to establish an umbrella group for local voluntary organisations so that their needs and responses could be coordinated.

For further information contact: Christopher Giotti, Principal Officer, Social Services

Barking, Havering and Brentwood Joint Consultative Committee

Beneficial area: London Boroughs of Barking and Dagenham, the Brentwood district of Essex County Council and Havering.

Objects: To get worthwhile schemes off the ground until they can be supported fully by the parent body. These should be schemes for the benefit of the community in a broad aspect.

Funding practices: Funding is spread across the health district and the authorities involved and is not apportioned specifically between the three local authority areas.

Joint finance budget: £1,060,000 (1992/93 and fully committed)

£300,000 is available for new schemes in 1993/94 onwards.

Details of voluntary projects funded: Grief Support Worker for St Francis Hospice (£7,170 in 1991/92)

Crossroads Care Attendant Scheme for Havering (£69,000 in 1992/93 and £66,000 in 1993/94)

Applications procedure: Application forms are available from the correspondents. Voluntary organisations may apply direct or through their representatives on the Joint Consultative Committee (JCC) or through one of the authorities represented. All applications are considered on their merits by a Joint Community Care Committee, one for each local authority area, and recommendations made to the JCC. In 1992 the applications procedure was under review.

Correspondents: Michael Cox, Contracts Manager, Priority Services or Janet de Bruin, Secretary to the authority

Address: Barking, Havering and Brentwood Health Authority, The Grange, Harold Wood Hospital, Gubbins Lane, Romford RM3 0BE (04023 49511)

Other information: The JCC meets approximately twice a year and the JCCC four times a year.

Voluntary sector representatives: Miss D Bunting (Parkinson's Disease Society), 7 Lime Avenue, Upminster RM14 2HY

Mrs E Hare (Dagenham Parish Church), 24 Osborne Square, Dagenham

Ms U Ebel (Barking and Dagenham Voluntary Services Association), 13 Hall Green Lane, Hutton, Brentwood CM13 2RA

Havering Arts Council

Beneficial area: London Borough of Havering

Objects: Promotion of the arts

Type of beneficiary: Organisations

Grant details: Primarily an advice-giving and co-ordination body, the council also has a small grants budget for affiliated societies.

Correspondent: Mr David A Partridge, Secretary

Address: c/o Central Library, St Edward's Way, Romford, Essex RM1 3AR (0708 758178)

Havering Lottery Fund (including the arts and sports bursary scheme)

Beneficial area: The London Borough of Havering

Objects: Support for recreational, artistic and cultural activities and for social welfare, educational and environmental projects.

Type of beneficiary: Local organisations and individuals

Income: £45,800 (1990/91)

Grant total: £27,730

Grant details: The net proceeds of Havering Council's lottery are allocated to the Lotteries Sub-Committee which distributes the money in the form of grants to local voluntary organisations and to individuals. Generally awards are made for activities which are not considered a priority by the council and are unlikely to receive funding. Grants tend to be under £300.

Grants to individuals: There is one bursary scheme for sport and another for the arts. The Sports Bursary Scheme assists sportsmen and sportswomen who have reached county or regional level but have not yet reached the standard at which grant aid is available from the Regional Sports Foundation.

The Arts Bursary Scheme fosters artistic endeavour and enables individuals to improve their standards in cultural or art-based activities. It is open to people of any age providing that they have lived in Havering for more than six months and have already achieved a high standard in their chosen field.

Bursaries can be awarded towards courses of further study or training, travel and the purchase of equipment or materials for a special project.

Grants to organisations: The lotteries scheme supports local organisations which seek funds for specific projects rather than ongoing commitments. Any group based in Havering is eligible for funding providing it can demonstrate:

sufficient stability to ensure that any grant made will be used efficiently

that it benefits communities in Havering

that the project for which assistance is sought is viable and has a reasonable chance of success

Applications procedure: Application forms and further information about grants to organisations can be obtained from the correspondent.

Correspondent: Borough Treasurer at the Town Hall, Main Road, Romford RM1 3BB (0708 746040 ext 3600).

The Lotteries Subcommittee meets quarterly to consider applications.

Application forms and further information about the Arts Bursary Scheme can be obtained from the Arts Officer, Central Library, St Edwards Way, Romford RM1 3AR (0708 746040 ext 3600).

Further information about grants for sporting activities can be obtained from the Director of Leisure Services, Mercury House, Mercury Gardens, Romford RM1 3DX (0708 746040 ext 4611)

Major Local Companies

P C Henderson Ltd (garage door manufacturers), Tangent Close, Ashton Road, Romford, Essex RM3 8UL (04023 45555) supports local charities. Contact Mrs Susan Farrow, Secretary to the Managing Director.

Murex Ltd, Murex Works, 89/95 Ferry Lane, Rainham, Essex (04027-53322) donates to the St Francis Hospice and a few local charities. Contact Mr B Walsh, Personnel Manager.

Romford Brewery Co, The Brewery, High Street, Romford (0708 766088) supports local charities. Contact Violet Roome, Stock Controller.

Save & Prosper Group Ltd, Hexagon House, 28 Weston Road, Romford, Essex RM1 3BL (0708 766966) supports local schools, and colleges. Contact John Shelley, Director, Save & Prosper Educational Trust, 1 Finsbury Avenue, London EC2M 2QY (071-588 1717)

Sherwood Computer Services plc, North House, 11 St Edward's Way, Romford, Essex RM1 4DJ (0708 724411). Charitable appeals are dealt with at Head Office, Sherwood Computer Services, Renslade House, Whitfield Street, Gloucester GL1 1NA (0452-500777) Contact Mr Kevin Crane.

Sources of Advice

Havering Adult Education Centre, Abbs Cross School, Abbs Cross Lane, Hornchurch, RM12 4YB (daytime 04024 40832/53242 evening 04024 53242)

Hillingdon

London Borough of Hillingdon

Civic Centre, High Street, Uxbridge, Middlesex UB8 1UW (0895-250111)

Correspondent:

Voluntary organisations wishing to apply for funding should contact: Nigel Cramb, Community Resources Officer (0895 250394)

Grant totals 1991/92: £912,730 in main programme funding

Funding: Voluntary organisations are funded from four distinct budgets held by the following departments :

Grants Budget 1991/92

Social Services	£414,000
Finance	£360,170
Education and Community Services	£102,750
Housing Services	£38,800
TOTAL	£912,730

Under the council's new scheme of delegation Chief Officers have powers to approve ongoing grant aid to community organisations. However, it is normal practice for officers to make recommendations about the level of funding to the appropriate committee for approval on an annual basis.

Social Services: Funding is targeted to borough organisations which provide services in addition and complementary to those provided by the social services department. Priorities include services for the disabled, the provision of respite care, services for people with mental health problems, services and advice for the elderly.

Finance: Applications are invited from organisations in the borough which primarily provide an information or advice service or which act as a coordinating body for other voluntary groups. Examples of organisations currently funded include Citizens' Advice Bureau and the Community Relations Council.

Housing Services: Organisations whose services complement those provided by the Housing Services Department are considered for funding. Resources are currently targeted on the provision of services for young single homeless people and a refuge for women and children.

Education and Community Services: Applications are considered from all borough youth and community groups or sports organisations, affiliated to the Education and Community Services Department. Grants are allocated as a contribution towards: running costs; building works limited to health and safety works; roof repairs and sanitary installation; specific items for equipment (one-offs).

Mental Illness Specific Grant: In 1990/91 Hillingdon received a total of £107,000 in central government funding and £12,000 was given in grants to voluntary organisations.

Drug and Alcohol Specific Grant: In 1990/91 the council was unsuccessful in its bid to receive central government funding.

Applications procedure: The council has adopted a standard application form and procedure irrespective of which committee or grants-budget community groups are applying to. The availability of grants is advertised in local newspapers and application forms are available from late August and must be returned by 1 November.

Contracting and the Community Care Plan

In March 1992 the Social Services Department was funding organisations through its grants allocation process. It planned to introduce agreements between itself and voluntary organisations on the range and level of service to be provided in return for a specific amount of grant.

These agreements will not be contracts in the strict sense of the word as 'contract' implies a legal agreement between parties which both the council and the voluntary sector are keen to avoid. Instead 'Understandings of Agreements' will be negotiated with the six main voluntary sector beneficiaries. One contract, however, has been made with the Women's Royal Voluntary Service to provide a dining centre service. It has no set term and is reviewed annually.

All future agreements will be individually negotiated between the Social Services Department and the organisation concerned to ensure the agreement best meets the needs of both parties.

Local organisations were involved in developing Hillingdon's Community Care Plan but the majority of them wish to leave the direct provision of services to the statutory sector. They will retain their current status but play an increased advisory role.

Hillingdon Council is keen to promote its role as an enabling authority and forge agreements with community organisations to provide certain services in return for financial assistance. The Education and Community Services Department recently entered into a partnership with a local group to run the borough's Outdoor Activity Centre.

For further information contact: Nigel Cramb, Community Resources Officer

Hillingdon Arts Association

Beneficial area: London Borough of Hillingdon

Grant details: The association makes a certain number of grants each year to affiliated organisations. The association is primarily an advice and co-ordination body but also acts as an umbrella organisation for the four local arts councils within the borough to whom local arts societies are affiliated (the Hayes and Harlington, the Ruislip and Northwood and the West Drayton Art Councils, and the Uxbridge Guild of Arts).

Correspondent: Secretary, Keith French

Address: c/o Villa Bijou, Beaconsfield Road, Farnham Royal, Bucks, SL2 3BP (0753 644782)

Hillingdon Joint Consultative Committee

Beneficial area: London Borough of Hillingdon

Funding practices: Applications for funding are considered annually, normally during March. Funding for approved projects is committed for a period of one to three years with the level of funding reviewed annually. It has become practice in certain cases to extend funding for up to five years.

Total expenditure: £641,000 (1991/92), expenditure on voluntary organisations, £335,720

Details of Projects: Voluntary organisations receiving funding through Joint Finance in 1991/92

included Crossroads Attendant Scheme (£127,650), Hillingdon Action against Alcohol Misuse (HAGAM £23,600), MIND (£32,000) and the Independent Living Centre (£18,000).

Applications procedure: For an initial discussion about applications contact the correspondent or Dino Oddi, Director of Planning, Hillingdon Health Authority (0895 279109)

Correspondent: Nigel Cramb, Community Resources Officer

Address: Social Services Department, London Borough of Hillingdon, Civic Centre, Uxbridge, Middlesex UB8 1UW (0895-250394)

Other information: The committee meets up to four times per year depending on the amount of business to be discussed.

There is also a Subcommittee which considers applications for up to £500 from voluntary sector groups. It had a budget of £10,000 in 1991/92 and uses it primarily to encourage new projects or new groups to provide facilities which complement or are in addition to those provided by the health authority or local authority.

Harefield Parochial Charities

Beneficial area: Ancient Parish of Harefield

Main grant areas: General benefit of the poor

Type of beneficiary: Individuals

Income: £3,990 (1988/89)

Grant total: £1,240

Grant details: About 200 cash grants between £10 and £60 were made for the relief of need.

Applications procedure: To the correspondent

Correspondent: Mrs D South, Honorary Treasurer

Address: 2 Meadow View, Springwell Lane, Harefield, Middlesex UB9 6PQ (0895 822387)

Harmondsworth United Charities

Beneficial area: Ancient Parish of Harmondsworth

Objects: General benefit of the poor, and the payment of stipends to poor persons of good character over 60 years old

Type of beneficiary: Individuals

Income: £625 (1974)

Grant total: £380

Grant details: Grants were given in the form of pensions. No further information available.

Correspondent: The Church Wardens

Address: St Mary's Vicarage, Harmondsworth, UB7 0AQ (081-897 2385)

Other information: No accounts are on file since 1974. The last named correspondent was Rev Hammerton.

The only other information is contained in a booklet, published in 1880 and entitled "The History of the Charities and Fishing Rights of Harmondsworth", which describes the work of the Harmondsworth United Charities under the heading "Malice to None, Charity to All".

Hillingdon Mayor's Fund

Beneficial area: London Borough of Hillingdon

Objects: To raise money for general charitable purposes

Type of beneficiary: Each year a specific charity is supported depending on the Mayor's choice. In 1988/89, Hillingdon's Children with Disabilities was the chosen charity, while in 1987/88, arthritis charities were supported.

Income: Usually around £20,000

Correspondent: The Mayor or the Mayor's Secretary

Address: Civic Centre, High Street, Uxbridge, UB8 1UW (0895-250111)

Hillingdon Partnership Trust

Beneficial area: London Borough of Hillingdon

Objects: To join local industry and the business sector with local charities

Type of beneficiary: Organisations

Grant details: The trust, which when it was established was one of the first of its kind, acts as a broker between charities and companies in Hillingdon, organising contacts and partnerships between the two as a way of boosting the income of local welfare organisations.

Applications procedure: Charities should get in touch with the correspondent with full details of their project and the sort of funding needed.

Correspondent: Wally Richards, Liaison Officer

Address: 274 High St, Uxbridge, Middlesex UBX 1LQ (0895 272911).

St Paul's Harefield Trust

Beneficial area: The village of Harefield

Objects: Any charitable purpose

Latest figures: 1980

Income: £1,800 (interest and donations)

Grant details: No grants were made and no further information is available.

Applications procedure: To the correspondent

Correspondent: E J Whistance

Address: 21 Hall Drive, Harefield, Middlesex (0895 822384)

Other information: The charity was established in 1979. The only accounts on file at the Charity Commission are for 1980, when the trustees reported, "This small charity has had an uneventful year. Thankfully there have been no calls on its funds. This has enabled the trustees to accumulate monies in readiness until required." Our attempts to contact the correspondent remained unanswered.

The Sullivan Trust for Deaf Children

Beneficial area: London Borough of Hillingdon

Objects: Welfare of deaf children

Type of beneficiary: Individuals

Income: £570 (1989/90)

Grant total: £960

Grant details: Grants were made towards the cost of a Christmas party, for a school uniform and to a family to help towards the cost of equipment for their deaf child.

Applications procedure: To the correspondent.

Correspondent: Mr Sullivan, Chairman

Address: 31 Crescent Gardens, Eastcote, Ruislip HA4 8SZ (081-866 3763)

Other information: Further information can be sought from Mrs Valery Soloway, Secretary to the Social Services Director, at the Civic Centre (0895 250526). Applications can also be channelled through the council's education and social services departments.

A P Taylor Fund

Beneficial area: Hayes and Harlington

Objects: To improve the lives of the inhabitants, partly through recreation

Type of beneficiary: Organisations

Income: £56,800 (1990/91)

Grant total: £8,250

Grant details: 25 grants were made, ranging between £100 and £800, and most were recurrent. Generally assisted organisations are involved with young people (scouts, guides, boys brigade units and youth clubs), disability (disabled riding school, stroke club, special school), arts (local arts council, record club, operatic society, choir), old people (club and welfare committee) and others (horticultural and locomotive societies).

Applications procedure: To the correspondent

Correspondent: E Stanmore, Secretary

Address: 267 Church Road, Hayes End, Middlesex

The Uxbridge United Welfare Trusts

Beneficial area: Uxbridge

Objects: General charitable purposes

Type of beneficiary: Individuals and organisations

Income: £172,175 (1986)

Grant total: £40,000 (1988)

Grant details: The charities consist of the Manor and Borough Charities and the Michael Pearce Charity (for almshouse purposes and the relief of poverty); the Clarke Charity (welfare of the sick poor); Lord Ossulton's Charity and the Foundation of Mr Henry Pease (educational grants).

The bulk of the income is derived from the Manor and Borough/Pearce Charities, and much of the expenditure has been connected with almshouses: some £400,000 in recent years for refurbishment and construction. However, in 1988 £40,000 was set aside for grants to welfare organisations (including a holiday scheme and groups operating with the disabled) and to individuals in need. One-off grants are made either in cash or for furniture, equipment, clothing and help with fuel bills. Educational grants are also available.

Applications procedure: To the correspondent from any source.

Correspondent: The Chairman

Address: Trustee Room, Woodbridge House, New Windsor Street, Uxbridge, UB8 2TY (0895 232976)

Major Local Companies

Chibnalls Bakeries Ltd, Springfield Road, Hayes, Middlesex UB4 0LU (081-573 3601) occasionally supports local charities such as Age Concern through gifts of the company's products. Contact Brian Thorpe, Sales Manager.

EMI Music Service UK Ltd, 1-3 Uxbridge Road, Hayes, Middlesex UB4 0SX (081-561 8722). Employees raise money, through raffles etc. for children's homes in the Hillingdon area. Sometimes, if money is left over, it is given to charities which have written in with an appeal. Contact Mike Brooklyn, Employee Relations Coordinator, Human Resources.

Express Foods Group International, 430 Victoria Road, South Ruislip HA4 0HS (081-842 5000) supports local charities through the Hillingdon Partnership Trust. Contact Jackie Blanchflower, Personnel Department or Wally Richards, Liaison Officer, Hillingdon Partnership Trust, 274 High St, Uxbridge, Middlesex UBX 1LQ (0895 272911).

H J Heinz & Co Ltd (head office), Hayes Park, Middlesex UB4 8AL (081-573 7757) supports local charities, particularly those concerned with nutrition and health. Contact Mrs Ann Banks, Donations Coordinator.

Nestlé UK Ltd, PO Box 22, Nestles Avenue, Hayes, Middlesex UB3 4RQ (081-573 3811) supports local charities. Contact Mr Follett, Financial Accountant.

Thorn EMI Electronics Ltd, 120 Blyth Road, Hayes, Middlesex UB3 4RQ (081-573 3888) supports one charity each year related to the defence forces. Contact Mr Paul Calderwood, Public Relations Manager.

Wimpey Laboratories Ltd, Beaconsfield Road, Hayes, Middlesex UB4 0LS (081-573 7744). Support for charitable appeals is decided at head office. Contact Stefan Bort, Secretary to the George Wimpey Charitable Trust, 27 Hammersmith Grove, London W6 7EN (081-748 2000)

Sources of Advice

Hillingdon Association of Voluntary Service,
'Communicare', Christ Church, Redford Way,
Belmont Road, Uxbridge, Middlesex UB8 1SZ
(0895 239830)

Director: Janet Morris
Opening hours: 9.00-4.45

Hillingdon Arts Association, (see separate
entry)

Hillingdon Adult Education Office, 86 Long
Lane, Ickenham, Uxbridge UB10 8SX (0895
676690)

Hounslow

London Borough of Hounslow

Civic Centre, Lampton Road, Hounslow, Middlesex TW3 4DN (081-570 7728)

All enquiries about grants and voluntary sector funding should be directed to the Community and Economic Development Unit in the first instance.

Correspondent:
Roger Coombes, Community and Economic Development Unit, Policy Department (081-862 5071/2)

Total grants budget 1992/93: £2,201,200 (excluding contributions to the London Boroughs Grants Scheme)

Funding: The grants system in Hounslow is currently in the process of being reorganised with effect from 1 April 1992. All grants management and policy will be administered by the Community and Economic Development Unit within the Policy Department, with all grant decisions being taken by the Grants Subcommittee of the Policy Committee. Service Departments and their committees (for example, Education, Leisure Services and Social Services) will retain responsibility for funding voluntary organisations and community groups which are integral to their mainstream activities through other, non-grants arrangements (such as service level agreements, guarantees against loss or 'pump-priming'). The funding priorities of the Grants-Subcommittee will be reviewed during 1992/93 as part of the development of a corporate grants strategy on which the local voluntary sector will be consulted.

Through a training budget the Grants Subcommittee enables funded organisations to develop good practices, proper systems of financial and management control, and alternative sources of funding. The council will also consider providing rate relief, rent subsidy and other support services to voluntary organisations in the borough.

The Children Act 1989: In 1992 the new legislation had not affected Hounslow's grant-making policy but Hounslow recognises that additional funds may be needed so that local groups comply with the new legal requirements.

Mental Illness Specific Grant: In 1991/92 Hounslow received funding from the Department of Health and funded its own services for the mentally ill.

Drug and Alcohol Specific Grant: In 1991/92 Social Services received £17,656 and funded Ethnic Alcohol Counselling in Hounslow.

Eligibility: The council expects funded projects to observe good financial and management practices, demonstrate a commitment to equal opportunities and consult users about their services. Organisations are also expected to seek funds actively from other sources.

Applications procedure: Application forms are available from August onwards and should be returned by early October together with supporting information (i.e. accounts, constitution, annual report). Decisions are made from January to March of the following year. At present it is difficult to approve new grants or provide increased funding to existing organisations because of budget constraints. However, there is some flexibility towards grant-making within the general pressure on resources.

Contracting and the Community Care Plan
In 1992 Hounslow Social Services funded voluntary organisations through grants via the Grants Subcommittee and there were no specific plans to change to contracts.

The voluntary sector was greatly involved in the borough's community care planning process, with representatives being invited to attend all working groups. Initially this was co-ordinated by the local Council for Voluntary Service and later channelled through a Community Care Forum, a separate body which was about to become independent.

Other departments at Hounslow were funding voluntary voluntary organisations through grants in 1992.

For further information contact: Leanda Richardson, Voluntary Services Manager, Social Services

Hounslow Joint Consultative Committee

Beneficial area: The local authority area of the London Borough of Hounslow. (The former Hounslow and Spelthorne Joint Consultative Committee has been disbanded and reconstituted separately in the Hounslow and Spelthorne areas.)

Objects: To plan jointly areas of service to which the health authority, family health services authority, local authority and voluntary sector all contribute.

Funding practices: Usually expenditure is divided into the following categories: 60% to the elderly (within this category top priority to be given to the elderly mentally infirm); 25% to the mentally ill; and 15% to the handicapped. Funding practices are likely to be reviewed in the light of Community Care Planning and the establishment of the new Hounslow Joint Consultative Committee (JCC).

Expenditure on voluntary organisations: £94,500 in 1990/91, £131,260 in 1991/92.

It must be noted that these figures represent expenditure by the Hounslow and Spelthorne JCC before its disbandment. The new Hounslow JCC has yet to allocate joint finance.

Details of projects: In 1991/92 examples of voluntary organisations funded were: Hounslow Carers Drop-in Centre (£4,775) and Training Programme for Home Care Staff (£5,000).

Applications procedure: Still to be determined by the new JCC. Contact the correspondents below for further information.

Correspondents: Deputy Director of Finance, Hillingdon Health Authority, District Offices, St Johns, Kingston Lane, Uxbridge, Middlesex UB8 3PL (0895 279055)

James Allen, Principal Committee Administrator and Secretary of the Joint Consultative Committee, London Borough of Hounslow, The Civic Centre, Lampton Road, Hounslow TW3 4DN (081-862 5081)

Other information: The committee meets twice a year in November and March. It is advisable to contact the District Health Authority at an early stage, and if applicable, the relevant local authority. Initial contacts are:

Hounslow and Spelthorne HA: Robert Nicholls (081-570 7715) and Hillingdon HA

London Borough of Hounslow: James Allen (081-862 5081) and Carol Caporn (081-862 6046).

Given the Hounslow JCC was only established in April 1992 there may be some subsequent changes to the information above.

Hounslow Council For The Arts

Beneficial area: London Borough of Hounslow

Objects: Promotion of the arts

Type of beneficiary: Organisations

Grant details: Principally an advice and co-ordinating body, the council also has a small grants budget for affiliated arts societies.

Correspondent: Colin Bloxham, Honorary Secretary

Address: c/o the London Borough of Hounslow, Leisure Services Department, Civic Centre, Lampton Road, Hounslow, TW3 4DN (081-862 5805)

The Heston and Isleworth United Charities

Beneficial area: Ancient Parishes of Heston and Isleworth

Objects: Relief of poverty and sickness

Type of beneficiary: Individuals

Income: £7220 (1989/90)

Grant total: £1,580

Grant details: A number of charities are administered, the largest connected with almshouses, and several smaller funds such as the Fuel Allotment Fund and the Haden Trust for the relief of sickness and poverty. In 1989/90 £1,420 was given in pensions and £160 in Christmas gifts.

Applications procedure: To the correspondent.

Correspondent: Mrs Worboys, Clerk to the trustees

Address: Clerk's Office, Tolson Lodge, North Street, Old Isleworth, TW7 6BY (081-569 9200)

Other information: This entry was not confirmed by the trust.

The Bowman, Taylor and Vaughan Charities

Beneficial area: The Parish of Brentford

Objects: Relief of poverty

Type of beneficiary: Individuals

Income: £3,930 (1990)

Grant total: nil

Correspondent: The Manager

Address: Bowman Trust, Residents Hall, Bowman Close, Ealing W5

Other information: The Bowman Taylor and Vaughan Charities derive their income from the Estate Charities of John Bowman and Richard Taylor. This Estate Charity was established to fund ecclesiastical work and to distribute money in the parishes of Ealing and Old Brentford. In practice this involves supporting St Mary's Church (through The Bowman Ecclesiastical Charity), Ealing Consolidated Charities (which appear to be concerned solely with almshouses), and The Bowman Taylor and Vaughan Charities, described above.

In the 1989/90 accounts on file at the Charity Commission, the Estate Charity handed on £3,350 of its income to its three dependent charities. The surplus of £960 was reinvested. This pattern of under-expenditure and reinvestment occurs on a regular basis.

Brentford and Chiswick Merged Charities

Beneficial area: Brentford and Chiswick

Objects: Relief of poverty and sickness

Type of beneficiary: Individuals

Income: c14,000 (1990)

Grant total: c14,000

Grant details: The Brentford and Chiswick Merged Charities are made up of several trusts. The bulk of the income is given in educational grants, and one-off donations are made for such items as telephone installation and bedding. In the past small pensions to two pensioners and Christmas gifts of £5 to widows have been paid. More information about the trust would be welcomed.

Applications procedure: To the correspondent.

Correspondent: Mrs Thelma Lewis, Honorary Clerk and Treasurer

Address: 285 Staines Road, Hounslow TW4 5AL (081-570 9789)

Hanworth Poors Land Trust and Coal Fund

Beneficial area: Ancient Parish of Hanworth

Main grant areas: Purchase of fuel for the poor

Type of beneficiary: Organisations and individuals

Income: £870 (1989/90)

Grant total: £620

Grant details: Main grant areas are the purchase of fuel and other assistance for destitute families. Each year grants are made to about 10 families, and a few individuals.

Applications procedure: Only through referral by Social Services, health visitors, probation officers, Citizens Advice Bureaux and Welcare.

Correspondent: E J Pittman

Address: 6 Shakespeare Way, Hanworth, Middx., TW13 7PE

Other information: The trust's income is from fixed interest stock so with inflation is constantly declining in value. The Rev Dr Burgess Charity for Education is also administered. In 1985 its income of £280 was spent on garden activities in Oriel School and on the LB of Hounslow Youth and Community Service to subsidise the cost of residential activity holidays.

The James and Portia Hawes Trust

Beneficial area: Parish of Feltham

Main grant areas: Relief of need.

Type of beneficiary: Individuals

Grant total: £190 (1991)

Grant details: Small grants can be made exclusively within the parish. A recent example was a grant towards a water rate bill for a mentally and emotionally disturbed girl who had three children and could not cope. The Feltham United Charities, administered along with this trust and principally concerned with almshouses, has a General Account and Distress Fund which have been used in the past to provide winter fuel. This service was cut back because of diminishing resources but in 1988/90 gave £350 in fuel donations.

Applications procedure: Only through social service departments, the parish vicar and the trustees.

Correspondent: Mrs P K Essery, Clerk

Address: 33 Hatton Road, Bedfont, Middx., TW14 8JN (081-751 0968)

Hounslow Mayor's Fund

Beneficial area: London Borough of Hounslow but often national charities are also supported.

Objects: To raise money through charity events and donations for charities of the Mayor's choice.

Income: Usually between £4,000 and £7,000

Correspondent: The Mayor

Address: Civic Centre, Lampton Road, Hounslow, Middlesex TW3 4DN (081-570 7728)

Brentford Relief in Need Charity

Beneficial area: Former ecclesiastical parishes of Brentford, St Lawrence with St Paul and St George and Brentford St Faith.

Main grant areas: General relief of poverty

Type of beneficiary: Individuals

Income: £1,000 (1991)

Grant total: £1,000

Grant details: One-off grant cash grants to individuals.

Applications procedure: Directly to the correspondent or through social services, welfare agencies etc.

Correspondent: Rev M Bridger

Address: 3 The Butts, Brentford, Middlesex, TW8 8BJ (081-568 6502)

Other information: In 1989 a scheme amalgamated The Thomas Layton Charity for the Poor and several smaller charities to form The Brentford Relief in Need Charity.

Need and Taylor's Educational Charity

Beneficial area: Brentford and Chiswick

Objects: Promoting the education of needy children

Type of beneficiary: Individuals and organisations

Grant total: £9,000 (1988)

Grant details: Cash grants are paid to schools to help with the costs of educational visits, equipment (especially hired), expensive musical instruments and to individual children.

Applications procedure: Contact the correspondent; local headteachers are also informed about the charity's work. Grants are distributed in October to November.

Correspondent: Ms Anne Best, Honorary Clerk

Address: 185 Linkfield Road, Isleworth, Middlesex TW7 6QY

Major Local Companies

BAA plc, Heathrow Airport Ltd, Hounslow, Middlesex TW6 1JH (081-759 4321) makes donations to local charities. Contact Jenny Bradley, Director of Public Affairs.

SmithKline Beecham Group plc, Beecham House, Great West Road, Brentford, Middlesex TW8 9BD (081-560 5151) has a substantial donations programme with an emphasis on healthcare. It considers projects regarding social welfare and education, requests from charities where the company has a presence, and national appeals. Contact Margaret Bailey, Contributions Coordinator (081-975 2293).

British Airways plc (head office), Speedbird House, Heathrow (London) Airport, Hounslow TW6 2JA (081-759 5511) supports local projects. Contact Mrs Jackie Ive, Charities Administrator.

Gillette UK Ltd, Great West Road, Isleworth, Middlesex TW7 5NP (081-560 1234). Write to Ms Rawlings, Consumer Bureau Manager.

Agfa-Gevaert Ltd, 27 Great West Road, Brentford, Middlesex TW8 9AX (081-560 2131). The company supports selected charities largely through the donations of goods and services rather than cash. Local appeals relevant to the business are preferred. Contact P Miller, Corporate Relations Manager.

Sources of Advice

Hounslow Voluntary Action, Voluntary Action Centre, 51 Grove Road, Hounslow, TW3 3PR (081-577 3226)

Office Manager: Enid Watts
Opening hours: 9.30-5.30

Hounslow Adult Education, Spring Grove Centre, Thornbury Road, Isleworth TW7 4HG (081-569 8484)

Islington

London Borough of Islington

Town Hall, Upper Street, London N1 2UD (071-226 1234).

Correspondent(s):

Policy Development Office: For further information, telephone 071-226 1234 ext 3334

Inner City Unit: Phil Gagg, Partnership Manager, c/o Policy Development Office (071-477 3027)

Economic Development Unit: Tony Wallis, Principal Employment Officer, (17 Islington Park Street)

Race Equality Unit: Eugene Dofoo, Race Equality Officer, address as above

Leisure Services Department: Lawrence Baylis, Arts and Entertainments Officer, 345 Holloway Road, London N7 ORS (071-607 7331)

Education Department: Vaughan West (Community Education), Clive Leach (Youth Services), Sian Williams (Under 5s), Janine Brady, Alison White, Alison Ruddock, Skevos Louizou (Play), Laycock Street N1 1TH

Neighbourhood Services: Jill Boon (Social Services) Angela McTiernan, (Housing). There are 24 Neighbourhood Managers at individual Neighbourhood Offices. For further information on these offices contact Jill Boon.

Planning Department: Lester Pritchard, Planning Officer, 227/229 Essex Road, N1 3PW (071-477 3642)

Grant totals 1991/92:

Main programme funding	£9,832,946
Urban Programme funding	£779,795

Funding: Islington Council has seven grant-making committees whose 1991/92 budgets can be broken down as follows:

Policy Committee	£1,172,091
Neighbourhood Services Committee	£2,832,862
Race Equality Committee	£1,623,278
Leisure Committee	£446,524
Education Committee	£2,906,125
Employment & Economic Development Subcommittee	£1,566,121
Environment Committee	£65,740
TOTAL	£10,612,741

Policy Committee: The Policy Committee funds advice and information groups, law centres and coordinating groups such as the Islington Voluntary Action Council.

Neighbourhood Services Committee: This committee funds housing advice and special needs housing, organisations dealing with older people and people with disabilities, social service organisations, community centres, local amenity societies, local advice and community projects. Grants to Under 5s organisations are administered through neighbourhood offices but funded by the Education Committee. Mental illness grants and drug/alcohol grants are also administered by the Neighbourhood Services Committee.

Race Equality Committee: Projects are funded which reduce racial disadvantage and discrimination, and promote community development amongst black and other ethnic minority groups. Organisations which provide specific services to particular ethnic communities including nurseries, pensioners' clubs etc are funded by the committee specialising in that service.

Leisure Committee: Arts, entertainments and sports organisations are supported.

Education Committee: This committee funds community education, supplementary and mother tongue teaching projects, playschemes and youth clubs but these are dealt with administratively by individual neighbourhoods.

Employment & Economic Development Subcommittee: This committee supports projects which enhance the economy of the area.

Environment Committee: Organisations are supported which work on environmental and planning issues.

There is also a Women's Committee which although it does not have a grant-aid budget, can advise women's organisations on making applications to other committees. Contact Marian Scott, Head of the Women's Equality Unit.

Mental Illness Specific Grant: In 1991/92 Islington received a grant of £15,727 towards providing services for the mentally ill and funded Islington Mental Health Consortium (£3,000), Islington Mental Health Forum (£3,000), Family Welfare Association for a volunteering scheme, (£8,275), and Islington MIND towards an employment project (£4,452).

Drugs and Alcohol Specific Grant: In 1991/92 Islington received a grant of £48,569 and funded two voluntary projects: Milton House (£24,295) and the Angel Project (£24,274).

Applications procedure: The deadline for submission of application forms is October for main programme funding and September for the Urban Programme. Final decisions are taken in January/February but budgets are set in October or November of the previous year.

Other support: This includes Unified Business Rate Relief, hire of council transport, special lease arrangements for council owned premises and in some circumstances, leasing of computers. General advice and support are given by the Liaison Officers listed above on finance, fundraising, constitutions, management etc. Islington Voluntary Action Council also gives help and advice, training and financial services (see Sources of Advice).

Contracting and the Community Care Plan
In 1992 Social Services wished to negotiate service level agreements with some voluntary projects but was reluctant to enter into SLAs for three years because of Islington Council's uncertain financial situation. Instead it planned to introduce a tighter specification for provision of service in the context of grant-aid and will encourage organisations to establish operational policies which clearly state the group's aims, objectives, service provided and ways of working.

In 1992/93 Social Services will probably negotiate with organisations to set up contracts for specific projects such as domiciliary care. Proposed contracts are:

Organisation	Budget
Islington Mind, (for an Employment Worker)	£8,904
Family Welfare Association (Volunteer Organiser)	£10,550

Discussions about community care were held with voluntary groups which included The Islington Voluntary Action Council, small local voluntary groups and large national organisations such as Age Concern, Pensioners' Link, Elfrida Rathbone, Islington, MENCAP and their users .

In 1992 other departments within the council were also starting to fund voluntary organisations through contracts: The Policy Development Office made contracts with law centres; the Economic Development Unit had a contract with Islington Voluntary Action Council to fund an Employment Worker; and the HIV/AIDS Unit was gradually moving towards funding voluntary organisations through contracts/service level agreements.

For further information contact: Ann Graham, Islington Neighbourhood Services, (071-477 4082)

Islington Joint Consultative Committee

Beneficial area: The London Borough of Islington.

Objects: The Joint Consultative Committee (JCC) agrees and monitors the Joint Collaboration Programme and oversees the Joint Finance Programme. At present, this involves only the health and local authorities but may be widened to include FHSAs (Family Health Services Authorities) and voluntary organisations.

Funding practices: The JCC is not a funding body as such. It does not have the power to make grants outside the Joint Finance Programme.

Expenditure on voluntary organisations: Nil. Responsibility lies with the two statutory authorities.

Details of projects: The Joint Finance Programme reflects the joint collaboration programme. No grants are made to voluntary organisations through this mechanism at present, but this is not precluded.

Applications procedure: Applications are dealt with through non-statutory organisation grant procedures operated by the two authorities. If considered suitable an application could then be submitted for inclusion on the Joint Finance Programme - but the purpose of the procedures is to ensure that non-statutory organisations have access to a full range of funding sources - not just Joint Finance.

Correspondent: Mike Whelan, Business Support Officer

Address: Bloomsbury and Islington Health Authority, District Headquarters, 110 Hampstead Road, London NW1 2LJ (071-383 4888 ext 8233)

Other information: The committee meets in February and September.

Clerkenwell Welfare Trust

Beneficial area: Ancient Parish of St James Clerkenwell within the former Metropolitan parish of Finsbury

Objects: Relief of need, hardship and distress.

Type of beneficiary: Individuals and organisations

Income: £6,800 (1979/80)

Grant total: £3,760

Grant details: £3,000 to local welfare organisations, the remainder to local churches. No further information available.

Applications procedure: To the correspondent.

Correspondent: P S Rust, The Secretary

Address: 61 West Smithfield, London EC1A 9EA (071-606 5711)

See also St Sepulchre (Finsbury) United Charities and Thomas Kifford's Educational Foundation.

Richard Cloudesley's Charity

Beneficial area: The ancient Parish of St Mary Islington (roughly the modern Borough, excluding the area south of the Pentonville and City Roads)

Objects: The relief of sick poor residents; support of local C of E churches and medical and welfare charities.

Type of beneficiary: Individuals and organisations

Income: £250,000 (1990)

Grant total: £250,000

Grant details: Grants to organisations ranged between £50 and £28,500, and were nearly all recurrent. 39 medical charities were supported and grants over £5,000 were made to nine churches. Welfare groups such as The Islington Reader Service for the Blind (£100) and the Islington Victim Support Scheme (£700) also received donations as well as projects providing counselling in bereavement and on drugs and sexual problems.

About £21,000 was given to individuals through the charity's Welfare Fund, with grants averaging £50. Two important points should be noted: firstly that applications, except in very exceptional circumstances, should be made through the social services, GP, CAB or similar agency. Secondly, that the terms of the charity's deed empower grants to be made only to poor sick residents of the ancient parish of Islington, and that applications for help with cases other than sickness or disability cannot be considered. The charity foresaw that the fast and flexible help it can give would become increasingly valuable with the introduction of the Social Fund.

Applications procedure:

There are two separate procedures:

Applications from or on behalf of individuals are administered by the Honorary Almoner, Miss Kerala Thomson, c/o 166 Upper Street, London N1 1XU. (081-883 5809)

Approaches from organisations should be made in the first instance in writing to Mr Wallace at the address below.

Correspondent: K Wallace, Clerk to the Trustees

Address: c/o Richards Butler, Beaufort House, 15 St Botolph Street, London EC3A 7EE (071-247 6555)

Other information: The charity was endowed by the will of Richard Cloudesley in 1517 and is now an important and innovative trust in the area. Full annual reports and accounts are on file at the Charity Commission. The grant budget has risen from £30,000 to £250,000 in just seven years, and the charity's income is expected to rise as the renovation and sale of its property continues.

City of London and East London Dispensary Fund

Beneficial area: City of London and the Metropolitan Boroughs of Shoreditch and Finsbury

Objects: Relief of need

Type of beneficiary: Organisations

Income: £2,350 (1989/90)

Grant total: £1,100

Grant details: Donations of £300 were made to the National Listening Library, St Joseph's Hospice and the Phyllis Tuckwell Memorial Hospice. Another group was supported with a donation of £200. Most of these grants are recurrent.

Applications procedure: To the correspondent

Trustees: R Bliss, V C Bliss, R A Ottaway, R W Young;

Correspondent: R H C Bliss,

Address: 1 Town Walk, Cheriton Place, Folkestone, Kent (no telephone number listed)

Other information: This entry was not confirmed by the trust.

The Cripplegate Boys' Scholarships Charity

Beneficial area: The Parish of St Luke, Old Street

Objects: Educational grants for boys under 25 living or studying in the beneficial area

Type of beneficiary: Individuals

Latest figures: 1990

Income: £2,580

Grant total: £1,010

Grant details: Cash grants for schoolboys, to a usual maximum of about £150 (depending on age), to help with books, equipment, clothing or travel.

Grants to help with school, college or university fees or to supplement existing grants.

Applications procedure: At any time, but preferably between March and June.

Correspondent: The Chief Executive

Address: St Luke's Parochial Educational Foundation, 90 Central Street, London EC1V 4AQ (071-250 4144)

Other information: See also the entry for St Luke's Parochial Trust. This entry was not confirmed by the trust.

Cripplegate Foundation

Beneficial area: The ancient Parish of St Giles, Cripplegate, together with the former parish of St Luke's, Old Street i.e. the present-day City of London and the southern part of the London Borough of Islington

Objects: Relief of need, hardship and distress and the improvement of the quality of life

Type of beneficiary: Individuals and organisations

Income: £1,187,980 (1990)

Grant total: £1,166,521

Grant details: Because of the large amount of money to be spent in this restricted area, many local projects are able to benefit. These include local community and charitable activities located nearby where some of the people to be helped are from the area of benefit.

Grants to organisations were made under the following categories (in order of total of grants made): schools and training, social and community service, the disabled and handicapped, the young, the inadequate, the old, recreation and the arts, hospitals.

Educational grants can be made for school children or students attending educational establishments or living in the area, if their education is being disrupted by financial need.

Applications procedure: To the correspondent. The foundation employs a staff of three and welcomes a preliminary approach by telephone or in writing to establish if an application is likely to be considered.

Correspondent: The Clerk to the Governors

Address: 87 Worship Street, London EC2A 2BE (071-247 2106)

Other information: This entry was not confirmed by the trust.

The Cripplegate Girls' Scholarships Charity

Beneficial area: The Parish of St Luke, Old Street

Objects: Educational grants for girls under 25 living or studying in the beneficial area

Type of beneficiary: Individuals

Latest figures: 1990

Income: £1,260

Grant total: £1,700

Grant details: Cash grants for schoolgirls, to a usual maximum of about £150 (depending on age), to help with books, equipment, clothing or travel.

Grants to help with school, college or university fees or to supplement existing grants.

Applications procedure: At any time, but preferably between March and June.

Correspondent: The Chief Executive

Address: St Luke's Parochial Educational Foundation, 90 Central Street, London EC1V 4AQ (071-250 4144)

Other information: See also the entry for St Luke's Parochial Trust.

This entry was not confirmed by the trust.

The Margaret Desmond Charitable Trust

Beneficial area: The Parish of St Joan of Arc, Highbury, London N5

Main grant areas: General charitable purposes

Grant details: No information available

Applications procedure: In writing to the correspondent with full details of the grant required and the benefit to be gained from it.

Correspondent: G McEwen

Address: L B Marks & Co, 39/41 Queen Anne's St, London W1A 3AX (071- 224 0422)

Other information: The charity was registered in 1985. A copy of Margaret Desmond's will detailing the bequest of the testator's house (at Northolme Road, Highbury Park) and estate to the trustees is on file at the Charity Commission. The correspondent told us that the trust is not very large.

Finsbury Dispensary Relief in Sickness Charity

Beneficial area: Finsbury

Main grant areas: Welfare of sick, convalescent, disabled and handicapped people

Type of beneficiary: Individuals

Income: £1,400 (1987)

Grant total: £1,400

Grant details: One-off grants of £25 to £100.

Applications procedure: Through social services, hospital, CAB etc.

Correspondent: Doreen Scott

Address: c/o IVAC, 322 Upper Street, London N1 (071-226 4862)

Finsbury Park Community Trust

See entry in the Haringey section

Lady Gould's Charity

Beneficial area: Highgate, comprising the whole of the N6 postal district and part of the N2, N8, N10 and N19 districts.

Objects: Relief of poverty

Type of beneficiary: Individuals

Income: see 'Other information'.

Grant total: c£12,000 (1991)

Grant details: Grants are made to individuals either through the Reverend J J Fielding of the Parish of St Michael, Highgate (081-340 7279) or by the trustees through Bower, Cotton and Bower, Solicitors.

Applications procedure: Applicants are required to complete a form obtainable from the correspondent.

Correspondent: J Talbot, Secretary

Address: Bower Cotton & Bower, 36 Whitefriars Street, London EC4Y 8BH (071-353 3040)

Other information: The major assets of the trust are two properties which have been recently let and renewed. The trustees believe that their disposable income will leave a clear £30,000 for distribution in 1992.

Islington Mayor's Charity

Beneficial area: London Borough of Islington

Objects: General charitable purposes

Type of beneficiary: Each year money is raised for a specific charity of the Mayor's choice. In 1990/91 this was the Islington Under Fives Development Trust.

Income: This depends on how much fundraising is done by the Mayor. In 1990/91 £8,000 was raised, whilst in the previous year, £15,000 was raised.

Correspondent: The Mayor or the Mayor's Secretary

Address: Town Hall, Upper Street, London N1 2UD (071-477 3113)

Islington Relief in Need Charities

Beneficial area: Islington and Upper Holloway

Main grant areas: Relief of poverty and distress

Type of beneficiary: Individuals

Income: £4,000 (1987)

Grant total: £4,000

Grant details: One-off grants of £25 to £100 to individuals

Applications procedure: Through social services, hospitals, CAB etc.

Correspondent: Doreen Scott

Address: c/o IVAC, 322 Upper Street, London N1 (071-226 4862)

Islington Relief in Sickness Charity

Beneficial area: Islington

Main grant area: Welfare of sick, convalescent, handicapped and disabled people.

Type of beneficiary: Individuals

Latest figures: 1987

Income: £650

Grant total: £600

Grant details: One-off grants of between £25 and £100

Applications procedure: Through social services, hospitals, CAB etc.

Correspondent: Doreen Scott

Address: c/o IVAC, 322 Upper Street, London N1 (071-226 4862)

Thomas Kifford's Educational Foundation

Beneficial area: Parish of St Sepulchre, Islington, with a preference for that part of the parish which is within the former Metropolitan Borough of Finsbury

Objects: Educational grants for residents under 25

Type of beneficiary: Individuals

Latest figures: 1975

Grant details: In 1975, the most recent year for which accounts are on file at the Charity Commission, £115 was given in educational grants, leaving an unallocated surplus of income over expenditure of £1,500.

Applications procedure: To the correspondent

Correspondent: P S Rust, Secretary

Address: 61 West Smithfield, London EC1A 9EA (071-606 5711)

Other information: Further information would be welcomed.

See also St Sepulchre (Finsbury) United Charities.

Dame Alice Owen's Eleemosynary Charities

Beneficial area: Parishes of St Mary, Islington, and St James Clerkenwell

Objects: Welfare of poor widows over 50 years old, resident in the beneficial area for at least two years.

Type of beneficiary: Individuals

Income: £850 (1987)

Grant total: £825

Grant details: Pensions are paid to five pensioners. The number of pensioners and the amount are reviewed from time to time.

Applications procedure: The local vicar and social services are told when vacancies arise, but direct applications can also be made.

Correspondent: The Clerk of the Worshipful Company of Brewers

Address: Brewers' Hall, Aldermanbury Square, London EC2V 7HR (071-606 1301)

Other information: This entry was not confirmed by the trust.

Reeve's Foundation

Beneficial area: The ecclesiastical Parish of St Sepulchre or the ancient Parishes of Clerkenwell and St Andrew, Holborn. This includes parts, but not all, of the areas of Holborn, Clerkenwell, Finsbury and Pentonville. In practice, it covers the area east of Goswell Road and Giltspur Street; north of Ludgate Hill, Chancery Lane and High Holborn; west of Great Ormond Street, Mount Pleasant and Kings Cross Road; and south of Wynford Road and Culpepper Street.

Objects: Educational grants for people under 26 years old who have lived or worked, or whose parents have lived or worked, in the beneficial area for at least 12 months prior to application or for at least two of the previous ten years.

Type of beneficiary: Individuals

Grant total: £150,000-£200,000

Grant details: The trust states that : "the beneficiaries of the local education trusts are generally in LEA schools - due largely to the area of benefit that we cover. The support for these is normally in the form of clothing grants for younger children, with additional sums for sports equipment, books, cost of projects, musical instruments and tuition, school trips, special courses etc., available for older children. The trust also helps with emergency payments for local college and university students whose parents fail to make up their grants. It also gives students book grants for their courses. In fact, the trustees will consider any request for a grant which can be considered educational where the beneficiary is under the age of 26 years. Furthermore, "if a request for help cannot be considered by the trustees then it is normally passed on to someone who is in a position to consider the applicant's request."

Applications procedure: Applications should be made on a form available from the correspondent. Meetings are normally held in February, May, July, September and December. Most requests are either received through the local headteachers or student welfare officers, or notified by them. Where this is not possible a visitor normally calls to discuss the need.

Correspondent: The Clerk

Address: 90 Central Street, London EC1V 8AQ (071-250 4144 ext 49).

St Luke's Parochial Educational Foundation

Beneficial area: The Parish of St Luke, Old Street

Objects: Educational grants for residents under the age of 25.

Type of beneficiary: Individuals

Income: £17,230 (1990)

Grant total: £17,230

Grant details: Cash grants for school pupils to a usual maximum of about £150 (depending on age), to help with books, equipment, clothing or travel.

Grants to help with school, college or university fees or to supplement existing grants. Help towards the cost of education, training, apprenticeship or equipment for those starting work.

Applications procedure: At any time, but preferably from March to June.

Correspondent: The Chief Executive

Address: St Luke's Parochial Educational Foundation, 90 Central Street, London EC1V 4AQ (071-250 4144)

Other information: See entry for St Luke's Parochial Trust. This entry was not confirmed by the trust.

Saint Luke's Parochial Trust

Beneficial area: The ancient Parish of St Luke's, Old Street in the former Metropolitan Borough of Finsbury

Objects: Payment of pensions; relief of need; running of Community Centre

Type of beneficiary: Individuals and organisations

Income: £739,200 (1990)

Grant total: £198,230 (£147,980 on pensions and related benefits; £50,260 on other benefits including grants and holidays). This figure excludes running costs of the Community Centre and expenditure on the trust's other social welfare and community programmes.

Grant details: The largest part of the grant budget was taken up with the provision of pensions for the elderly, with weekly allowances of £3 per week for a single person and £4 per week for a married couple. Note that applicants for pensions must have lived in the parish for 5 years before application, or for 15 years out of the previous 30 years. Elderly people who once lived within the beneficial area but were forced to move away because of the war, slum clearance or similar cause will also be considered.

The trust also provides grants, mainly for the elderly, for TV licences, Christmas gifts and individual help where necessary.

Educational grants are channelled through three other charities administered by the trust -St Luke's Parochial Educational and Apprenticing Charity, The Cripplegate Girls' Scholarships Charity and The Cripplegate Boys' Scholarships Charity (see separate entries).

Grants are also available for organisations. During the year grants totalling £32,390 were made to 16 organisations working in the area of relief in need. Of these, five were for the welfare of children and young people.

The focus of the trust's activities in the area is the community centre it established and now runs, where lunches are provided for pensioners. Holidays and outings are arranged and the trust's visiting service ensures that isolated or house-bound elderly people are visited and offered practical help and support.

Applications procedure: To the correspondent at any time.

Correspondent: K C S Wood, The Chief Executive

Address: 90 Central Street, London EC1V 8AQ (071-250 4144)

St Sepulchre (Finsbury) United Charities

Beneficial area: Parish of St Sepulchre, Islington

Objects: Benefit of needy residents, especially the elderly

Type of beneficiary: Individuals

Income: £20,330 (1991)

Grant total: £17,440

Grant details: £17,410 was paid in weekly pensions and £30 in grants. No further information available.

Applications procedure: To the correspondent.

Correspondent: P S Rust, Secretary

Address: 61 West Smithfield, London EC1A 9EA (071-606 5711)

See also Thomas Kifford's Educational Foundation.

Dame Sarah Temple's Educational Foundation

Beneficial area: The Parish of Islington

Objects: Educational grants for school children living in the beneficial area

Type of beneficiary: Individuals

Grant total: £1,000 (1990/91)

Grant details: Small, one-off grants are made to school children for items such as books and travel expenses. The foundation is too small to offer help with fees or to receive applications from students in further education.

Applications procedure: Grants now are only given on recommendation of Islington education welfare officers. No other requests will be considered or acknowledged.

Correspondent: Rev G L Claydon

Address: St Mary's Vicarage, Upper Street, London N1 1BU (071-226 3400)

A number of small charities are also administered from the church. Their beneficial area again covers the parish of Islington, they have very specific objects (e.g. married members of the C of E who are over 50) and their combined income is probably not much over £500.

The Throckmorton Trotman Educational Foundation

Beneficial area: Greater London, with a preference for the Parishes of St Giles, Cripplegate, and St Luke's, Old Street

Objects: Educational grants for residents in the beneficial area. Junior exhibitions are available to boys and girls over the age of 11 and under 14 on 31st May each year. Senior exhibitions are awarded to students over 16 and under 25 at the date of the award.

Type of beneficiary: Individuals

Latest figures: 1988

Grant total: About £13,600

Grant details: The foundation's aim is "to assist those eligible and who might otherwise be deprived."

Junior exhibitions (about 10 a year) are available at any approved secondary school and Technical Exhibitions are available at any institution of technical, professional or industrial training. Grants are usually up to about £250 each.

Senior exhibitions (about five a year) are available at any college, university or professional institution. Grants are usually up to about £1,000, either by single payment or spread over a maximum of four years.

Applications procedure: Juniors proposing to sit examinations must give notice in writing by 28 February. Seniors may apply in writing at any time.

Correspondent: The Clerk

Address: The Worshipful Company of Haberdashers, Haberdashers' Hall, Staining Lane, London EC2V 7DD (071-606 0967)

The Worrall and Fuller Exhibition Fund

Beneficial area: Finsbury with preference for those in the Parish of St Luke, Old Street, Islington

Objects: To help with the educational needs of those resident in the beneficial area.

Type of beneficiary: Individuals (usually between the ages of 5 and 25) but also Church of England aided schools needing repair.

Income: £20,000 (1990/91)

Grant total: £13,850

Grant details: Grants are made for the cost of

school, college or university fees, books, travel and other equipment expenses and to help those wishing to study music and the arts or intending to start work. This includes help with clothing tools etc. to beneficiaries on leaving school or university to help them enter a trade or profession.

Applications procedure: Applications should be made on forms available from the correspondent.

Correspondent: Mr D C Smith

Address: 23 Whitehouse Way, Southgate, London N14 7LX (081-368 2715)

Major Local Companies

Automagic Cleaning Services Ltd, 242-244 St John's Street, London EC1V 4PQ (071-250 4148). Write to the Managing Director.

National Westminster Bank, King's Cross House, 200 Pentonville Road, London N1 9HL (071-239 8000). This company generally helps voluntary organisations and groups achieve financial effectiveness and enterprise through its community contributions. For further information contact Jan Rayment, Community Relations Manager, National Westminster Bank, 1/2 Broadgate, London EC2M 2AD (071-714 4000).

The Royal Bank of Scotland, The Royal Bank of Scotland Regional Office, Regents House, 42 Islington High Street, London N1 8XL (071- 833 2121) makes donations to local charities. Contact Julian Gouge, Business Development Officer.

Sources of Advice

Islington Voluntary Action Council, 322 Upper Street, Islington, London N1 2XQ (071-226 4862).

General Secretary: Andy Gregg
Opening hours: 10.00-5.00

Islington Community Adult Education has twelve branches and is decentralised. Information about courses can be obtained from any branch of which Archway is one: Archway Branch, School Buildings, Holland Walk, (off Duncombe Road), London N19 3EU (071-226 9190).

Education Advice Service for Islington Adults (EASIA) gives free advice on education for adults over 19 years of age, 12 Barnsbury Road, N1 OHB (071-278 3761).

Kensington and Chelsea

Royal Borough of Kensington and Chelsea

The Town Hall, Hornton Street, London W8 7NX (071-937 5464)

Correspondents:
For general enquiries about grants contact:
Community Liaison Department: Tina Dubois, Voluntary Organisations Liaison Officer, (ext.2156)

For specific enquiries about grants contact:
Planning and Development: Jennifer Lyon, Manager of Planning and Development, ext 2597 (central government specific grants, mental illness, drug/alcohol abuse, HIV/AIDS)

Libraries and Arts: Ms Terry Slasberg, Administrator, (081-743 4559)

Urban Programme: Graham Taylor, Chief Community Liaison Officer (ext 2308)

Grant totals 1990/91: £5,060,000 in main programme funding

£721,000 through the Urban Programme

Funding practice: Kensington and Chelsea has six grant-making committees: Social Services; Housing (private sector); Youth; Continuing Education and Employment; Corporate Management; and Libraries and Arts. Their 1990/91 grant-making budgets can be broken down as follows:

Social Services	£1,934,000
Libraries and Arts	£129,000
Corporate Management	£1,439,000
Housing (private sector)	£434,000
Youth	£1,037,000
Continuing Education and Employment	£84,000
TOTAL	£5,060,000

Social Services: The Social Services committee is the largest grant-maker, allocating (in 1990/91) around 38% of the main programme budget. Nearly 50 welfare organisations were funded with grants ranging from £600 to £362,000. Support is given across the field of social services organisations. A

further £160,000 of grants to voluntary organisations has been made in 1990/91 under the AIDS Allocation of Special Joint Finance.

The Children Act 1989: In March 1992 the council was reviewing the implications of the new legislation for both its own services and voluntary sector provision. This has led to the funding of a new voluntary sector respite care scheme and is likely to lead to further changes in the pattern of grants to voluntary organisations in future years.

Libraries and Arts: This committee funds arts projects. Beneficiaries in 1990/91 included Caribbean Cultural International and Film Work Group. A grant is made annually to Kensington and Chelsea Arts Council to enable them to make small, one-off grants to local arts projects.

Corporate Management: This committee funds advice services, co-ordinating/support agencies and community centres in the borough. In 1990 it supported 19 organisations, with annual grants ranging from £5,350 to £472,000.

Housing (private sector): In 1990/91 grants were made to nine groups concerned with housing advice and hostels. The Housing Action Centre received £179,000 and the remaining grants ranged from £4,800 to £73,000.

Youth: This committee funds youth and play provision and in 1990/91 supported over 30 organisations with annual grants ranging from £340 to £131,000.

Continuing Education and Employment: In 1990/91 grants ranging from £570 to £28,000 were given to mother tongue classes, employment projects and the Community Language Centre.

In addition to annual grants, each of the grant-making committees has a contingency fund to support small one-off grants. As only very limited funds are available, organisations are advised to contact the correspondent prior to making an application.

All of the above committees and their grant-making are co-ordinated by the Community Liaison Section of the Corporate Services Business Group, to which all initial enquiries should be addressed.

Urban Programme: The Royal Borough of Kensington and Chelsea is an Urban Programme Authority and grants are available for projects covering the five Northern Wards (St Charles, Golborne, Kellfield, Colville, Avondale), Earls Court and South Stanley. Of the £721,000 of grants given in 1990/91, 35% went on revenue funding and 65% on capital funding. A wide range of inner city projects, ranging from steel bands to enterprise units received UP funding. Many social projects are applying for revenue grants but there is currently more scope for economic and environmental groups to receive support.

Mental Illness Specific Grant: No voluntary sector projects were funded in 1991/92.

Alcohol and Drug Specific Grant: The council was successful in bidding for central government monies and funded three local voluntary organisations to a total of £102,490: Richmond Fellowship (£41,000), Turning Point (£49,770), and Self Help Addiction Recovery Project (SHARP) (£11,730).

Applications procedure: Applications for one-off small grants can be made throughout the year using a standard application form. There is limited scope for considering new bids for annual grants and the applications procedure is under review. Prospective applicants are advised to contact Tina Dubois, Voluntary Organisations Liaison Officer.

Other support: Kensington and Chelsea Council gives further support to voluntary groups in a variety of ways. The Audit Department assists with financial and bookkeeping advice, whilst the Voluntary Organisation Liaison Officers are available for advice on a wide range of issues. Some groups are given access to council vehicles, and a limited number use council premises at a peppercorn rent. Discretionary rate relief has been granted to many local voluntary groups. Payroll services are also offered to some voluntary organisations.

Contracting and the Community Care Plan
The Social Services department proposes to replace its grant-aid to voluntary organisations with service-level agreements by April 1993. It will probably devise a general format for these agreements and the level of detail will be appropriate to the organisation concerned.

In 1992 Social Services was using the introduction of service-level agreements to clarify its funding relationship with the voluntary sector and was creating a basis for future monitoring of quantity and quality of service.

Voluntary groups were consulted about community care, and senior managers visited organisations such as MENCAP, Crossroads, Pepperpot Lunch Club (Afro Caribbean) to discuss the Community Care Plan with users.

All departments in the council were moving towards a more contractual relationship with the voluntary sector in 1992.

For further information contact: Jim Mullany, Voluntary Organisations Liaison Officer, Social Services (071-937 5464 ext 2484)

Kensington and Chelsea Joint Consultative Committee

Beneficial area: The Royal Borough of Kensington & Chelsea catchment area.

Objects: To support health and/or social projects which benefit the residents of the borough. In previous years, priority has been given to people with learning difficulties; people with mental illness; the elderly mentally ill; the elderly; the physically disabled; substance misusers; the homeless; children; and ethnic minority groups. Priorities do change from year to year and this is reflected in the bidding criteria which are produced annually at the beginning of the bidding process.

Funding practices: Schemes may be given one-off capital allocations or receive revenue funding for three years. During the second year of funding a health authority officer initiates discussions with appropriate senior officers in the health and local authority so that possibilities of future funding are established.

Expenditure on voluntary organisations: £124,040 (1990/91)

Details of projects: Voluntary organisations supported in 1990/91 included: The SMART Project, sheltered workshop facilities for people with mental health problems; Earls Court Bed and Breakfast Scheme, a project providing services and support for homeless families in Earls Court; Crossroads Care Attendants Scheme, a project to support carers; The Asian Elders Welfare Council, a support and advocacy project for the Asian elders of the borough.

Applications procedure: Bids are required in November/December and are considered by the Kensington and Chelsea Joint Consultative Committee in February. Successful schemes are funded from 1 April.

Correspondent: Deborah Cottam, Joint Planning Officer

Address: Riverside Health Authority, 5/7 Parsons Green, London SW6 4UL (081-846 6741)

Other information: Due to limited funds, there will be no joint finance available for new schemes in 1992/93.

West London Task Force (formerly called the North Kensington Task Force)

Beneficial area: This Task Force has expanded to cover additional areas in the Borough of Hammersmith and Fulham (Avonmore, Brook Green Addison, White City, Shepherd's Bush, College Park and Old Oak) as well as the areas originally targeted in North Kensington (the wards of St Charles, Golborne, Kelfield, Colville and Avondale, all lying to the north of Notting Hill Gate.)

General: The Task Forces, of which there are four in London, were set up by the government in areas known to be seriously disadvantaged. The main objective is to create a thriving economy in these inner city areas. The goals of this initiative are the provision of jobs for local people, the encouragement of local enterprise, the enhancement of the employability of local people, and the improvement of the local environment when this is linked to economic factors.

Some of the work of the Task Forces is concerned with improving the take-up and the effectiveness of existing government programmes, and in enhancing their co-ordination. However, there are also numerous examples in which the Task Force works through voluntary organisations and community groups in the area. Examples in 1990/91 include groups such as the Kensington and Chelsea Project which works with the elderly (£5,000), The Moroccan Coordinating Committee which works within the Moroccan community (£19,000), MIND which organises the Many Hands Decorating Project, (£5,000) and the Task Force Management Skills Programme which enhances local people's management skills (£11,000).

Grant total: circa £1,250,000 annually

Correspondent: Ash Verma, Task Force Leader

Address: 2 Acklam Road, London W10 5QZ (tel: 071-960 8455, fax: 081-960 7264)

The Campden Charities

Beneficial area: The former Parish and Borough of Kensington.

Objects:

1. To support individuals resident and organisations located in the parish who are in need through sickness, poverty and misfortune.

2. To help with individual educational needs and with educational projects.

Type of beneficiary: Organisations and individuals

Income: £1,686,949 (1991)

Grant total: £1,376,290

Grant details: *Relief of need

1. Grants given direct to individuals in need. The award of pensions to needy people who are over 70 years of age and who have lived in the parish for not less than seven years dates back at least 200 years. The current pension is £260 a year. Christmas and birthday presents, television licences, holidays and other sundries are distributed.

The authorised number of pensions is 650, which is about as many as the charity's staff are able to administer. In the financial year 1990/91 Campden Pensions and gifts worth £182,772, television licences totalling £19,820, holidays costing a total of £8,120 were given to pensioners. Help with fuel bills worth a total of £1,300 was given to 10 people.

2. Grants given to individuals in need through agencies which have applied on their behalf. In this category a total of £121,580 was awarded to 606 people.

These grants vary a great deal in size and purpose from quite small sums for children's clothing and pocket money to large sums for equipment and the settling of debts.

3. Grants given through agencies set up to support people in need. £535,520 was distributed to a wide range of charitable organisations in 1991. Projects helping the elderly were again a priority with grants worth £25,630 being made to 50 clubs and associations in Kensington for Christmas parties presents and outings. Donations totalling £32,330 were also made for holidays for the sick and elderly. Housing and homeless projects received much support with seven grants totalling £84,951 being made. Several community centres were funded including the St Cuthbert's Church Centre (£10,000) and the Moroccan Women's Centre (£4,400) and two HIV/AIDS organisations also received support: the Red

Admiral Project (£4,400) and the Terrence Higgins Trust (£5,000). Other groups supported included the National Council for One Parent Families (£12,340), Action for Disability (£8,980) and MIND (£15,000).

* Education and training of young people

The educational part of the Campden Charities, was founded by the will of Lady Campden in 1643 with the intention of putting poor boys from Kensington into apprenticeships. Under the current Scheme which dates from 1990 the trustees' powers are much wider.

The basic requirements, set in 1643, have remained the same: all applicants must have been resident in the beneficial area for at least two years, must be under 30 years old (under 35 in exceptional cases) and in financial need. Grants totalling £237,480 and ranging between £75 and £6,500 were made for a wide variety of educational needs. They funded extra tuition for primary school children suffering from dyslexia as well as postgraduate studies. All subjects are covered, including music, art and sports, and also the provision of tools, books and equipment either while studying or to assist in obtaining employment.

The trustees have embarked on a scholarship scheme in six independent schools and an assisted places exhibitions scheme for able and gifted children resident in Kensington. Scholarships and exhibitions totalling £55,180 were awarded.

Grants are also made to educational projects and organisations. These totalled £205,570, and were allocated to a wide variety of projects including playgrounds and playschemes, youth organisations, sports ventures, holiday schemes, youth projects for the disadvantaged, and schools with building and equipment needs. Examples of grants made include a further grant to the Longridge Road Under 5s Centre, Earls Court, towards building an extension (£8,256) and Sion Manning School for a scheme to raise the expectations of disadvantaged young people to the possibilities of entering university (£6,000).

Applications procedure: Preliminary telephone enquiries are welcomed. Specific application forms are available for social work organisations seeking pensions or charitable relief for individuals in the parish and also for residents seeking educational support. There is no specific application form for organisations seeking grants for their work in the parish, but they should include a copy of their latest annual report and accounts with their letters of application. Applications are considered by the case committee, the education committee or the board of trustees as appropriate. Each of these meets monthly.

Correspondent: P R Lucas, Clerk to the Trustees

Address: 5 Hogarth Road, London SW5 0QH (071-370 1576)

Earl Cadogan's Charity

Beneficial area: London, especially Chelsea

Objects: Support of charitable organisations

Type of beneficiary: Organisations

Income: £135,780 (1990/91)

Grant total: £151,390

Grant details: Grants ranging between £100 and £46,400 were made to hospitals, medical charities, youth clubs, welfare groups, both national or local to London and particularly in the Chelsea area. The most common size of donation was £1,000 and the largest of £46,400 went to the Salvation Army.

Applications procedure: In writing, to the correspondent, who states, "Please note that contributions are given to a regular list of charities".

Correspondent: Miss J M Castle, Secretary to the Trustees

Address: 18 Cadogan Gardens, London SW3 2RP (telephone number is ex-directory)

Trustees: Earl Cadogan, Countess Cadogan, Viscount Chelsea, Miss P D J Molloy

Other information: The most recent accounts on file at the Charity Commission are for 1990/91.

Chelsea Non-Ecclesiastical Charities

Beneficial area: Chelsea

Objects: General benefit of the poor

Type of beneficiary: Individuals, particularly elderly women

Income: £1,100 (1987)

Grant total: £850

Grant details: One-off grants, usually for about £30, were made to individuals and organisations, which included Chelsea Social Council (071-351 3210) and Action for Disability (071-937 6726).

Applications procedure: To the correspondent

Correspondent: Miss B N Towle (071-352 5032)

Address: 17 Meridan Court, Chelsea Manor Street, London SW3 3TT (071-352 5032)

Other information: The trustees did not wish this entry to be included.

The Kensington District Nursing Trust

Beneficial area: Former Royal Borough of Kensington

Main grant area: Relief of need which falls outside the limits of aid provided by statutory bodies

Type of beneficiary: Individuals and organisations

Income: £62,280 (1989/90)

Grant total: £46,520

Grant details: £14,630 was given in grants for equipment, essential items etc. During the winter heating allowances totalling £5,750 were made to individuals. The trust cannot fund rent, rates (except water rates) or hire-purchase debts or fines.

Grants of up to £5,000 were made to organisations involved with sick and elderly people, handicapped children, and women's housing.

Applications procedure: Direct to the correspondent or through social services, district nurses, health visitors or GPs. The case committee sits monthly (except in August).

Correspondent: Mrs J Forbes, Clerk to the Trustees

Address: 20 Hogarth Place, London SW5 OQY (071-370 2305)

Mayor of Chelsea's Fund

Beneficial area: Chelsea

Objects: Any charitable purpose

Grant details: The fund has very limited resources. It distributes small grants perhaps twice a year for events such as pensioners' parties.

Applications procedure: To the correspondent.

Correspondent: Roger Barker, The Mayor's Secretary

Address: Mayor's Parlour, Town Hall, Hornton Street, London W8 7NX (071-937 5464)

Other information: This entry was not confirmed by the trust.

Notting Hill Parishes Charity Committee

Beneficial area: Area covered by the Notting Hill Council of Churches

Objects: Support of local voluntary and welfare organisations

Type of beneficiary: Organisations

Latest figures: 1988/89

Income: £3,500

Grant total: £3,500

Grant details: 30 grants ranging between £25 and £250 were made to organisations for the very young, for youth, people with physical of mental handicap, the elderly, and general social welfare groups and centres.

Applications procedure: To the correspondent, or through any of the churches listed below.

Correspondent: Rev J Fairhead

Address: 12 Powis Gardens, London W11 1JG (071-229 4766)

Other information: The following churches are involved in the charity committee, raising funds which are then distributed in the area: St John and St Peter, All Saints, St Clement and St James, St Mary Abbotts, St Helens, St Thomas. This entry was not confirmed by the trust.

The Pocklington Apprenticeship Trust

Beneficial area: London Borough of Kensington and Chelsea

Objects: Help towards the costs that individuals incur in obtaining education and training.

Type of beneficiary: Young people 21 or under who were either born in Kensington and Chelsea or who have lived there for more than 10 years. Also children of adults who were born in the borough or who have lived there for 10 years. Beneficiaries must be in need of financial assistance.

Annual Income: About £2,800

Grant details: Grants up to £400 are made.

Applications procedure: Contact the correspondent for an application form.

Correspondent: Peter Aykroyd, Chief Executive's Department, Royal Borough of Kensington and Chelsea

Address: Room 250, The Town Hall, Hornton Street, London W8 7NX (071-937 5464 ext 2262)

Major Local Companies

Associated Newspaper Holdings plc (head office), Northcliffe House, 2 Derry Street, London W8 5TT (071-938 6000) supports primarily local charities and charities associated with the news print world. Contact Major Vyvyan Harmsworth.

Elf Aquitaine UK (Holdings) plc, Knightsbridge House, 197 Knightsbridge, London SW7 1RZ (071-589 4588) does not have particular areas of support. Donations are usually given through the Charities Aid Foundation, and occasionally directly. Contact Ms A M Davis, External Relations Manager.

Virgin Group, 95-99 Ladbroke Grove, London W11 1PG (071-229 1282) has production facilities in the Notting Hill/North Kensington area and gives to local voluntary organisations. Contact Will Whitehorn, Head of Public Relations.

Sources of Advice

Chelsea Social Council, The Crypt, St Luke's Church, Sydney Street, London SW3 (071-351 3210)

Coordinator: Sara Copland
Opening hours: 9.30-5.00

Kensington and Chelsea Arts Council, Central Library, Phillimore Walk, Kensington, London W8 7RX (081-743 4559)

Administrator: Miss Terry Slasberg

Kensington and Chelsea Adult Education College has eight branches and a decentralised structure. Information about courses can be obtained from every branch of which the Chelsea Branch is one: Chelsea Branch, Hortensia Road, London SW10 (071-351 7127)

Kensington and Chelsea Youth Office, Campden Institute, 95 Lancaster Road, W11 1QQ (071-221 3743)

Kingston-upon-Thames

The Royal Borough of Kingston-upon-Thames

Guildhall, Kingston-upon-Thames KT1 1EU (081-546 2121)

Correspondents:

Housing and Leisure Services Committee: Nick Balchin, Manager

Social Services Committee: Principal Officer, Voluntary Sector Liaison (to be appointed) (081-547 6072, MINICOM)

Education Committee: No grant aid available

Youth and Community Advisory Committee: Roger Dibben, Principal Youth Community Officer

Grants totals: £509,300 (1991/92)

Funding: At present Kingston Council funds the local voluntary sector through four separate committees but may reorganise and establish a single grants committee by 1993. The current committees' grant-giving in 1991/92 can be broken down as follows:

Housing & Leisure	£246,800
Social Services	£220,000
Education	£24,500
Youth and Community	£18,000
TOTAL	£509,300

In addition the council runs a lottery scheme (*see separate entry*)

Housing and Leisure Services Committee: Leisure: Grants are made to increase the involvement and participation in the arts, particularly through the support of special projects and exceptionally gifted individuals. Sports organisations are funded which complement the Leisure Services Division's Development programme and to assist exceptionally gifted individuals. Support is also given to groups which work in leisure provision but are outside the scope of local/regional Sports and Arts Council funding.

Housing: Support is given to voluntary organisations working in the field of housing.

Youth and Community Committee: This supports a wide variety of groups which provide activities for young people and makes grants towards hire of premises, building maintenance, equipment, staff, training and headquarter costs. In 1991/92 Kingston and Malden Scout and Guide Band (£1,037), Tolworth District Guides (£3,470) Tolworth Gymnastics Club (£7,500) and Stoneleigh Youth Orchestra (£1,500) were among the organisations supported.

Education Committee: No funds are available for general grant-aid.

Social Services Committee: This gives recurring grants (totalling £320,870 in 1991/92) to a small number of local welfare, and advisory organisations. It also makes a few grants under £1,000.

In 1991/92 the largest beneficiaries were Kingston Voluntary Service Council (£76,200), Wel-care (£26,100) and Kingston Women's Centre (£19,270). Applications from organisations which are not currently funded by Kingston Council are considered on the same basis as other applications. Support for seedcorn funding is one of the council's overall priorities. £86,624 was transferred to the Elderly and Disability Division to cover Old People's Welfare Associations' service contracts.

The Children Act 1989: This new legislation put the spotlight on groups working with children and consequently Kingston Council has given them added priority. In particular its grant to the Childminders' Association was doubled in 1991/92.

Mental Illness Specific Grant: Kingston Council was awarded a grant of £70,000 from the DoH in 1991/92 and spent £100,000 on mental health services. Voluntary sector projects were funded to a total of £55,100 with MIND Kingston, Kingston Citizens Advocacy Scheme, MIND South East, and the Association of Respite Care receiving grants.

Drug and Alcohol Specific Grant: In 1991/92 Kingston Council received a £11,000 grant from the DoH and funded Kaleidoscope.

Applications procedure: All committees have the same application form. Criteria are different for each service area though all must follow the council's overall priorities.

Leisure grants of over £1,000 are allocated twice a year, with deadlines for the submission of completed application forms falling in November and July.

Applications for grants from Social Services should be submitted by 30 September and most are considered in January. Small amounts become available throughout the year and these are allocated in an ongoing way.

Youth and Community grants applications are considered on a year-round basis and forms can be submitted at any time.

Contracting and the Community Care Plan
In 1992 Social Services mostly funded voluntary organisations through grants but started three-year contracts with groups which target people who are not eligible for local authority day-care support. These were Kingston, Surbiton and Malden and Coombe Old People's Welfare Associations. Other kinds of organisations will probably become eligible for contracts.

Social Services sees community care as a collaboration between voluntary and statutory sectors. It discussed its Community Care Plan with the Kingston Council for Voluntary Service, the Kingston Community Care Forum, users and carers and via a series of open consultation meetings.

Other departments within the borough were beginning to fund voluntary organisations through contracts in 1992. The Youth and Community Committee contracted out transport for youth groups.

For further information contact: Principal Officer, Voluntary Sector Liaison (to be appointed)

Kingston and Esher Joint Consultative Committee

Beneficial area: Royal Borough of Kingston-upon-Thames and part of Elmbridge Borough Council which was formerly Esher Urban District.

Objects: Schemes which keep, or facilitate people out of hospital; schemes to achieve care group joint strategies. Since resources are limited, value for money (good cost: benefit ratio) is important.

Many grants are directed to community care for patients from long stay hospitals. Joint finance has been allocated to voluntary organisation care attendant and advocacy schemes.

Funding practices: Schemes which aim to keep people out of hospital may receive 100% joint finance for a maximum of ten years, tapering to zero

over three years. As a condition for granting joint finance, all schemes are subject to regular monitoring and review, including the provision of periodic scheme statements.

Total joint finance expenditure on voluntary organisations: £109,880 (1991/92)

Details of projects: In 1991 funded voluntary organisations included: Kingston Council for Voluntary Service Bereavement Counselling (£16,460), Kingston Council for Voluntary Service, Consumer and Voluntary Sector Coordinator (£10,550), Kingston Crossroads Care Attendant Scheme (£50,550), Kingston Citizen's Advocacy Group (£28,300), and Voluntary Work Project (£4,000).

Applications procedure: Applications forms are available from the Planning Manager, or Mrs Joy Damji, at the address below.

Correspondent: The Planning Manager

Address: Kingston and Esher Health Authority, 17 Upper Brighton Road, Surbiton KT6 6LH (081-390 1111 ext 4459)

Other information: The committee meets every four months – usually in February, June and October

Kingston-upon-Thames Arts Council

Beneficial area: London Borough of Kingston

Type of beneficiary: organisations

Grant total: £4,200 (1990/91)

Grant details: Principally an advice and co-ordinating body, the council also has a small grants budget for local arts organisations.

Correspondent: Peter Simmonds

Address: 52 Auckland Road, Kingston-upon-Thames, Surrey KT1 3BQ (081-549 5127)

The Gerald Bentall Charitable Trust

Beneficial area: Southern England generally; within London a distinct preference for Kingston and Ealing, i.e. the areas where the company has department stores

Objects: General charitable purposes, including the relief of poverty

Type of beneficiary: Organisations

Income total: £13,050 (1988/89)

Grant total: £12,840

Grant details: Grants are made to national charities and local organisations for general charitable purposes including the relief of poverty. Grants are in the region of £100 to £600, the most common donation being £100.

Applications procedure: In writing to the correspondent.

Correspondent: J F Noel Anstee

Address: Bentalls, Head Office, Anstee House, Wood Street, Kingston-upon-Thames KT1 1TS (081-546 2002)

Other information: The Rowan Bentall Charity Trust, which shares similar objects to the Gerald Bentall Charitable Trust, is also administered from the company.

Kingston and District Charity

Beneficial area: Kingston-upon-Thames and surrounding district

Objects: Welfare of disadvantaged or disabled children, and senior citizens

Type of beneficiary: Individuals

Income: £6,000 (1990/91)

Grant total: £5,500

Grant details: One-off grants, maximum £200. The charity cannot pay for debts or bills.

Applications procedure: Only through social services and the S.W. London Probation Office.

Correspondent: Mrs Kerr-Waller, Secretary

Address: 100 Maple Road, Surbiton, KT6 4AL (081-399 8599)

Kingston-upon-Thames Association for the Blind

Beneficial area: Kingston-upon-Thames

Objects: The welfare of blind and partially-sighted people

Type of beneficiary: Individuals

Income: £4,000 (1990)

Grant total: £5,500

Grant details: Grants towards holidays, house repairs, the Kingston Talking Newspaper for the Blind, amongst others, have been given. Contact the correspondent for further details.

Correspondent: G M Hancock

Address: 123 Raeburn Avenue, Surbiton, Surrey (081-399 4633)

Kingston-upon-Thames Central Aid Society

Beneficial area: Royal Borough of Kingston-upon-Thames

Objects: Relief of need

Type of beneficiary: Individuals

Grant total: £23,000 (1990/91)

Grant details: The Society provides assistance and support of the Borough's population not only through grant-making but also through its links with the area's voluntary sector (it is represented on old people's welfare committees, Soldiers', Sailors' and Airmen's Families Association/Forces Help Society (SSAFA) and Kingston Care Committee for Chest Heart and Stroke Association) and by being able to offer advice or arrange visits from its Fife Road offices.

During the year 599 grants were made for the relief of need, especially in cases of sickness or emergencies e.g. the repair or replacement of household furniture, and grants for or towards the cost of bedding, clothing, dentures or spectacles, fares, removals, heating bills, rent or rate arrears and TV licences. Help can also be provided towards much-needed convalescent holidays. Christmas gifts, toys and food parcels are also given.

Applications procedure: In writing, in person or through a welfare agency, social services etc.

Correspondent: Mrs M Chapman, Director Secretary

Address: Parman House, 36a Fife Road, Kingston-upon-Thames, KT1 1SY (081-546 6187)

Other information: Office hours are Mon, Wed, Fri, 10.0-4.00, and Tues, Thurs 10.30 to 12.30.

The society incorporates the Kingston & District Committee for Chest and Heart Diseases and Soldiers', Sailors' and Airmen's Families Association/Forces Help Society.

Kingston-upon-Thames Lottery Scheme

Beneficial area: The Royal Borough of Kingston-upon-Thames.

Objects: To assist projects which improve cultural, recreational, social and environmental amenities for residents of the borough.

Type of beneficiary: Organisations

Income: Variable; see under 'other information'.

Grant total: About £30,000 a year.

Grant details: The Lottery Fund makes one-off grants for durable items only. Grants cannot be given for running costs or for projects which the council is planning to carry out soon itself. Projects receiving a grant should be capable of being started at an early date. Grants are usually given for items such as vehicles, typewriters and cookers and for work such as essential building repairs. They normally range in size from £50 to a few thousand pounds.

Applications procedure: Application forms are available from the correspondent. Applications are processed twice a year, in September and March.

Correspondent: Ms Joy Millett, Administrative Assistant.

Address: Secretariat, Royal Borough of Kingston-upon-Thames, Guildhall, Kingston-upon-Thames KT1 1EU (081-547 5025).

Other information: The council's lottery has been operating since 1977. The amount of funds available for distribution depends entirely on the number of tickets sold.

The Mayor's Charity Fund

Beneficial area: The Royal Borough of Kingston-upon-Thames

Objects: General charitable purposes at the discretion of the mayor

Type of beneficiary: Organisations

Income: Variable

Grant details: The Mayor's Charity Fund supports a charity or charities of the mayor's choice throughout his/her year of office.

Applications procedure: To the correspondent

Correspondent: Mrs J Turk, Mayor's Secretary.

Address: Guildhall, Kingston-upon-Thames KT1 1EU (081-547 5030/5033)

The Charity of William Nicholl

Beneficial area: The former Royal Borough of Kingston-upon-Thames as constituted until 1964

Objects: Provision of fuel vouchers and pensions

Type of beneficiary: Individuals

Grant total: £2,540 (1990)

Grant details: 224 fuel vouchers were distributed at £5 each, and seven weekly pensions of £3 were paid.

Applications procedure: To the correspondent via local organisations

Correspondent: Head of Secretariat

Address: The Guildhall, Kingston-upon-Thames, Surrey, KT1 1EU (081-547 5021)

The Smedley Charitable Trust

Beneficial area: The Kingston area

Objects: Support of local charitable organisations

Type of beneficiary: Organisations

Income: £9,190 (1989/90)

Grant total: £4,940

Grant details: The trust supports local charities and the Kingston branches of national charities. Grants range between £250 and £1,000 and are made to groups involved in a wide range of work, including medical charities, the elderly, handicapped and social welfare.

Applications procedure: In writing to the correspondent.

Correspondent: David Smedley

Address: 22 Balaclava Road, Surbiton, Surrey, KT6 5PN

Other information: This trust did not wish to be included in the guide.

Major Local Companies

Bentalls plc, Anstee House, Wood Street, Kingston-upon-Thames (081-546 2002) supports local charities or branches of national charities in Kingston. Apply in writing to Mrs Brock.

Racal Radar Defence Systems Ltd, Wellington Crescent, New Malden, Surrey KT3 3PG (081-942 2233) supports local and national organisations. Contact Sheila Butler, Secretary to the Racal Charitable Trust, Western Road, Bracknell,

Berkshire RG12 1RG (0344 483244).

Marks & Spencer, 26 Clarence Street, Kingston-on-Thames, Surrey KT1 1NU (081-549 9933) has a small budget to make donations to local organisations. Contact the Personnel Manager.

Higgs and Hill (construction and property development), Crown House, Kingston Road, New Malden, KT3 3ST (081-942 8921) prefers to support local charities in areas of company presence, appeals relevant to company business and charities in which a member of staff is involved. Contact Joy Baldry, Secretary to the Higgs and Hill plc Charitable Trust.

Willis Wrightson (insurance brokers), Willis Wrightson House, Wood Street, Kingston, KT1 1UG (081-977 8888) supports local charities. Contact Mrs Christine Bevan, Secretary to the Charities Committee, Willis Corroon Group plc, 10 Trinity Square, London EC3P 3AX (071-488 8111).

Sources of Advice

Kingston-upon-Thames Council for Voluntary Service, 52 Grove Crescent, Kingston-upon-Thames, KT1 1SY (081-546 0184).

General Secretary: Myra Fulford
Opening hours: 9.00-5.00

Kingston-upon-Thames Arts Council (see previous entry)

Kingston Adult Education Service, North Kingston Centre, Richmond Road, KT2 5PE (081-547 6705)

Lambeth

London Borough of Lambeth

Lambeth Town Hall, Brixton Hill, London SW2
1RW (071-926 1000)

Correspondents:

Social Services Department: E Zephyrine, Principal Manager Community and Voluntary Services

Strategic Policy and Performance Unit: Ashford Francis, Grants Section (Urban Programme)

Housing Department: Clovis Reid, Grants Liaison Officer

Environmental Services: Sue Whittaker, Research and Information Officer

Education: Catherine Mullan, Principal Programming and Community Development Officer, Community Education

Grant totals to voluntary organisations in 1991/92:

£8 million in main programme funding

£6.1 million in capital funding, £2.25 million Urban Programme funding

£650, 000 Health Authorities

Environmental Services: The Environmental Services Committee manages a wide-ranging grant-aid programme affording significant social, economic and environmental benefits to many people in the borough. Over 250 different voluntary groups are funded annually to a total of almost £6 million. The following areas of work are eligible for grant-aid:

1. Social activities such as children's play facilities, arts, events, entertainments, sports and physical recreation.

2. Organisations which provide information and advice.

3. Groups which provide equal opportunities and work with disadvantaged groups such as community associations, groups which improve services for women and people with disabilities.

4. Economic projects, environmental work through the Urban Programme.

5. Employment and training.

Some of the projects funded in 1991/92 include: the Asian Community Action Centre; Lambeth Chinese Community Association and Project; Myatts Fields After-School Project; Charlie Chaplin Handicapped Adventure Playground Association; Brixton Music Development; Oval House Theatre; summer, Christmas and Easter holiday play grants to 125 local groups; Action Space; Lambeth Video; Stockwell Women's Lift Service; Lambeth Air Rifle Club for People with Disabilities; Union Place Community Resource Centre; Lady Margaret Hall Settlement, Horticultural and Employment Projects; Lambeth Women's workshop; Lambeth Unemployed Centre.

Education Committee: This committee gives priority to the following areas: Supplementary education; mother tongue classes, basic education projects; support for people with educational needs; voluntary youth organisations; educational provision for under fives; agencies giving advice and information on education to parents and pupils; and cultural groups providing educational services for ethnic minority communities.

All the voluntary organisations currently funded by this committee meet the needs of groups which are usually excluded from educational facilities. These were defined in the council's Community Information and Participation Strategy and include young unemployed black people, lone parents, members of black and ethnic minority communities and young people with special educational needs.

Social Services Committee: This department assisted a broad range of projects including children's day nurseries, work centres for the disabled, day centres for people with a mental illness, schemes for homeless people, women's refuges, advice services, resettlement schemes. Organisations recently funded by the department include: the North Lambeth Day Centre (for homeless people); Afro Caribbean Mental Health Association; Age Concern; One Love Children's Centre (a day nursery); Brixton Neighbourhood Community Association (day centre for the black elderly); and Ravenswood Housing Trust (residential facility for the severely disabled).

The department also makes a number of small, one-off grants for capital costs and non-recurrent schemes.

Housing Committee: Grant recipients include shelters for the homeless, tenants' associations, co-ops and housing repair pools. Grants are awarded to community estates towards maintenance costs.

Urban Programme

Capital and revenue grants are available for community organisations running innovative projects which provide services to Lambeth residents in the areas of training, housing, environmental improvements, community, social and leisure provision.

Resources are targeted to particular areas of the borough according to Lambeth's Council's policy priorities.

Most of the resources allocated by the Department of the Environment are spent on economic projects. Grants are made for capital rather than revenue expenses.

Applications procedure: Applications are dealt with annually, usually in January and February. The deadline for the return of completed applications for grant-aid varies with individual directorates but is generally between November and December.

Other support: All of the directorates offer advice and consultancy services for voluntary groups. Discretionary rate relief can be provided by the Social Services Department; and, occasionally premises can be provided by the Housing Department.

Contracting and the Community Care Plan

In 1992 most of Social Services' funding of voluntary organisations was through grant-aid. However it was envisaged that contracts would become the main form of funding, with a small amount of grant-aid retained for new projects and development. After three years of funding a new project through grant-aid, a contract would be introduced.

Contracts were very generally framed and only lasted for one year in 1992. But this will change, with detailed specifications for services being introduced and the duration being extended to two to three years.

In 1992/93 Social Services will probably enter into contracts for services for people with HIV/AIDS services and people with drug/alcohol problems. Few, if any, other departments within the borough are using contracts so Social Services was very much a trail-blazer.

The voluntary sector was involved in Lambeth's Community Care Plan through the Voluntary Sector Community Care Forum which united local voluntary groups and branches of large national agencies.

For further information contact: Nigel Golding, Head of Strategic Planning and Inspectorate, Social Services

West Lambeth Joint Consultative Committee

Beneficial area: Combined catchment area of West Lambeth Health Authority and London Borough of Lambeth.

Objects: Joint finance is for furthering the advancement of joint planning between statutory services and voluntary organisations. It is particularly concerned with the needs of the local community and is aimed at preventing the admission of people to hospital or helping their discharge.

Funding practices: Grants are usually paid quarterly in advance. Funding is guaranteed for two years with the possibility of extension thereafter.

Latest figures: 1991/92

Total expenditure: £413,000

Expenditure on voluntary organisations: c£290,000

Details of projects: In 1991/92 voluntary organisations which received funding included Age Concern (£15,600), Brixton Circle, a black mental health project, MENCAP (£10,000), Family Link, a project for children with special needs (£8,600), Lambeth Accord, an information service for people with disability (£13,600), and Lambeth Women's Children's Health Project (£13,400).

Applications procedure: Applications should be made by 31 December, for consideration by the JCC at their March meeting. Final approval depends on the funds available and the preparation of budgets for the next financial year.

The JCC meets about four times a year.

Correspondent: Joint Finance Monitoring Officer

Address: SELCA, Mary Sheridan House, 9/15 St Thomas St, London SE1 9RY (071-955 5000 ext 2425)

Other information: In March 1992 there were plans underway to reorganise the joint consultative committees in South East London along borough boundaries, with the result that there will be one JCC covering the whole of Lambeth.

Camberwell Joint Consultative Committee

Beneficial area: Camberwell, Lambeth, Southwark

Objects: To support projects which make a greater contribution to total care in the framework of health or local authority services and which show evidence of joint planning.

Funding practices: Priorities arise out of the joint planning process, particularly in relation to the NHS and the Community Care Act.

100% funding for three years is available with tapering possibilities reviewed at the end of the second year. Details of the bidding process are widely circulated to known voluntary organisations through umbrella organisations and the local press. All bids received are considered by the relevant Joint Care Planning Groups, that is the JCPG for elderly services, for physical disabilities, people with learning difficulties or for mental health.

Expenditure on voluntary organisations: £216,520 (1991/92)

Details of projects: Voluntary groups supported include: a carers' outreach scheme (£18,150); Southwark Disablement Association for an Advocacy Worker (£9,070) and Voluntary Sector Co-ordinator (£24,880); Crossroads Care Attendant Scheme (£43,130); and The Centre for Integrated Living (£29,880).

Applications procedure: Funding packs which include an application form, procedure bids and guidance on applications are available from the correspondent (see below). The funding process usually takes place between September and March. Advice and information on joint finance and related matters are available at any time. For further assistance contact Brian Stapleton, Planning and Strategy Manager, Southwark Social Services, Mabel Goldwyn House, 49 Grange Walk, London SE1 5DY (071-525 3791) or the correspondent below.

Correspondent: Joint Finance Administrator

Address: South East London Commissioning Agency, 15 St Thomas St, London SE1 (071-955 5000 ext 242)

Other information: The committee meets three to four times a year.

In April 1992 the future reorganisation of the JCC along borough boundaries was being considered.

The Brixton Dispensary

Beneficial area: 11 parishes in and around the centre of Brixton

Main grant area: Relief of need due to mental or physical illness

Type of beneficiary: Individuals

Income: £2,270 (1988/89)

Grant total: £1,130

Grant details: One-off grants, typically between £30 and £150. Christmas gifts of £15, mainly for the sick or elderly.

Applications procedure: Normally through the social services or welfare agencies.

Correspondent: Mrs M F Stedman, Clerk to the trustees

Address: 1 Kett Gardens, London SW2 1SS (071-737 1605)

Clapham Sick Poor Fund

Beneficial area: Clapham and immediate vicinity

Objects: Benefit of sick, poor residents

Type of beneficiary: Individuals

Income: £8,460 (1990)

Grant total: £10,400

Grant details: Grants are made for fuel, heating appliances, bedding, clothing, food and convalescent holidays.

Applications procedure: Via a social worker, DHSS, London Borough of Lambeth, WRVS, doctor, minister of religion or appropriate welfare agency.

Correspondent: Roy F Harding, Clerk

Address: 19 Highfield Park, Marlow, Bucks, SL7 2DE (06284 6293)

Other information: This trust has not confirmed the above entry.

A H Heddon Trust Fund

Beneficial area: London Borough of Lambeth

Objects: Payments for or towards holidays for persons in need over 65 years old

Type of beneficiary: Individuals

Income: About £500 (1988)

Applications procedure: To the correspondent

Correspondent: See below

Address: See below

Other information: This charity was in the process of being reorganised at the start of 1989. Further information about the new correspondent of this trust would be welcomed.

The Lambeth Endowed Charities

Income: £505,080 (1990)

Grant total: £515,120

Other information: The Lambeth Endowed Charities is a grouping of several Lambeth charities, the most important of which are Hayle's Charity and The Walcot Educational Charity. The origin of some of these charities goes back as far as the 17th century (Hayle's Charity, for example, was established in 1671 with money left over from a successful appeal for the restoration of the parish church). Nowadays the charities are still playing an active and involved role in the community, and each year produce an informative report outlining their policies and how they can respond to individual need and changing social circumstances.

The Charities:

1.) **The Walcot Educational Foundation:** The foundation is able to make grants within the London Borough of Lambeth and was established for various educational purposes, including the power to assist voluntary aided schools (grants in 1990 amounted to £23,570) and voluntary and non-voluntary aided schools in disadvantaged areas (£91,109 – 43 grants); to make grants to organisations and projects involved in education and the advancement in life of young people (£239,760); to assist young people in need under the age of 30 who are resident in the area of benefit with financial assistance for the purchase of books, outfits, instruments, tools etc. necessary for their entry into a profession, trade or calling, and with educational grants tenable at any place of learning approved by the Governors. In 1990 grants in these categories came to a total of £34,990 and were made to 101 students and 67 school pupils.

2.) **Hayle's Charity:** This charity's area of benefit is the London Borough of Lambeth, although in very exceptional cases the trustees may grant relief to persons otherwise eligible who are resident immediately outside the beneficial area. Since 1987 the charity has been operating under a new Scheme for the relief of need, hardship and distress which allows it to make grants to individuals or to the local organisations which care for them.

Grants for individuals fell into several categories (grant total in brackets): to 275 individuals or families in urgent need, minimum £30, maximum £100 (£19,240); and quarterly grants between £150 and £2,000 to 19 people with extraordinary needs who were mostly disabled (£10,965); monthly payments to chronically sick and disabled patients (£2,400); quarterly pensions for 110 pensioners (£23,420); the Electric Wheelchair Loan Scheme enabled 8 disabled people to receive wheelchairs, including two additional chairs which were bought in 1990 (£3,090).

Other donations included grants to ten pensioners' groups and organisations (£7,670), 21 projects organising Christmas parties and outings (£2,100), seven medical organisations and health projects (£9,000), six social work and counselling projects (£9,540), five community centres (£7,050), three disabled projects (£2,850), two employment and training projects (£4,000), three homeless support projects (£3,800) and five educational projects (£12,190).

3.) **The smaller charities:** During 1990 and 1991 four of the small Lambeth Endowed Charities were amalgamated with the Hayle's Charity. These were the United Charities, the Robert Forest's Pensioners Charity, the Benson and McArthur Charity and the Harry Clapham Charity. In addition the Lawrence & Spencer Foundation has been amalgamated with the Walcot Educational Foundation.

These amalgamations left only one of the small Lambeth Endowed Charities intact, the Walcot Non-Educational Charity which makes grants for individuals in special need.

Applications procedure: In all cases application forms may be obtained from the correspondent. Applications are normally considered four times a year, in February, June, September and November and should reach the correspondent at least one month beforehand for consideration at the next meeting. Points to note are as follows:

For individuals: applications from individuals and families must be supported by a recognized welfare agency or CAB, or by a doctor, social worker or minister of religion. Students applying for grants will be invited for interview.

For organisations: after submission of written details a personal visit will be arranged.

Exclusions: Where debts or bills have already been incurred; where funds are available from a statutory or other source; where applicants (individuals or organisations) live or operate outside the area of benefit; from students aged 30 and above.

Correspondent: Rev D I S Jones, Clerk to the Trustees

Address: 127 Kennington Road, London SE11 6SF (071-735 1925)

Lambeth Mayor's Fund

Beneficial area: London Borough of Lambeth

Objects: To raise money for individuals in need who cannot be helped by the relevant statutory bodies.

Income: Usually £5,000 to £6,000.

Grant details: Grants are usually around £20 to £30 each and are decided by the Mayor. The individuals helped are usually referred through social workers, Citizens Advice Bureaux etc, but individuals may also write in independently.

Correspondent: The Mayor

Address: Lambeth Town Hall, Brixton Hill, London SW2 1RW (071-925 1000)

Other information: This entry was not confirmed.

South London Relief in Sickness Fund

Beneficial area: London Boroughs of Lambeth and Wandsworth

Objects: Relief of sickness, disability, infirmity and handicap

Type of beneficiary: Individuals

Income: £6,810 (1991)

Grant total: £6,824

Grant details: One-off grants to individuals. Maximum grant size is normally £100.

Applications procedure: Only through social worker, GP, clergy, welfare agency. The trustees meet twice a year but grants can also be dealt with at the chairman's discretion.

Correspondent: Andrew Cottell, Clerk, London Borough of Wandsworth,

Address: Wandsworth Town Hall, High Street, London SW18 (081-871 6021)

Major Local Companies

T Clarke plc, Stanhope House, 116-118 Walworth Road, London SE17 1JL supports local charities (071-252 7676). Contact Mrs Mendham, Secretary to the Managing Director.

Executive Cleaning Services Ltd, 70 Stewarts Road, London SW8 4BR (071-720 2232). Contact Mr Chisholm, at head office, Executive Cleaning Services plc. Marlow House, 143/45 Larkhall Lane, London SW4 6RG (071-720 7972). The company is usually inundated with appeals.

Freemans plc, 139 Clapham Road, London SW9 0PU (071-735 7644) makes donations towards community groups local to Freemans' sites. Preferred areas of support are children, youth, social welfare, medical work and enterprise/training. Contact J J Pearmund, Director.

Otis plc (head office), 43-59 Clapham Road, London SW9 0JZ (071-735 9131). Contact David Littleford, Personnel Director.

Sources of Advice

Lambeth Adult Education (headquarters), Strand Centre, Elm Park, SW2 2EH (071-926 7293)

Lewisham

London Borough of Lewisham

Town Hall, Catford, London SE6 4RU (081-695 6000).

Correspondent(s):

For general enquiries contact: Nigel Massey, Head of Voluntary Sector Team, Community Affairs Unit

For specific enquiries contact: Lorna De Smidt, Grants Officer, (Race Relations and Women's Committees' grants) Equalities Development Unit

Leroy Phillips, Head of Community Affairs, City Challenge Funding

Colin Plant, Mental Health Services Manager, Mental Illness Specific Grant

Grant totals 1991/92:

£5,497,000 in main programme funding

£275,000 in Urban Programme funding (revenue)

Funding practice: All of Lewisham Council's main programme funding of voluntary organisations is given through the Voluntary Sector Committee which is serviced by the Community Affairs Unit. Other service committees, such as Social Services, make recommendations to the Voluntary Sector Committee. In 1991/92 Lewisham Council agreed to reduce the level of its grant-aid to the voluntary sector by £480,000. This meant that no new groups were accepted for funding during this period, and that grants to organisations already in receipt of funding from the council were either reduced or maintained at the same level in real terms. However Lewisham Council has recently established a number of small grant schemes which are as follows:

Fast stream Grants: Grants for new or currently unfunded voluntary organisations with a maximum of £1,000 per grant.

Volunteers Fund: This has a budget of £11,200 in 1991/92 and makes one-off grants to support recruitment, training and retention of volunteers. The maximum grant is £500.

Training Initiatives: The budget for this was £25,000 in 1991/92 and funds training programmes for voluntary organisations in a flexible way. A grant could be used to employ a consultant to train staff, for a group to run a course or for employees to attend a training course.

Service Development Block: This has a budget of £50,000 for one-off, largely capital grants which develop or enhance an existing service being provided by a voluntary organisation. The maximum grant is £5,000.

Major beneficiaries in 1991/92 included Lewisham Citizens' Advice Bureaux (£444,000), North Lewisham Law Centre (£200,700), Lewisham Academy of Music (£44,000), Lewisham Women's Aid (£101,000) and Age Concern (£201,000). Some priority was given to organisations offering direct services to individuals in need or to groups which provided services to ethnic minorities or women.

The Children Act 1989: In April 1992 an Early Years' Committee was established to provide an integrated service for children under eight in response to the Children Act and the new responsibilities of Lewisham as an education authority. The Early Years' Committee will probably make recommendations about grants to the Voluntary Sector Sub-committee, Policy and Resources.

Women's Committee: This committee makes one-off grants to women's groups and organisations.

Race Relations Committee: This committee makes one-off grants to organisations providing services for ethnic minorities.

Urban Progamme: Lewisham is an Urban Programme Authority, spending £2.5 million in 1991/92 on innovative local projects dealing with economic, environmental and social problems in the borough. Applicants for Urban Programme funding should contact Nigel Massey, Head of the Voluntary Sector Team, as above. Applications are invited in July and the closing date is the end of September.

City Challenge: Lewisham was invited to bid for City Challenge at the Department of the Environment and was successful in securing funds for Deptford and New Cross from April 1992. Over a period of five years Lewisham will receive £37.5

million, of which about £2.5 to 3.4 million will be targeted towards local voluntary sector initiatives run by local people to meet local needs.

Mental Illness Specific Grant: In 1991/92 Lewisham was successful in its bid for funding and received £167,000 towards mental health services. It spent a total of £238,600 and grant-aided three voluntary organisations: Lewisham MIND (£26,000), Lewisham Users' Forum (£1,800) and a black mental health group (£14,000).

Drugs and Alcohol Specific Grant: Lewisham received less funding than it applied for in 1991/92 and made one grant of £7,900 to Drugs in Deptford.

Applications procedure: Applications for main programme funding are reviewed annually, normally in December. Applications must be returned to the council by the end of September each year. One-off grants from the Women's Equality Unit are considered in July; one-off grants from the Race Equality Unit are considered at various times of the year.

Other support: Lewisham Council also gives occasional practical support to local voluntary organisations in the form of materials and equipment in kind, free premises for some groups, discretionary rate relief, advice and consultancy on fundraising, finance and management issues, and training courses. The contact for any of these forms of assistance is, in the first instance, Nigel Massey, as above.

Contracting and the Community Care Plan
In 1992 Lewisham Social Services mainly funded voluntary organisations through grants. It was not actively planning to use contracts because it already makes considerable use of the voluntary sector for residential placements and provides significant grant-aid to voluntary groups providing social services.

But it was prepared to enter contractual arrangements whenever voluntary agencies prefer this and in 1992 made contracts with two children's agencies at their request. These contracts tend to be fairly general and usually last for three years.

Social Services was in close contact with the voluntary sector over its Community Care Plan: Local voluntary organisations were represented on the multi-agency Service Planning Groups; Voluntary Action Lewisham serviced the Community Care Forum which had links with statutory agencies and co-ordinated 'shadow' planning groups; a conference was held with the voluntary sector to improve joint-planning and more were planned.

For further information contact: Bob Scribbins, Coordinator of the Community Care Plan, Social Services

Lewisham and North Southwark Joint Consultative Committee

Beneficial area: Lewisham and North Southwark

Objects: The money should make a greater contribution to total care than if spent on local or health services alone. The scheme should show evidence of joint planning.

Funding practices: Priorities arise out of the joint planning process particularly in relation to the NHS and the Community Care Act.

Details of the bidding process are widely circulated to known voluntary groups through umbrella organisations and in the local press. All bids received are considered by the relevant Joint Care Planning Groups (JCPGs). For example, one JCPG considers services for elderly people with physical disabilities, another considers people with learning difficulties.

Expenditure of voluntary organisations: £249,000 from a total allocation of £791,000 (31%) in 1991/92.

Details of projects: Voluntary organisations funded in 1991/92 include: Camberwell Citizen Advocacy Office, for an advocacy worker for people with learning difficulties (£16,950); Isis, a black mental health group, for a development worker (£20,490); Drugline, for a women and family worker (£15,820); and Crossroads, for a Saturday playscheme (£5,300).

Applications procedure: Funding packs which include an application form, procedure bids and guidance on applications are available from the correspondent (see below). The funding process usually takes place between September and March. Advice and information on joint finance and related matters are available at any time.

The committee meets three to four times per year.

Correspondent: Alyson Bunn, Joint Finance Administrator

Address: Lewisham & North Southwark Health Authority, Mary Sheridan House, 15 St Thomas's Street, London SE1 9RY (071-955 5000 ext 2425)

Other information: In early 1992 the London Boroughs of Lewisham and Southwark and the

Lewisham and North Southwark Health Authority agreed that the Joint Consultative Committee (JCC) should become borough-based as opposed to health-authority-based. This means that Lewisham and North Southwark JCC will become two separate JCCs. Contact the above correspondent for further information.

Deptford Task Force

Beneficial area: The London Borough of Lewisham (Grinling Gibbons, Marlowe, Pepys, Drake Evelyn and the northern half of Ladywell wards only).

General: These Task Forces, of which there are four in London, have been set up by the government in areas known to be seriously disadvantaged. The main objective is to create a thriving economy in these inner city areas. The goals of this initiative are the provision of jobs for local people, the encouragement of local enterprise, the enhancement of the employability of local people, and the improvement of the local environment, especially through crime reduction and the improvement of safety.

Much of the work of the Task Forces is concerned with improving the take-up and effectiveness of existing government programmes, and in improving their co-ordination, but there are also numerous occasions in which the Task Force works through voluntary organisations and community groups in the area. Examples include: The Adun Society which runs courses to equip women from ethnic minorities with the business skills needed to set up their own enterprises (£23,675); The Grand Metropolitan Community Services which gives local people the skills to become milk roundsmen/women (£28,505); The Pagnell Street Youth Centre which is developing a business plan to present to its main funders through the aid of a consultant (£3,500).

Grant total: Circa £1.1 million 1991/92

Correspondent: Joseph Montgomery, Task Force Leader

Address: Unit 1, City Link Court, 471-473 New Cross Road, London SE14 6TA, (tel: 081-694 9276, fax: 081-694 9314)

Deptford into the 90s Trust

Beneficial area: Parliamentary constituency of Deptford

Objects: Assisting people through supporting small local initiatives

Type of beneficiary: Organisations

Income: £1,700 (1991)

Grant total: £1,400

Grant details: Grants made for clubs and festivals.

Applications procedure: Apply in writing to the correspondent.

Correspondent: Owen Beament

Address: 22 Erlanger Road, London SE14 5TG (071-639 3497)

Other information: The trust also organises local events which celebrate the international diversity of Deptford.

The Deptford Pension Society

Beneficial area: Deptford

Objects: Provision of pensions to aged householders

Type of beneficiary: Individuals

Income: £3,220 (1977)

Grant total: £3,200

Grant details: Cash payments rather than pensions

Applications procedure: To the correspondent

Correspondent: Mrs Alison Claremont-Davies, Honorary Secretary

Address: c/o All Saints' Church, 105 New Cross Road, London SE14 5DJ (071-639 2889)

Other information: This entry was not confirmed by the trust.

Deptford St Paul Charity

Beneficial area: Former Metropolitan area of Deptford

Objects: Relief of the elderly

Type of beneficiary: individuals, organisations

Grant total: about £4,000 per annum

Grant details: £3,500 was donated to organisations working with the elderly at Christmas and pensions of £7 were given to 40 people per month. Pensions are administered by the Deptford Pension Society.

Applications procedure: Organisations should apply directly to the correspondent. Individuals seeking pensions should apply to the Deptford Pension Society (see entry).

Correspondent: Mike Brown, Honorary Secretary,

Address: Chief Executive's Department, London Borough of Lewisham, Lewisham Town Hall, Catford, London SE6 4RU (081-695 6000)

'56 Aid Club

Beneficial area: Lewisham

Objects: Relief of poverty

Type of beneficiary: Individuals

Income: £3,180 (1989/90)

Grant total: £1,890

Grant details: No information available.

Applications procedure: To the correspondent.

Correspondent: Sean O'Sullivan, Secretary

Address: 121 Houston Road, Forest Hill, London SE23 2RL (the telephone number is ex-directory)

Other information: This entry was not confirmed by the trust.

The William Hatcliffe Educational Charity

Beneficial area: The ancient Parish of Lee in Lewisham

Objects: Educational grants for young people between 16 and 25 years of age

Type of beneficiary: Individuals

Grant total: £100 (1991)

Income: £100

Grant details: This small trust makes limited grants to assist with further education.

Applications procedure: Direct to the correspondent D J Swales

Address: 39 Brownhill Road, Catford, London SE6 2HB (081-697 8528)

The Christopher Boone's Charity

Beneficial area: The ancient Parish of Lee in Lewisham

Objects: Educational grants for young people

Type of beneficiary: Individuals

Grant total: £100 (1991)

Income: £100

Grant details: This small trust makes limited grants for pupils at secondary schools.

Applications procedure: Direct to the correspondent

Correspondent: D J Swales

Address: 39 Brownhill Road, Catford, London SE6 2HB (081-697 8528)

The William Hatcliffe Non-Educational Charity

Beneficial area: The ancient Parish of Lee in Lewisham

Main grant area: Relief of need among people who have lived in the beneficial area for at least 5 years

Type of beneficiary: Individuals

Grant total: No information available

Grant details: The trust's priorities are elderly and handicapped people. Regular allowances are given which currently stand at £146 per annum.

Applications procedure: Direct to the correspondent

Correspondent: D J Swales

Address: 39 Brownhill Road, Catford, London SE6 2HB (081-697 8528)

Other information: According to the terms of the charity's constitution, the London Borough of Lewisham has to nominate trustees onto its governing body.

The Mayoress of Lewisham's Committee for Local Charities

Beneficial area: London Borough of Lewisham

Objects: General charitable purposes at the discretion of the mayoress

Type of beneficiary: Organisations

Income: About £10,000 but variable (£11,320 in 1990/91)

Grant total: About £10,000

Grant details: Beneficiaries are chosen by the mayor/ess in office, but are not normally organisations already in receipt of a local authority grant. Donations are given for a wide variety of purposes, such as the training of guide dogs for blind Lewisham residents, the purchase of an electrocardiogram for a local health centre and the purchase of equipment for local hospitals. Donations vary in size according to need; the largest award in 1990/91 was £3,000 for the Lewisham Hospital Scanner Appeal.

Applications procedure: Applications should be in writing and addressed to the Mayor in office.

Correspondent: The Mayor/ess

Address: The Mayor's Office, London Borough of Lewisham, Lewisham Town Hall, London SE6 4RU (081-695 6000)

Major Local Companies

Franklin Mint Ltd, 138 Bromley Road, London SE6 2XG (081-697 8121) supports local charities but most giving is controlled by the American parent company and therefore tends to be directed to national charities. Contact James Lothian, Public Relations Director.

Marks and Spencer plc, 122 Lewisham High Street, London SE13 6JG (081-318 9444). Contact Joanne Ladbury, Training Coordinator, Personnel Department,

The Body Shop, 40a Lewisham Centre, High Street, SE13 5JX makes small donations to local organisations (081-852 5252). Contact Hilda Mills.

Sources of Advice

Voluntary Action Lewisham, 120 Rushey Green, Catford, London SE6 4HQ (081-695 6000 ext 3340).

Coordinator: Nigel Spalding
Opening hours: 10.00-5.30

Lewisham Arts Council, 44 Doggett Road, London SE6 (081-690 0431). Contact Mrs Olga Webb, Secretary.

Community Education Lewisham (headquarters), Mornington Road Centre, Stanley Street, London SE8 4BL (081-691 5959).

Merton

London Borough of Merton

Merton Civic Centre, London Road, Morden, Surrey SM4 5DX (081-543 2222)

Correspondents:

The Grants Unit (for all grants except those for youth organisations and mental illness and drug/alcohol specific grants): Sandra Jones, Acting Principal Grants Officer, Surinder Vassal, Grants Officer, (081-545 3646)

Youth Committee: Mark Clark, Youth Officer, The London Borough of Merton, Youth Officer, The Pavilion, Farm Road, Morden, Surrey SM4 6RA (081-640 7050)

Social Services (Drugs and Alcohol Specific Grant, Mental Illness Specific Grant): Colin Willard, Principal Policy Development and Inspection Officer, (Mental Health) (081-545 4002)

Grant total 1992/93: £2,483,880

Funding: Merton has a Grants Services Committee which awards grants to local voluntary groups in the following nine categories:

Arts, Leisure and the Environment

Housing

Disability and Health

Elderly people

Children and Families

Information, Advice and Counselling

Support/Umbrella organisations

Community/Family Centres

Welfare Support

In 1992/93 56 groups received annual revenue grants ranging from £3,000 to £223,000. Most grants were between £4,000 and £80,000.

The committee also has a budget of £10,000 for non-recurrent grants and in 1992/93 a new initiative was launched to support the training of staff in local voluntary groups. This has a budget of £5,000.

There is also a Small Grants Programme to provide 'start-up' finance to allow new projects to become established and give one-off funding. Grants range from £50 to £2,000.

The Children Act 1989: In 1992/93 a few grants to children's organisations were increased to meet training requirements of the new legislation.

Youth Committee: This committee funds voluntary youth organisations affiliated to it and has a budget of about £65,000 a year. Grants ranging from £50 to £500 are made towards staffing costs, premises, equipment, materials, and residential weekends for young people. Small grants are awarded to regional youth organisations and new youth groups.

Mental Illness Specific Grant: In 1991/92 the Merton Council received DoH funding for mental health services and funded Merton MIND for an information and advice project and weekend drop-in centre (c£27,000) and the Richmond Fellowship for a Sheltered Workshop for a Work Placement Officer (c£8,000).

Alcohol and Drugs Specific Grant: Merton Council did not apply for alcohol/drugs funding in 1991/92 but was waiting to hear about its bid for 1992/93 when this book went to press.

Lottery Fund: (*see separate entry*)

Applications procedure: Application forms are available from the Grants Unit and usually should be completed by the end of September. Grant decisions are made in November and January.

The Youth Committee makes grants all year round. Applications should be made using the standard application form available from the Youth Office.

Other support: Merton supports local voluntary groups in further ways by providing access to cheap printing facilities; professional advice on legal, personnel and financial matters, tailored to the service provided; use of premises on a free or reduced cost basis; the loan of council-owned vehicles; payroll services (whereby staff pay and contributions are administered on behalf of voluntary groups).

Contracting and the Community Care Plan

Social Services developed its Community Care Plan for 1992/93 through consultation with all sections of the voluntary sector. Merton Community Care Forum co-ordinated contributions from a wide range of organisations. Additional consultation was arranged with groups representing the borough's ethnic minority communities and with local housing associations.

For further information contact: Trevor Knowles, Director of Housing and Social Services

Merton and Sutton Joint Consultative Committee

Beneficial area: London Boroughs of Merton and Sutton

Funding practices: Many projects are sponsored by the health authority or/and the local authorities. Funding pump-primes new schemes which cater to both health and social care needs of the local population. It is tapered, usually over seven years, after which a sponsoring authority must intend to fund the project from its main allocation.

Total expenditure: £827,000 (1990/91)

Joint finance budget: £931,000 for 1991/92 (please note that the programme is fully committed until 1995/96).

Details of projects: Over 50 different organisations were funded in 1990/91, including MIND (£12,500), MENCAP (£17,000) and Crossroads (£26,400).

Applications procedure: For up-to-date guidance for voluntary organisations contact the Director of Social Services at the London Borough of Merton (081-543 2222) or the Director of Social Services at the London Borough of Sutton (081-770 5000) or the health authority contact given below.

Correspondent: Ms Laura Cummings, Planning Manager

Address: Merton and Sutton Health Authority, Wilson Hospital, Mitcham, Surrey CR4 4TP (081-648 3021)

Other information: The committee meets three times a year but joint finance bids are considered once per year.

The Black Family Trusts

Beneficial area: National; Merton and Wimbledon area

Objects: Mainly Christian churches and groups; also social welfare and young people

Type of beneficiary: Organisations

Grant total: c£162,648 (1987/88)

Grant details: Although these trusts make grants nationally, a high proportion of the beneficial organisations are local to the Wimbledon and Merton areas where the family trusts and business (CWB Finance Co Ltd) are based.

Most grants are made for Christian causes, especially those of an evangelical bent, be they individual churches or groups, or church-sponsored projects. Other donations are given to youth work and a few are given for social welfare purposes – local beneficiaries in recent years have also included the Wimbledon Community Association, Mitcham Senior Citizens' Club, Wimbledon Guild of Social Welfare, Merton Association for the Welfare of the Blind, Merton Women's Aid, as well as local churches, clubs, schools, YMCA, the light opera society and the ladies' bowls club. It should be noted that the majority of the grants are for £100 or less.

Applications procedure: The Black family trusts are three in number but operate as one. Applications in writing to the correspondent.

Correspondent: Mr Bilcher, Secretary

Address: 6 Leopold Road, Wimbledon, London SW19 7BD (081-947 1041)

Directors: Sir Cyril Black, Lady D J Black, A W Black, K R Crabtree, Mrs J D Crabtree

Other information: This entry was not confirmed by the trust.

The Lady Tyrrell Giles Gift

Beneficial area: National but with a preference for Wimbledon

Objects: To assist 'ladies in reduced circumstances' (women of the upper, middle and professional classes in financial need).

Type of beneficiary: Individuals

Income: £5,590 (1991)

Grant total: £3,420

Grant details: Preference is shown to ladies who have or have had connections with Wimbledon. Grants are one-off and usually range from £100 to £500. In 1991 six grants were made.

Applications procedure: An application form is available from the correspondent and can be submitted at any time by the person in question or through a social worker, Citizen's Advice Bureau or other welfare agency. It is important to state the purpose for which the grant is required.

Correspondent: The Charities Clerk

Address: The Skinners' Company, 8 Dowgate Hill, London EC4R 2SP (071-236 5629)

The Ronald Greenwood Music Trust Fund

Beneficial area: London Borough of Merton

Objects: Material assistance to young people living in the beneficial area who show a talent in music and who are in need of help by reason of financial circumstances

Type of beneficiary: Individuals

Grant total: £700 (1989/90)

Grant details: Two grants were made during the year.

Applications procedure: Applications should be submitted on forms available from the correspondent not later than June 30th and are considered from January to June. Urgent applications will be considered outside this period.

Correspondent: G J Norris, Honorary Secretary

Address: 8 Langley Road, Merton Park, London SW19 3NZ (081-540 3459)

Alf and Hilda Leivers Charity Trust

Beneficial area: London Borough of Merton

Objects: Assistance of young people under 18 whose parents or guardians have lived in the beneficial area for at least five years

Type of beneficiary: Individuals

Grant details: Probably help with the cost of books, clothing and other essentials for those at school.

Applications procedure: In writing to the correspondent. The trust will be advertised locally.

Correspondent: A Leivers

Address: 171 Coombe Lane, Raynes Park, London SW20 0QX (081-947 2800)

Other information: This trust was formed in 1989. No further information available.

Merton Lottery Fund

Beneficial area: London Borough of Merton

Objects: General charitable purposes in the borough.

Type of beneficiary: Organisations

Latest information: 1991

Grant total: £25,000 shared with the council's Community Chest Fund.

Grant details: The Lottery Fund is used to finance part of the London Borough of Merton's Small Grants Programme (see entry for local authority). It makes small grants, principally for new initiatives (£2,000 maximum) but also assists existing voluntary action where there is a clear community need.

Applications procedure: Application forms are available from the correspondent. Grants are allocated four or five times a year; this means that applicants should not normally have to wait longer than three months before a decision is made. Applicants should contact the correspondent to find out the precise deadlines.

Correspondent: Barbara Conaty, Grants Officer, Grants Unit

Address: London Borough of Merton, Crown House, London Road, Morden, Surrey SM4 5DX (081-543 3646)

Other information: Merton Council no longer runs a lottery. The Lottery Fund's income comes from the interest of the invested sum.

Merton Mayor's Charity

Beneficial area: London Borough of Merton

Objects: Support for organisations

Grant details: Each year the Mayor fundraises for several charities of his choice and in 1991/92 these were St Raphael's Hospice and Merton Crossroads, a care attendant scheme.

Correspondent: Deanna Manley, the Mayor's Secretary, or the Mayor

Address: The Mayor's Office, London Borough of Merton, Crown House, London Road, Morden, Surrey SM4 5DX (081-545 3517)

Mitcham United Charity

Beneficial area: Former Metropolitan Borough of Mitcham

Objects: Relief of need

Type of beneficiary: Individuals

Income: about £2,000 (1990)

Grant details: Christmas gifts and one-off grants

Applications procedure: To the correspondent for an application form

Correspondent: Brenda Bull,

Address: Age Concern (Merton), 277 London Road, Mitcham, Surrey, CR4 3NT (081-648 5792)

Other information: In early 1992 Age Concern had just taken over the administration of the trust from the London Borough of Sutton and was reorganising its finances.

The Wimbledon Guild

Beneficial area: Wimbledon and part of SW20

Objects: Relief of sickness, hardship and distress

Type of beneficiary: Individuals

Grant total: £3,380 (1988/89)

Grant details: Grants of up to £200 are made. The guild can consider applications for the relief of most sorts of need.

Applications procedure: To the correspondent, not necessarily through social services or a welfare agency. There is an application form.

Correspondent: Head of Social Work

Address: The Guild House, 30/32 Worple Road, Wimbledon, London SW19 4EF (081-946 0735)

Major Local Companies

Brown and Root UK Ltd (Engineering Construction), 150 The Broadway, Wimbledon, London SW19 1RX (081-544 5000). Contact John Collins, Public Relations Manager.

Morfax Ltd (precision engineers), Morfax House, 1 Greenlea Park, Prince George's Road, Colliers Wood, London SW19 2JD (081-648 7040) makes donations to local organisations. Contact the Personnel Department.

Racal Avionics Ltd, 88 Bushey Road, Raynes Park, London SW20 0JH (081-946 8011). Donations are decided on a corporate basis with some consideration of local charities in areas of company presence. Contact Sheila Butler, Secretary to the Racal Charitable Trust, Western Road, Bracknell, Berkshire RG12 1RG (0344-483244).

Sources of Advice

Merton Voluntary Service Council, Vestry Hall, London Road, Mitcham, Surrey CRY 3UD (081-685 1771)

General Secretary: Christine Frost
Opening hours: 9.30-5.00

Merton Arts Council, 1st Floor Office, Wimbledon Library, Wimbledon Hill Road, London SW19 7NB (081-947 6545). Contact Maurice Hedden, Chairman (Tuesday, Wednesday, Thursday mornings).

Merton Adult Education Institute, Whatley Avenue, London SW20 9NS (081-543 9292)

Newham

London Borough of Newham

Town Hall, East Ham, London E6 2RP (081-472 1430)

Correspondent: Sue Thomas, Head of Central Grants Unit

Grants totals 1990/91:

£4,082,605 in main programme funding (including small grants)

£1,585,228 in Urban Programme funding

£450,440 in Joint Finance

£501,901 Joint Funding with the London Docklands Development Corporation

Funding: In 1987 Newham established a Central Grants Unit through which all of its grant-making is now carried out. This co-ordinates awards made through the council's various grant-making committees. Grants made in the period 1990/91 can be broken down as follows:

Community Affairs Sub-committee	£917,144
Economic Development	£465,678
Education	£247,365
Environment and Planning	£18,663
Housing	£214,223
Leisure	£998,091
Policing and Community Safety	£29,050
Race Equality	£216,248
Social Services	£976,143
TOTAL	£4,082,605

Most of the money detailed above is given through the standard main programme. Some, however, is given in the form of small grants – usually for the purposes of seedcorn funding of community groups. This, for example, is the principal function of the Community Chest and the Arts in the Neighbourhood Funds. Similarly, many small grants are awarded by the Race Equality Committee. As the Central Grants Unit acts as a 'clearing house' for all the council's grants to the voluntary sector, applicants should approach this unit for further advice and information.

In 1990/91 the council made a 10% reduction in its voluntary sector budget and a few large organisations lost their funding. However, £200,000 was retained and redirected to meet new voluntary sector initiatives from 1991/92.

The Children Act 1989: In 1992 Newham realigned existing funds so that it could give equipment grants for groups working with children between five and eight and will probably award grants for building adaptations for playschemes and out-of-school clubs. Larger grants were being made to a smaller number of after-school clubs, holiday playschemes, and play projects so that the council ensured that the adult/child ratio and training facilities required by the Act were met by the organisations it funds. This means that some groups will lose their funding altogether.

Urban Programme: Newham is an Urban Programme (UP) authority. UP voluntary sector grants are dealt with through the Central Grants Unit, and would-be applicants should approach this unit for further information and advice. In 1990/91 voluntary sector projects comprised 40% of Newham's overall UP approvals. Of this, 59% was for capital projects and 41% for revenue commitments.

Mental Illness Specific Grant: In 1991/92 Newham received funding towards mental health projects and supported its local branch of MIND (£6,000). For further information contact: Margaret King, Divisional Manager of Assessment, Social Services (071-474 7070).

Alcohol and Drugs Specific Grant: Newham did not receive any central government funding in 1991/92 and was waiting to hear if its bid has been successful in 1992/93 when this book went to press. For further information contact Keith Harris, Mental Health Development Worker (081-534 4545 ext 25013)

Applications procedure: Main programme grants are dealt with annually. The deadline for submission of completed application forms normally falls in September. Small grants, however, are given according to different procedures set by individual committees, and can be awarded at various times during the year. Applicants should approach the

Grants Unit for further information.

Other support: Newham gives some support in kind to local groups. This includes the rental of buildings at a peppercorn rent to a few specific organisations, the loan of certain materials and equipment (such as play equipment), and the secondment of local authority staff to some voluntary groups, especially youth groups. Secondments will increase in the future due to the council's proposals to use the Section II grant to fund outreach workers within community groups.

Contracting and the Community Care Plan

In 1992 Newham Social Services mostly funded voluntary organisations through grants but discussions were taking place about the nature and extent of the reorientation of the borough's grant system necessary to meet the requirements of the Community Care legislation. According to the borough's lawyers Newham's current approval system was legally a 'contract' but would need improving and adapting.

Social Services has always had formal contracts with organisations such as Barnardos to provide residential care. No new contractual arrangements are envisaged in 1992/93 as a result of the Community Care Plan and any new measures are likely to take effect during 1993/94 at the very earliest. In 1992 other departments at Newham Council were not using contracts although their grant approval system was already fairly tight and specific.

Newham developed its Community Care Plan through consultation with umbrella organisations including its Council for Voluntary Service and the local Council for Racial Equality. The local Health Forum, made up of voluntary sector representatives and an ethnic minorities community health forum also played an active role. The Central Grants Unit and the Social Services Department worked together on this issue through meetings with all local groups providing personal social services.

For further information contact: Cath Roff, Principal Officer, Voluntary Sector, Social Services Department, (081-534 4545, ext 25043)

Newham Joint Consultative Committee

Beneficial area: London Borough of Newham

Objects: To pump-prime new schemes through joint finance funding. Specific criteria for supporting projects were developed in accordance with Community Care requirements.

Funding practices: The major part of the joint finance allocation is already committed to existing schemes. However funds do become available for new schemes as underspendings occur and existing schemes reach the end of their agreed funding period. In 1992/93 the allocation for Joint Finance was given to schemes which were already receiving funding. For 1993/94 there will be £287,300 available for new schemes commencing on 1 April 1993.

Total expenditure: £2,285,230 (1992/93)

Expenditure on voluntary organisations: £515,200 (1992/93)

Details of projects: Voluntary organisations receiving support include: Newham Drugs Advice Project (£29,880), Children's Centre (£11,730), Family Welfare Association Bereavement and Loss (£27,660), Mind,(£78,620), Springboard Housing Association (£75,710), Newham Housing Association (£133,100), Newham Alcohol Advisory Service (£19,360), Respite Care for Children with Special Needs (£39,310), Newham Health Forum (£11,010), and Newham Drugs Advice Project (£18,370).

Correspondents: Julia Lane and Sylvia West, Planning Managers

Address: Newham Health Authority, 1 Helena Road, London E13 (tel no: 081-472 1444, fax no: 081-552 0848)

Other information: The committee meets every three months.

Aston Charities Trust Ltd

Beneficial area: London Borough of Newham and immediate surroundings

Main grant area: General social welfare (but see below)

Type of beneficiary: Organisations

Income: £915,390 (1991)

Grant total: £28,840

Grant details: The trust supports its own community centres and single housing in Newham and a holiday hotel for the elderly near Southend. It will only be able to make very limited grants to local organisations in financial crisis.

Grants are not made towards the revenue costs of former statutory projects.

Applications procedure: In writing to the correspondent

Correspondent: R J Speyer, Secretary

Address: Durning Hall, Earlham Grove, Forest Gate, London E7 9AB (081-555 0142)

The Clarnico Trust

Beneficial area: Stratford area

Objects: Welfare of former employees

Type of beneficiary: Former employees

Income: £2,800 (1990)

Grant total: £2,900

Grant details: The company's main area of support is the welfare of their former employees, especially in the Stratford area where the company used to be based.

Applications procedure: In writing to the correspondent.

Correspondent: Kathleen Blackett, Secretary

Address: Clarke, Nickolls & Coombs plc, 33 High Street, Sunninghill, Ascot, Berks, SL5 9NR (0344 28721)

Mary Curtis Maternity Charity

Beneficial area: London Borough of Newham

Objects: Welfare of poor women before and after confinement

Income: £3,200 (1986)

Grant total: £2,900

Grant details: No information available.

Applications procedure: To the correspondent.

Correspondent: Geoffrey Hooper, The Chairman

Address: South West Ham Child Welfare Society, c/o Mansfield House University Settlement, 310 Barking Road, London E13 8HL (071-476 1505)

Other information: This entry was not confirmed by the trust.

The Samuel Montagu Charitable Trust

See entry in the City of London section

Mayor of Newham's Benevolent Fund

Beneficial area: London Borough of Newham

Objects: General charitable purposes at the discretion of the mayor

Type of beneficiary: Organisations

Income: About £4,000 but variable; relies on fundraising.

Grant total: £3,000 to £5,000

Grant details: Donations are given to a wide variety of local groups. The main criterion is that a beneficiary should be a local group (or a local branch of a national organisation) with few other financial resources. Donations are usually given to help pay for specific items. Maximum payments are normally for about £200. Very occasionally grants may be made to individuals.

Applications procedure: Applicants should write to the mayor in office. Donations can be made at any time, but most money tends to be spent at the end of the mayoral year when most fund-raising has been completed (ie. in May).

Correspondent: The Mayor

Address: The London Borough of Newham, Mayor's Parlour, Town Hall, Barking Road, East Ham, London E6 2RP (081-472 1430)

The Tate and Lyle and Newham Sixth Form Scholarship Trust

Beneficial area: London Borough of Newham

Objects: Educational grants for school pupils living or being educated in the beneficial area

Type of beneficiary: Individuals

Grant total: £20,000 (1990)

Grant details: Cash grants are made to school pupils taking A Level courses, to help with books, equipment, clothing or travel. Grants are awarded for a two year period.

Applications procedure: Applications should be submitted by head teachers by the January of each year.

Correspondent: Miss K Taylor

Address: Tate and Lyle Sugars, Thames Refinery, Silvertown, London E16 2EW (071-476 4455)

Major Local Companies

Barclays Life Assurance Co Ltd, 252 Romford Road, London E7 9JB (081-534 5544). Staff have collected for charity through raffles etc. but this is not a regular occurrence. Recipient charities are decided by the Sports and Social Club. For further information contact Mr King in the Pensions Department. Most donations are given through the head office of Barclays plc, Fleetway House, 25 Farringdon Street, London EC4A 4LP (071-489 1995). Contact B J Blair, Deputy Head of Barclays Community Enterprise.

Manufacturers Hanover Trust Company, 1 Gerry Raffles Square, London E15 1XG (071-932 3000) occasionally makes donations but does not have a donations budget. The parent company in New York mostly makes donations for organisations in America. Contact Andrew Brown, Public Relations Department.

J P Morgan Incorporated Ltd, 17-19 The Mall, Stratford, London E15 1XG (071-600 2300) makes charitable donations. Contact Anita Gallow, Personnel Department.

Tate & Lyle Sugars (part of Tate & Lyle plc), Plaistow Wharf, North Woolwich Road, London E16 2AG (071-476 1161) and Thames Refinery, Factory Road, Silvertown, London E16 2EW (071-476 4455). Cash and product donations are made and staff raise money for charity through raffles. A few standard charities are supported through contributions from employees' salaries but most donations are administered centrally. Contact Dennis Dickson, Employee Services Manager, Thames Refinery or Mr Richard Hogg, Product Group Manager, of Tate & Lyle Sugars, Enterprise House, 45 Homesdale Road, Bromley, Kent 3R2 9TE (081-464 6556).

Sources of Advice

Newham Voluntary Service Council, c/o Family Welfare Association, 20 Baxter Road, Customs House, London E16 3HP (071-511 3553/3773)

Contact: Ann Batchelor
Opening hours: 9–5

Newham Community College, East Ham Centre, High Street South, London E6 4ER (081-472 1480)

Redbridge

London Borough of Redbridge

PO Box 2, Town Hall, 128-142 High Road, Ilford, Essex IG1 1DD (081-478 3020)

For initial enquiries and information for all grants contact the correspondent.

Correspondent: Shamus Kenny, Grants Liaison Officer, Grants Committee

Grant totals in 1991/92:

£679,720 in main programme funding

Funding: In 1991/92 grant-giving can be broken down into the following committees:

Central Grants Committee	£436,000
Recreation and Amenities Committee	£9,500
Education Committee	£6,920
Social Services (including service agreements)	£227,300
TOTAL	£679,720

Central Grants Committee: This provides the following types of funding:

Key Organisation Funding:

a) Umbrella organisations are supported which represent the arts, children, young people, disabled people, the elderly, the mentally ill, sports, recreation and the underfives. In 1991/92 grants totalling £151,532 were awarded and among groups funded were Redbridge Arts Council (£16,790), Redbridge Conference of Voluntary Youth Organisations (£490), Age Concern (£5,900), Mental After Care Association (£9,310), and the Jewish Youth and Community Centre (£27,000).

b) Organisations providing advice and counselling are supported. In 1992/92 grants totalling £118,050 were made and examples of funded groups are: Citizens' Advice Bureau (£52,960), Asian Women's Association (£25,720), Relate (£13,000), Victims' Support (£22,550) and the Samaritans (£3,020).

c) Organisations which represent the interests of the voluntary sector receive funding and in 1991/92 £92,380 was awarded in grants. Redbridge Council for Voluntary Service (£30,000) and the Volunteer Bureau were amongst the organisations supported.

Pump-priming Funding: This enables new organisations or projects to become established, usually for a maximum of five years, with funding tapering appropriately over this period. At the end of the pump-priming organisations should either be self-financing or suitable for agency funding by Service Committees (Social Services, Education, Recreation and Amenities). In 1991/92 a total of £66,178 was made in grants.

The council refers all requests for small grants (under £500) to the Redbridge Community Trust (*see separate entry*).

Education Committee: In 1991/92 this committee made grants to the Preschool Playgroup Association (£2,880), to NELREC, the North East London Religious Education Centre, (£1,920), 33rd Epping Forest Scouts (£2,070) and a Special Activities Course (£150).

Recreational and Amenities Committee: Grants were made for sports and recreation groups. Typical beneficiaries are sports and horticultural groups.

Social Services Committee: In 1991/92 a wide variety of organisations received funding, including Age Concern (£15,990), Redbridge Talking Newspaper Association (£880), Royal Association in Aid of Deaf People (£535) and RESPITE (£805).

Mental Illness Specific Grant: In 1991/92 Redbridge received £107,000 from the Department of Health and funded five projects, some of which were from the voluntary sector.

Drugs and Alcohol Specific Grant: Redbridge was successful in its bid for funding from the Department of Health and made grants to three voluntary initiatives: the Pegasus Project (£10,230), Redbridge Alcohol Project (£11,000) and Drugline Essex (£29,000).

Applications Procedure: New groups requesting assistance should contact Shamus Kenny, Grants Liaison Officer, in the first instance. Applications are dealt with on a year-round basis and in October forms are sent out to funded groups and should be returned by the first week of December. Grants are made by the above mentioned committees or a service agency agreement is drawn up.

Other support: Redbridge's Education Department also lends materials and equipment to local groups (especially youth groups), usually on an indefinite loan basis. The Grants Committee occasionally makes grants specifically to cover the rental costs of council-owned accommodation.

Contracting and the Community Care Plan
In 1992 Redbridge Social Services funded voluntary organisations through grants and contracts and did not see this changing greatly for a while.

A few 'agency agreements' were made in 1991/92 and during 1992/93 some contracts will probably be used. These will be tailored to the specific organisation and services required and will usually run for one year.

Redbridge Social Services discussed its Community Care Plan with the Redbridge Voluntary Services Association, small local voluntary groups such as Redbridge Association for Handicapped People, and large voluntary organisations.

For further information contact: Mrs Joyce Phillips, Development, Information and Property Services, (081-478 3020 ext 4078)

Redbridge Joint Consultative Committee

Beneficial area: London Borough of Redbridge.

Objects: To co-ordinate the planning of services to "priority groups". These groups include the elderly, people with learning difficulties, people with physical or sensory disabilities, people with a mental health problem.

The government is keen to see Joint Finance used to support services in other key areas such as drug and alcohol misuse, children with special needs, support for carers of elderly or dependent people and the terminally ill. Joint Finance can also be used to recruit staff and purchase equipment so long as it is an essential part of the proposed scheme or project.

Funding practices: All Joint Finance schemes are monitored on a six monthly basis and progress reports are considered by the Chief Officers Advisory Team and then by the Joint Consultative Committee.

Expenditure on voluntary organisations: £80,670 (1991/92)

Details of projects: Support includes £1,050 to Drugline Essex (Helpline scheme); £4,220 to the Alzheimer's Disease Society (the Green Elms Project, Activity Session); £14,560 to the Carers' Worker Scheme; £36,040 to MACA Respite Care Project; £17,350 to the Redbridge Care Attendant Scheme (Alzheimer's Disease Project) and £7,450 to the Redbridge Forum (secretarial support scheme).

Application procedure: Applications must be received by the Joint Planning Officer by 1 November. They are considered by the Chief Officers' Advisory Team (COAT) in January. COAT makes recommendations to the JCC which considers the applications and allocates joint finance in February.

Correspondent: Vee Bonga, Assistant Joint Planning Officer

Address: Redbridge Health Authority, District Management Board, West Wing, King George's Hospital, Eastern Avenue, Ilford 1G2 75J (081-518 2299)

Other information: The committee meets quarterly. Voluntary organisations thinking of applying for Joint Finance should seek advice from:

Vee Bonga, Redbridge Health Authority/London Borough of Redbridge (081-518 2299 ext 3510)

Geoff Pearce, Directorate of Finance, the London Borough of Redbridge (081-478 3020 ext 4444)

Ian Clay, Redbridge Health Authority (081-590 6060 ext 2493)

Ivan King, Redbridge Council for Voluntary Service (081-554 5049)

Redbridge Arts Council

Beneficial area: London Borough of Redbridge

Type of beneficiary: Organisations

Grant details: Primarily a co-ordinating and advisory body, the council also has a small grants budget for the benefit of affiliated societies.

Correspondent: Nigel Maxwell, Honorary Secretary

Address: Central Library, Clements Road, Ilford, Essex IG1 1EA (081-478 7145 ext 300)

Ilford Charities

Beneficial area: London Borough of Redbridge, Ilford, Essex

Objects: Distribution of grants to elderly, needy residents

Type of beneficiary: Individuals over sixty years of age

Grant total: £3,680 (1991)

Grant details: This year 245 elderly people received a £15 grant on the 17 December, 1991.

Applications procedure: Details of the distribution are advertised locally in day centres, etc. frequented by the elderly. Application forms are available from the Town Hall during the first three weeks in October. The form asks for brief details of age, income, expenses etc., how long the applicant has lived in Ilford and other districts administered by Redbridge. The Assistant Clerk to the trustees, Mrs E L Cook works at the Town Hall information desk and can be contacted on 081-478 3020 ext 2126.

Correspondent: Miss R D Felton, Clerk to the Trustees

Address: 40 Somersby Gardens, Redbridge, Ilford, Essex IG4 5EA (081-550 6311)

Other information: The charity is also responsible for publicising and finding elderly beneficiaries for the annual visit of members of the Worshipful Company of Poulters who distribute a £10 note to each of the 80 people at a ceremony attended by the Mayor, in the Town Hall in June of each year. Applications forms are available during the first three weeks in April.

The Ilford Charities' income is derived from investments of legacies from former residents of the borough.

The Mayor's Fund

Beneficial area: The London Borough of Redbridge

Objects: The relief of needy residents

Type of beneficiary: Individuals

Income: Variable but very small; relies on an annual donation of £100 from the Ford of Britain Trust and fund-raising by the Ilford South Carnival Association.

Grant total: About £500

Grant details: This is a very limited fund. Donations are given for specific items or purposes to residents who have fallen on hard times, such as a local pensioner whose pension was stolen and a disabled child needing a holiday.

Applications procedure: Most applicants are referred by the council's Social Services department. However, applicants can write directly to the Mayor.

Correspondent: The Mayor

Address: Mayor's Parlour, London Borough of Redbridge, Town Hall, Ilford, Essex IG1 1DD (081-478 3020)

Other information: This entry was not confirmed by the trust.

Redbridge Community Trust

Beneficial area: London Borough of Redbridge

Objects: to benefit the local community through support of the voluntary sector

Type of beneficiary: Voluntary organisations

Income: £22,000 (1990/91)

Grant total: £6,000

Grant details: £500 is the maximum grant made, and in 1990 Hainault Community Centre (£500), the Catholic Handicapped Fellowship (£500) Asians Senior Citizens Welfare Association (£300), The Advisory Council on Alcohol and Drug Education (£300), Arthritis Care, Redbridge (£100), were among the organisations supported.

In 1992 the trustees plan to launch a Community Trust Innovation Award Scheme whereby £5,000 will be given to a proposed project which benefits Redbridge in an original way. The proposal must involve one of the following: young people, the environment, multi-culture, the arts, health and welfare, recreation and leisure, education.

Application procedure: In writing to the correspondent for an application form.

Correspondent: Shamus Kenny, Clerk to the Trustees

Address: PO Box 77, Ilford, Essex IG1 1EB (081-553 9469)

Other information: The trust is raising sponsorship from local businesses so that it can broaden its work.

Major Local Companies

Polygram Record Operations Ltd, Clyde Works, Grove Road, Chadwell Heath, Romford, Essex RM6 4QR (081-590 6088) donates its products to general charities in the Redbridge area. No cash is donated. Contact John Lloyd.

Wiggins Teape Stationery Ltd, Grove Road, Chadwell Heath, Romford, Essex RM6 4XL (081-590 7777) supports local charities. Contact the Personnel Manager.

John Lelliot (building construction), 52/54
Peregrine Road, Hainault Industrial Estate, Ilford,
Essex IG6 3SZ (081-501 4040) sponsors St
John's Ambulance and runs a raffle to raise
money for it. Usually gives to local charities but
due to economic constraints, is not making any
donations at the moment. When there has been an
upturn in the economy contact Nick Fowler,
Public Relations Department.

Kelvin Hughes Ltd (radar equipment), Lew
North Road, Hainault, Ilford, Essex IG6 2UR
(081-500 1020) gives product donations such as
barometers and nautical clocks and has a small
charitable budget for local organisations. Donations of £50 are made. Contact Mrs Margaret
Bundy, Personnel Department.

**The Exchange (shopping centre run by
Norwich Union),** High Road, Ilford IG1 1RS
(081-553 3000) Contact Mr Knight.

Sources of Advice

Redbridge Council for Voluntary Service, 1st
Floor, Broadway Chambers, 1 Cranbrook Road,
Ilford, Essex 1G1 4DU (tel 081- 554 5049, fax
081-478 9640)

Director: Ivan King
Opening hours: 9.00-5.00

Redbridge Institute of Adult Education,
Gearies Centre, Gaysham Ave, Gants Hill, Ilford
1G2 6TD (081-550 2398)

Richmond-upon-Thames

London Borough of Richmond-upon-Thames

Municipal Offices, York House, Twickenham, Middlesex TW1 3AA (081-891 1411)

Correspondent: All enquiries should be addressed to Ms N Rowe, Principal Officer (grants), Voluntary Organisations Subcommittee (081-891 7151).

Grant totals 1991/92:
£666,500 in main programme funding

Funding practice: Richmond Council has centralised its grantmaking structure so that the majority of applications from voluntary organisations are dealt with by the Voluntary Organisations Sub-Committee. Grants in 1991/92 included £207,500 to Richmond-upon-Thames Citizens' Advice Bureau, £200 to Barnes and Mortlake History Society, and £8,875 to the Richmond and Barnes Mental Health Association.

Policy: The criteria used by Richmond-upon-Thames in grant-aid decisions are, on the whole, standard guidelines relating to:

- eligibility (any organisation seeking a grant must be non-profit-making, must be benefiting local residents and must be able to demonstrate that a grant will be spent effectively);
- need (evidence must be supplied showing that the service provided by the organisation is needed and that the organisation in question can provide it);
- cost-effectiveness.

Mental Illness Specific Grant: The council was awarded £90,000 and used it to develop its own services for the mentally ill.

Drug and Alcohol Specific Grant: The council received central government funding of £7,000 and with it funded a local voluntary group called SPEAR (Single Person's Emergency Accommodation in Richmond).

Applications Procedure: The majority of applications are considered in February although applications may be considered at other times at the discretion of the Voluntary Organisations Sub-Committee. Normally applications should be returned to the Council by the end of September of each year.

Other support: The Community Services Department gives some help to certain voluntary organisations in the form of discretionary rate relief, free and subsidised accommodation, administrative help, financial advice, seconded staff, and, in the case of the Richmond Festival, free telephone and postage facilities. The Education Department also gives some help in the form of administrative assistance, assistance with transport and the provision of free accommodation. This assistance is, on the whole, restricted to certain organisations; however, from time to time the council will give similar help to small local groups.

Contracting and the Community Care Plan

In 1992 the Chief Executive's Department funded voluntary organisations through grants and was not using contracts or planning to in 1992/93.

Richmond Social Services worked with Richmond Council for Voluntary Service to organise interest groups and a public forum to develop community care plans. These have provided a basis for future consultation and representation of voluntary organisations, users and carers.

For further information contact: Margaret Edwards, Departmental Planning Officer, Social Services

Richmond Joint Consultative Committee

Beneficial area: London Borough of Richmond upon Thames and Richmond, Twickenham & Roehampton District Health Authority (DHA).

Objects: In conjunction with the District Health Authority, Family Health Service Authority (FHSA) and the voluntary sector to identify needs in health and personal social services which are common to the statutory authorities and to promote initiatives which are seen to be in the best overall interest of health care.

Funding practices: An annual programme is set up

and bids from either statutory authority or voluntary organisations are considered in the previous October. It is open to any voluntary organisation to seek Joint Finance but they must secure a sponsor - either local authority or district health authority - to guarantee funding once Joint Finance support has expired.

Expenditure on voluntary organisations: £52,000 (in 1992/93, total available for new bids was £80,000).

Details of projects: Voluntary sector projects supported in 1992/93 are follows:

Alcohol Counselling (Problem drinkers)	£9,120
Crossroads (supporting frail and disabled)	£31,200
Volunteer Drivers Expenses	£14,500
Youth Counselling	£4,300
Homeless (Chiropody)	£800
CVS Coordinator	£10,000

Applications procedure: Formal submissions to the correspondent in September

Correspondent: Anne Bogod, CVS General Secretary

Address: 51 Sheen Road, Richmond, Surrey TW9 1YQ (081-940 6235)

Other information: The Joint Consultative Committee (JCC) meets quarterly. All JCC proposals must be endorsed by the DHA. The amount of uncommitted monies in any one year is extremely limited and considerably narrows scope for any new bids.

Barnes Relief in Need Charity and The Bailey and Bates Trust

Beneficial area: The former Borough of Barnes

Objects: Residents in need; educational grants for residents under 25

Type of beneficiary: Individuals and organisations

Income: £5,310 (1990)

Grant total: £3,810

Grant details: Small grants were made to pensioners from the Relief in Need Charity. Educational grants are made from the Bailey and Bates Trust.

Applications procedure: In writing to the correspondent.

Correspondent: T M Sutton-Mattocks, Clerk

Address: Bank Chambers, 1 Rocks Lane, Ranelagh Gardens, Barnes, SW13 0DE (081-876 8811)

Other information: Note that the beneficial area is restricted to the former borough of Barnes. The trust has recently been receiving applications from as far afield as Newcastle.

Barnes Workhouse Fund

Beneficial area: Ancient Parish of Barnes (in practice SW13)

Main grant areas: Relief of poverty, sickness and distress, and improving the conditions of life of the inhabitants

Type of beneficiary: Individuals and organisations

Income: £106,160 (1989/90)

Grant total: £60,040

Grant details: £25,000 was given to Richmond-upon-Thames Churches Trust towards their Vera Gray House Appeal. Grants were made to 23 other local organisations, including primary schools, football club, community centre, old persons' welfare, music club, youth theatre and counselling groups. Comparison with previous years' accounts shows few of the grants to be recurrent, although the same broad areas are supported each year.

A total of £220 was given in miscellaneous grants to individuals.

Applications procedure: By letter to the correspondent. Applications for personal grants preferably via social services, CAB or welfare agency.

Correspondent: T M Sutton-Mattocks

Address: Bank Chambers, 1 Rocks Lane, Ranelagh Gardens, Barnes, London SW13 0DE (081-876 8811/2/3)

The Hampton and Hampton Hill Philanthropic Society

Beneficial area: Civil Parishes of Hampton St Mary and All Saints and Hampton Hill St James

Objects: Relief of financial distress

Type of beneficiary: Individuals and organisations

Income: £1,400 (1990/91)

Grant total: £400

Grant details: No information available

Applications procedure: To the correspondent.

Correspondent: J L Reed, Secretary

Address: 4 Cardinal's Walk, Hampton, Middlesex TW12 2TS (081-979 2872)

Hampton Fuel Allotment Charitable Trust

Beneficial area: Primarily the ancient town of Hampton, being the present areas of Hampton and of Hampton Hill, also the former Borough of Twickenham and the remainder of the present London Borough of Richmond-upon-Thames.

Objects: The relief of people in need or who are sick, convalescent, disabled, handicapped or infirm; the provision of educational grants to assist children and young persons in financial need; the provision of grants to schools for providing special benefits not normally provided by the local education authority; the provision of recreational facilities not normally provided by the local authority to improve the quality of life for residents; and other charitable purposes.

Type of beneficiary: Individuals and organisations

Income: £1,861,290 (1991)

Grant total: £1,946,230

Grant details:

Relief of need: £107,390 was given to individuals in need, with £68,930 in heating grants, £7,120 for emergency alarm systems and the remaining £31,334 for various items and facilities.

General provision for relief in need: £255,300 was donated to hospitals and related organisations, including the League of Friends, Teddington Hospital (£106,000), the Cassel Hospital (£50,000), Princess Alice Hospice, (£35,000), the Royal Hospital and Home, Putney (£6,500) and St John's Ambulance, Twickenham and Whitton (£5,000).

The mentally ill and handicapped: £86,900 was given in grants to organisations as varied as Elizabeth Fitzroy Homes (£25,000), Sons of Divine Providence, Molesey Venture (£20,000), the Twickenham and District Association for Mental Health (£7,000), the Multiple Sclerosis Society, Richmond Branch, (£5,000), the National Society for Epilepsy (£2,000) and the Portcullis Trust (£2,000).

Social and medical welfare: £36,800 was given in

grants to organisations including the Richmond upon Thames Arthritis Care (£11,000), the Hampton Old People's Welfare Association (£5,000), the Hampton Hill Old People's Welfare Committee (£5,000) and Twickenham Club for the Blind (£2,000).

Housing: Grants totalling £1,208,440 were made to housing associations and trusts, with major grants being awarded to Richmond upon Thames Churches Housing Trust, Oak Avenue (£461,290), to Cecil Houses, Homestead, (£359,890), to Richmond upon Thames Churches Housing Trust, Seymour Road, (£220,850) and Richmond-upon-Thames Churches' Housing Trust, Cedars Road, (£150,000). Smaller grants were also awarded including £115 to Mortlake Almshouses, to Shenehom Housing Association and £3,800 to Richmond Housing Cooperative.

School Projects and other council related matters: A total of £555,550 was given in grants, primarily to schools, colleges and educational projects, including the Rectory School (£375,000), Buckingham Primary School (£8,500), Heathfields Schools Association (£5,000) and the Richmond Adult and Community College (£1,000).

Youth work: £352,470 was given to youth groups including the Barnes/Richmond Scouts Division (£30,000), the Twickenham Division Girl Guides (£105,520) and Barnes Eagles FC (£1,000).

Community work: £720,920 was given in grants to 23 organisations including Hampton and Hampton Hill Community Care Group, Citizens' Advice Bureau, (£56,700), Elleray Hall Day Centre (£35,000), Richmond-upon-Thames Welcare (£9,000), Richmond Borough Crime Prevention Panel (£5,000) and Mediation in Divorce (£2,000).

Recreation and Leisure Time Occupation: £80,220 was awarded in grants to diverse groups and organisations including the Richmond-upon-Thames Boat Project (£2,000), the Teddington Cricket Club (£7,000), Twickenham and Thames Valley Bee Keepers' Association (£500), the Orange Tree Theatre (£10,000), Richmond-upon-Thames Arts Council (£1,250) and the Hampton Choral Society (£2,000).

Pre-school groups: £7,300 was given in grants to toddler groups, playgroups, a toy library, a primary school and a nursery.

Applications procedure: Application forms are available from the correspondent.

Correspondent: A W B Goode, Clerk

Address: 15 Hurst Mount, High Street, Hampton, Middlesex TW12 2SA (081-941 7866)

Other information: After a spectacular series of financial and political manoeuvrings, the charity succeeded in selling its ten acre allotment site to J Sainsbury plc for more than £21 million. The trustees have developed a new scheme with the Charity Commissioners for the management of the charity, that takes into account its vastly increased resources. The new arrangements entail a widening of the objects of the charity and an extension of the area of benefit.

Hampton Wick United Charity

Beneficial area: Parish of St Mark, Teddington and St John the Baptist, Hampton Wick

Objects: Benefit of the poor and educational grants for the young

Type of beneficiary: Individuals and local organisations

Income: £51,920 (1989/90)

Grant total: £22,960

Grant details: One-off cash grants (with the possibility of future reapplication) are made, with no fixed minimum or maximum value. Churches, old people's welfare and youth groups have been supported in the recent past.

Educational grants are also available for children and young persons being residents of one year's standing who through financial need are unable to begin or complete a course of higher or further education.

Applications procedure: To the correspondent. Applications are normally processed at meetings of the full body of trustees which take place in or about February, May and September.

Correspondent: R R H Ellison

Address: Foley Edge, Walpole Avenue, Chipstead, Surrey, CR3 3PP (0737 554291)

Other information: The United Charity is an amalgamation, under a Charity Commission Scheme of 1990, of the Hampton Wick Parish Lands, John Jones, John Turner, Cyrus Maigre and William Cole charities and the Hampton Wick Educational Foundation.

Mayor's Appeal Fund

Beneficial area: London Borough of Richmond upon Thames

Objects: General charitable purposes at the discretion of the mayor and the trustees.

Type of beneficiary: Organisations

Income: £10,000 but variable; depends on fund-raising.

Annual grant total: About £10,000 (£8,110 in 1990/91)

Grant details: Donations are allocated at a meeting of the trustees each April, at the end of the mayoral year. Many recipients are regular beneficiaries of this fund, but other welfare and voluntary organisations are welcome to apply. Awards normally range from £50 to £375 in size; they can be for any purpose.

Applications procedure: In writing to the correspondent at any time of the year.

Correspondent: The Mayor

Address: London Borough of Richmond-upon-Thames, Mayor's Office, York House, Richmond Road, Twickenham, TW1 3AA (Direct line to the Mayor's office, 081-891 7163).

Petersham United Charities

Beneficial area: Parish of Petersham

Objects: General benefit of the poor

Type of beneficiary: Individuals

Latest information: 1987

Income: £2,250

Grant total: £1,175

Grant details: Grants to a maximum of £250, including Christmas and birthday gifts and heating allowances, are made. Pensions are also given. Support cannot be given where statutory funding is available.

Applications procedure: In writing to the correspondent. Applications are considered quarterly in January, April, July and October.

Correspondent: R M Robinson, Clerk to the Trustees

Address: Dixon Ward & Co, 16 The Green, Richmond, Surrey, TW9 1QD (081-940 4051)

Other information: This entry was not confirmed by the trust.

The Richmond Aid in Sickness Fund

Beneficial area: London Borough of Richmond

Main grant areas: Relief of poverty and sickness

Type of beneficiary: Individuals

Income: £2,700 (1987)

Grant total: £635

Grant details: One-off and recurrent grants for Christmas parcels and gifts, groceries, bedding, fuel bills, rent, funeral expenses, recuperative holidays and small cash grants.

Applications procedure: In writing to the correspondent.

Correspondent: R M Robinson, Clerk to the Trustees

Address: Dixon Ward & Co, 16 The Green, Richmond, Surrey, TW9 1QD (081-940 4051)

Other information: This entry was not confirmed by the trust.

Richmond Charities' Almshouses

Beneficial area: Former borough of Richmond

Objects: Relief of need, hardship and distress, educational grants for people under 25 years old, welfare of widows, provision of pensions

Type of beneficiary: Individuals

Grant total: £1,810 (1989)

Grant details: Small, one-off grants.

Applications procedure: Either direct or through social services, CAB, GP etc.

Correspondent: H R Stinson, Clerk to the Trustees

Address: 9 The Green, Richmond, Surrey, TW9 1PU (081-940 0017)

Other information: The William Hickey's Almshouse Charity, Bishop Duppa's Almshouse Charity, Houblon's Almshouse Charity, Sir George Wright's Almshouse Charity and Michel's Almshouse Charity were amalgamated in 1990 to form the Richmond Charities' Almshouses.

Richmond Parish Lands Charity

Beneficial area: The former Civil Parish of Richmond (roughly that part of the present-day borough that is bounded by Kew Gardens and the Old Deer Park to the west, the Thames and Petersham Road to the south, Sandycombe Road, Manoir Road and Richmond Park to the east, and Broomfield Road to the north), and now Kew and North Sheen.

Objects: Relief of poverty, sickness and distress and the aged; the provision and support of recreational facilities; any charitable purpose for the benefit of the inhabitants

Type of beneficiary: Organisations and individuals

Grant total: £528,640 (in 1990/91, but varies considerably from year to year)

Grant details: Revenue grants, and some capital grants are given, principally to organisations through a wide range of programmes:

1. *Relief of poverty:* The charity supports organisations such as the Richmond Philanthropic Society and Richmond Group for the single homeless, as well as a variety of social welfare charities. Donations totalling £74,270 were made.

In addition a Small Grants Scheme is operated, whereby cases of individual hardship are brought to the trustees' attention by welfare organisations.

2. *Support for social and medical welfare:* Grants are made to hospices, counselling groups, hospitals and local medical charities.

3. *Support for the mentally ill and handicapped:* Hostels, housing associations, and groups like MENCAP (£6,600) and RABMIND (£19,590) are supported.

4. *Support for the physically handicapped:* Projects which provide information and services such as RAID were supported. A capital grant of £20,000 was made to the Royal British Legion Poppy Factory to install central heating in the flats of workers, many of whom are disabled.

5. *Education:* In 1987 an Education Fund was set up to support local people of any age on courses of study, and in particular during post-school education when it can be difficult to obtain funding from the local education authority. Grants are made towards fees, books, travel and the cost of apprenticeships. School fees are paid only in exceptional circumstances. Grants are also made to organisations operating educational schemes.

In 1990/91 £72,132 was awarded in grants to over 250 students. General education projects were supported such as Drama Workshops in Schools, Youth Theatre projects, a children's safety scheme and a music group.

6. *Youth and community work:* Youth clubs, sports centres and projects involving young people are generally supported. In 1990/91 the Richmond and Barnes Scout Council (£1,870), The Richmond Sports Council (£100), and the Richmond Youth Centre (£200) were among the organisations supported.

7. *Welfare of pre-school children:* Playgroups, nurseries, and projects involving young children are supported. In 1990/91 the Cygnets' Playgroup (£1,350), The Richmond and Kew Holiday Scheme (£400) and St Matthias Playcentre (£250) were among the groups awarded grants.

8. *Welfare of the elderly:* Residential homes, day centres and groups providing services for the elderly are supported. There is also a WARM Campaign whereby heating vouchers are distributed to the elderly.

9. *Community initiatives:* The charity has undertaken major programmes of construction, support and maintenance of community centres, facilities and housing. The bulk of its funding in 1990 was spent on organisations like the Orange Tree Theatre and Kew Neighbourhood Association.

10. *Music and the arts:* £12,470 was donated to various orchestras, operas, societies and arts groups.

11. *Environmental improvements:* Small grants are made to organisations such as the Richmond Tidy Group (£300).

12. *Local societies:* Small grants are made to all kinds of local groups such as the Scientific Society (£80); Society of Voluntary Guides (£120); and Writers' Circle (£160).

Applications procedure: By letter to the Clerk at any time. The trustees meet each month. Note that national appeals cannot be considered.

Correspondent: The Clerk to the Trustees

Address: The Vestry House, 21 Paradise Road, Richmond, Surrey, TW9 1SA (081-948 5701)

Other information: Two other points are worth noting. Firstly, the charity has extended its beneficial area to encompass Kew and North Sheen and hopes eventually to include the remainder of the Surrey side of the borough. Secondly, the charity produces a detailed and informative annual report and accounts which can be obtained free of charge from the Clerk.

Richmond Philanthropic Society

Beneficial area: Former Parish of Richmond-upon-Thames

Objects: Relief of poverty and need

Type of beneficiary: Individuals

Grant total: About £7,000 in 1988

Grant details: Small one-off grants to a maximum of £50.

Applications procedure: Only through social services or a welfare agency.

Correspondent: B Cook

Address: 20 Whitecliff Crescent, Parkstone, Poole, Dorset BH14 8DT (0202 741953)

Richmond-upon-Thames Fund for the Mentally Handicapped

Beneficial area: Richmond-upon-Thames

Objects: The welfare of mentally handicapped people

Type of beneficiary: Organisations

Income: £1,000 (1990)

Grant total: £1,000

Grant details: Four grants totalling £1,000 were made. The trust's main work in recent years has been its collaboration with Elizabeth Fitzroy Homes to build the 'Silver Birches' home for mentally handicapped people in Richmond.

Applications procedure: In writing to the correspondent

Correspondent: Mr A J Baldwin, The Treasurer

Address: 33 Defoe Avenue, Kew, Richmond, Surrey (081-876 8824)

Other information: The chairman of the trust is Victor Dembo (081-876 5980) who is happy to give information about the trust.

Ann Elizabeth Savage's General Charities

Beneficial area: Ancient Parish of Kingston-upon-Thames

Objects: Welfare of widows, nursing care, Christian education

Type of beneficiary: Individuals

Income: £4,970 (1989/90)

Grant total: £800

Grant details: Annuities of £100 and occasional grants to individuals are made. The Kingston Nursing Association is supported.

Applications procedure: To the correspondent or through the churches of All Saints and St John Evangelist

Correspondent: The Vicar of Kingston

Address: 15 Woodbines Avenue, Kingston-upon-Thames, Surrey, KT1 2AZ (081-546 2644)

Major Local Companies

Courage Ltd, 14 Mortlake High Street, London SW14 8JD (081-876 3434) supports a few local charities especially when a business client is involved. Contact Linda Gregory, Sales Operations Executive. Most donations are made through head office, Courage Ltd, Ashby House, No 1 Bridge Street, Staines, Middlesex, TW18 4TP (0784 466199). Contact M Reynolds, Executive Director of Public Affairs.

Thames Television plc, Teddington Lock, Teddington, Middlesex TW11 9NT (081-977 3252) gives preference to general charities in the Teddington area. Contact Linda Coe, Company Secretary.

William Grant & Sons Ltd, Independence House, 84 Lower Mortlake Road, Richmond, Surrey TW9 2HF (081-332 1188) prefers to support local charities across a broad spectrum of causes. Contact Karen Ambrose, Public Relations Manager.

Sources of Advice

Richmond Council for Voluntary Service, 51 Sheen Road, Richmond, Surrey TW9 1YQ (081-940 6235)

General Secretary: Anne Bogod
Opening hours: 9.30-4.00

Richmond-upon-Thames Arts Council, Arts Council Officers, Parkshot Centre, Parkshot, Richmond, TW9 2RE (081-940 7217). Contact Alistair Davidson, Secretary, Mondays to Fridays, 9.30-1.30.

Richmond Adult and Community College, Main Centre, Clifden Road, Twickenham TW1 4LT (081-891 5907)

Southwark

London Borough of Southwark

The Town Hall, Peckham Road, London SE5 8HB, (071-237 6677)

In the first instance all grant enquiries should be addressed to Stan Dubeck, Unit Head, Community and Social Services Programming Unit (071-525 7402)

Correspondents:

Community Services and Programming Unit: Stan Dubeck, Unit Head

Urban Programme: David Sanderson, Programme Officer, Community Services and Programming Unit,

Social Services Committee: Doug Adams, Planning and Development Officer, Jeff Doodson, Planning Officer, Mental Health, for information on Mental Illness and Drugs/Alcohol Specific Grants,

Central Services Committee: Mike Cantor, Principal Community Development Officer,

Development Services Committee: Malcolm Smith, Deputy Borough Planner and Economic Development Officer,

Leisure and Recreation Committee: E Williams, Grants Coordinator,

Housing Committee: John Hebditch, Grants Officer,

Women's Equality Committee: Rita Stallard, Women's Officer,

Race Equality Committee: Colin Hunte, Grant Liaison Officer,

Education Committee: Lincoln Williams, Community Education Officer.

Grant totals 1991/92:

£7,419,524 in main programme funding
£2,700,000 in Urban Programme Funding
£112,000 in Joint Funding

Funding: Southwark has a central Grants Subcommittee serviced by a central team of officers in the Community Services and Programming Unit. Grants in 1991/92 can be broken down as follows:

Social Services	£1,560,000
Central Services	£1,411,830
Leisure and Recreation	£668,110
Development Services	£691,782
Housing	£334,450
Women's Equality	£304,996
Race Equality	£351,000
Education	
(community education)	£439,000
(under 8s)	£1,218,383
(Youth Service)	£439,973
TOTAL	£7,419,524

Community Services and Programming Unit: Services and advises the Central Grants Sub-committee on grants and other voluntary sector matters. It receives all grant applications.

Central Grants Sub-committee: The Sub-committee has overall responsibility for the allocation of grant resources to grant-giving committees as well as the allocation of individual grants. Grant giving committees are responsible for implementing and monitoring the programmes approved by the Sub-committee. Details of the activities supported are identified below.

Central Services: Funded activities include advice centres, community centres, and generalist provision for the elderly and the disabled.

Development Services: Local employment and economic development initiatives are funded including job training schemes, local planning and environmental projects.

Education: Projects are supported which relate to community education (including literacy and mother tongue projects), under 8s provision and youth services. Grant-making policy towards organisations working with young children remains unaffected by the Children Act 1989.

Housing: Projects are supported which relate directly to the provision of housing services.

Leisure and Recreation: Sports, arts and other recreational initiatives are funded.

Race Equality: The promotion of racial equality in the borough through support to local ethnic minority organisations and projects.

Social Services: Organisations providing welfare and social services are supported.

Women's Equality: Local projects are supported which provide services for women and girls.

Urban Programme: Southwark is an Urban Programme Authority. The availability of grant-aid through this programme is advertised in late spring for the following financial year. Categories under which applications are considered are economic, environmental, and social. Almost half of the resources available are directed towards economic projects. For further information contact David Sanderson, Programme Officer, Community Services and Programming Unit.

Mental Illness Specific Grant: In 1991/92 Southwark received central government funding and made one-off grants to a number of voluntary organisations: Crossways (£11,250) to set up a work assessment project with the London Docklands Development Corporation contributing the additional 30%; MIND (£3,560) to provide a user-friendly guide for people using mental health services in the borough and to purchase computer packages on welfare rights (£3,500); and the Lorrimore Centre, for general redecoration and the purchasing of new chairs (£4,000). Southwark council is waiting to hear if its bid for funding from the DoH in 1992/93 has been successful.

Drugs and Alcohol Specific Grant: In 1991/92 Southwark received DoH funding and supported two drugs projects: CADA (Committee Against Drug Abuse) with a grant of £14,000 for a worker to set up an assessment project; and MAYA Project, a residential house, for childcare workers to help women with drug problems look after their children (£27,000). Southwark council is waiting to hear from the DoH of its bid for funding in 1992/93 has been successful.

Applications procedure: Southwark's conditions of grant-aid are fairly standard, detailing constitutional requirements and organisational practice. Grants are made on an annual basis and new groups seeking funding can apply at any time, using the standard application form available from the Community Services and Programming Unit. Grants to organisations already funded are considered for renewal prior to the start of the financial year. The availability of small, one-off grants is occasionally advertised locally.

Would-be applicants should note that Southwark's grants budget for 1991/92 was almost fully committed to organisations funded previously. However relevant organisations seeking support are encouraged to make applications so that their needs can be assessed against existing programmes and as an indication of need within the borough.

Other support: The council can offer discretionary rate relief, premises (market rents are charged but can be offset by applications for rent grants), training including fundraising strategies, management and supervision of staff and business development plans. The initial contact for these is the Community Services and Programming Unit.

Contracting and the Community Care Plan

In March 1992 Southwark launched pilot service agreements in all departments with a view to the majority of voluntary organisations being funded through Service Level Agreements (SLAs) by April 1994.

The service level agreements of the council-wide pilot schemes will be specific and detailed whilst social services was developing a variety of SLAs tailored to the voluntary organisation and service provided. Block/individual residential placements, and services for people with HIV/AIDS will be among the first to be funded through contracts.

In March 1992 Social Services was starting contracts with new service developments and hoped to use the experience to consider contracting service provision at a later stage. It was looking into joint commissioning with SELCA and the Family Health Services Authority. Joint commissioning for each client group was also being considered and it was believed that this could lead to a need for multi-sectoral purchasing and contracting arrangements.

Discussion with the voluntary sector about Southwark's Community Care Plan was achieved through Southwark Community Care Forum. Voluntary sector representatives for each of the Joint Community Care Planning Groups were appointed and public meetings held for users, carers and voluntary groups. Draft plans were circulated widely and comments invited.

For further information contact: Doug Adams, Purchasing and Contracts Development Manager, Social Services

Camberwell Joint Consultative Committee

Beneficial area: Camberwell, Lambeth, Southwark

Objects: To support projects which make a greater

contribution to total care in the framework of health or local authority services and which show evidence of joint planning.

Funding practices: Priorities arise out of the joint planning process, particularly in relation to the NHS and the Community Care Act.

100% funding for three years is available with tapering possibilities reviewed at the end of the second year. Details of the bidding process are widely circulated to known voluntary organisations, through umbrella organisations and the local press. All bids received are considered by the relevant Joint Care Planning Groups, that is the JCPG for elderly services, for physical disabilities, people with learning difficulties or for mental health.

Expenditure on voluntary organisations: £216,520 (1991/92)

Details of projects: Voluntary groups supported include: a carers' outreach scheme (£18,150); Southwark Disablement Association for an Advocacy Worker (£9,070) and Voluntary Sector Co-ordinator (£24,880); Crossroads Care Attendant Scheme (£43,130); and The Centre for Integrated Living (£29,880).

Applications procedure: Funding packs which include an application form, procedure bids and guidance on applications are available from the correspondent (see below). The funding process usually takes place between September and March. Advice and information on joint finance and related matters are available at any time. For further assistance contact Brian Stapleton, Planning and Strategy Manager, Southwark Social Services, Mabel Goldwyn House, 49 Grange Walk, London SE1 SDY (071-525 3791) or the correspondent below.

Correspondent: Joint Finance Administrator

Address: South East London Commissioning Agency, 15 St Thomas St, London SE1 (071-955 5000 ext 242)

Other information: The committee meets three to four times a year.

In April 1992 the future reorganisation of the JCC along borough boundaries was being considered.

Lewisham and North Southwark Joint Consultative Committee

Beneficial area: Lewisham and North Southwark

Objects: The money should make a greater contri-

bution to total care than if spent on local or health services alone. The scheme should show evidence of joint planning.

Funding practices: Priorities arise out of the joint planning process particularly in relation to the NHS and the Community Care Act.

Details of the bidding process are widely circulated to known voluntary groups through umbrella organisations and in the local press. All bids received are considered by the relevant Joint Care Planning Groups (JCPGs). One JCPG considers services for elderly people with physical disabilities, another considers people with learning difficulties.

Expenditure on voluntary organisations: £249,000 from a total allocation of £791,000 (31%) in 1991/92.

Details of projects: Voluntary organisations funded in 1991/92 include: Camberwell Citizen Advocacy Office, for an advocacy worker for people with learning difficulties (£16,950); Isis, a black mental health group, for a development worker (£20,490); Drugline, for a women and family worker (£15,820); and Crossroads, for a Saturday playscheme (£5,300).

Applications procedure: Funding packs which include an application form, procedure bids and guidance on applications are available from the correspondent (see below). The funding process usually takes place between September and March. Advice and information on joint finance and related matters are available at any time.

The committee meets three to four times per year.

Correspondent: Alyson Bunn, Joint Finance Administrator

Address: Lewisham & North Southwark Health Authority, Mary Sheridan House, 15 St Thomas's Street, London SE1 9RY (071-955 5000 ext 2425)

Other information: In early 1992 the London Boroughs of Lewisham and Southwark and the Lewisham and North Southwark Health Authority agreed that the Joint Consultative Committee should become borough-based as opposed to health-authority based. This means that Lewisham and North Southwark JCC will become two separate JCCs. Contact the correspondent for further information.

North Peckham Task Force

Beneficial area: Part of North Peckham, primarily the North Peckham and Gloucester Grove housing estates.

General: The Task Forces, of which there are four

in London, have been set up by the government in areas known to be seriously disadvantaged. The main objective is to create a thriving economy. The goals of this initiative are the provision of jobs for local people, the encouragement of local enterprise, the enhancement of the employability of local people, and the improvement of the local environment, especially through crime reduction and increased safety.

Much of the work of the Task Forces is concerned with improving the take-up and the effectiveness of existing government programmes, and in enhancing their co-ordination, but there are also numerous occasions in which the Task Force works through voluntary organisations and community groups in the area. Examples include: The Sojourner Trust Youth Association, a local black-led community group (at least £50,000 in 1991), Jobs in the City which helps local people find jobs (£161,000 in 1990/92), and the Vietnamese Employment Training and Enterprise Centre (£40,000 in 1988/91).

Grant total: Between £500,000 and £1,000,0000 a year

Correspondent: Steve Bowen, Task Force Leader

Address: 2nd Floor, 72 Rye Lane, London SE15 5DQ (tel: 071-358 9018, fax: 071-358 9770)

The Mabel Asprey Trust

Beneficial area: Parish of St Agnes, Kennington Park

Objects: Relief of need

Type of beneficiary: Individuals

Income: £140 (1975)

Grant total: Not known

Grant details: Usually one-off. No grants for payment of rates, taxes etc.

Applications procedure: To the correspondent

Correspondent: C P Woolley, Secretary

Address: 195 Cornisborough Crescent, London SE6 2SF (081-698 4437)

Camberwell Consolidated Charities

Beneficial area: Camberwell, Peckham and Dulwich

Objects: Pensions for the aged poor

Type of beneficiary: Individuals

Grant total: £13,000 (1988)

Grant details: About 430 pensions of £5 are paid every two months.

Applications procedure: Vacancies are advertised by social services area offices, Age Concern etc; application forms can also be picked up from the Town Hall. Trustees meet usually in July and December to consider new pensions.

Correspondent: Ms Lesley John, The Clerk to the Trustees

Address: Town Hall, Peckham Road, London SE5 8UB (071-525 5000)

The Camberwell and Dulwich Benevolent Society

Beneficial area: Former Parish of Camberwell

Objects: Relief of need of people over 60 years old

Type of beneficiary: Organisations and individuals

Income: £600 (1987)

Grants: £360

Grant details: Monthly pensions of £6 are given.

Applications procedure: To the correspondent

Correspondent: L R Clayton

Address: 2 Clayhill Cottages, Lamberhurst, Kent TN3 8AY (0892 890247)

Other information: This trust is now being administered by the Peckham and Kent Road Pension Society (see entry).

Camberwell Provident Dispensary Fund

Beneficial area: Two mile radius of the church of St Giles, Camberwell

Objects: Relief of sickness

Type of beneficiary: Individuals

Income: £600 (1990)

Grant total: £600

Grant details: 30-40 one-off grants are made to sick poor people for help towards holiday expenses, food, clothing, fuel and medical expenses. Funds cannot be paid for the relief of rates or taxes.

Correspondent: Rev Andrew Davey

Address: St Luke's Vicarage, 123 Farnborough Way, London SE15 6HL (071-703 5587)

Other information: Rev Andrew Davey is administering another trust in the area, the St Luke's and Camden Schools' Trust, but it was not operational in early 1992.

The Christchurch Church of England Educational Foundation

Beneficial area: In the following order of priority: Parish of Christchurch, Southwark; former Borough of Southwark; present London Borough of Southwark

Objects: Promotion of education

Type of beneficiary: Individuals

Grant total: £3,000 (1990)

Grant details: Cash grants promoting education 'in accordance with the principles of the Church of England'. No age limit applies. Applications from organisations may also be considered.

Applications procedure: Direct to the correspondent. Applications are considered in May and November.

Correspondent: Canon P B Challen

Address: Christchurch Industrial Centre, 27 Blackfriars Road, London SE1 8NY (071-928 4707)

Other information: Figures above also refer to the Emily Temple West Trust (*see separate entry*)

Christ Church United Charities,

incorporating Edward Edward's Charity and Vaughan's Pension Charity; also St Mary Newington United Charities, St George the Martyr Charities, Walworth United Charities

Beneficial area: The former Metropolitan Borough of Southwark (in general, the northern part of the present London Borough of Southwark)

Objects: Welfare of elderly people who have lived in the beneficial area for at least five years

Type of beneficiary: Individuals and organisations

Grant total: About £41,370 (1989)

Grant details: Most of the charity's income is used to maintain its almshouses but it also provides pensions for the elderly (£25,000), Christmas parties (£3,500) and gifts (£2,700) and makes grants to other organisations helping the elderly in this area. (two grants of £5,000).

Applications procedure: To the correspondent.

Correspondent: W F Plowright, Clerk to the trustees

Address: The Charity Office, Municipal Offices, 151/3 Walworth Road, London SE17 1RY (071-703 5464)

Other information: This entry was not confirmed by the trust.

Newcomen Collett Educational Foundation

Beneficial area: The London Borough of Southwark but preference is given to applicants from the Parish of St Saviours.

Objects: To help school pupils with books, equipment, clothing or travel. To help with school, college or university fees or to supplement existing grants.

Help towards the cost of education, training, apprenticeship or equipment for those starting work.

To help educational groups such as playgroups and toy libraries.

Type of beneficiary: Individuals under the age of 25 and educational groups.

Grant total: c£120,000 per annum

Grant details: Grants are one-off and range from £25 to £1,000 but are usually below £500.

Applications procedure: In writing to the correspondent stating how long the applicant has been resident in Southwark. Every application must be accompanied by a supporting statement from the school head or tutor or other suitably qualified instructor or supervisor. The statement need not exceed 50 words and should give an opinion of the suitability of the applicant for the object of the application. Applications are considered in March, June, September and December.

Correspondent: Edward B Van Loock

Address: Marshall House, 66 Newcomen Street, London Bridge, London SE1 1YT (071-407 2967)

Other information: This trust is the result of the amalgamation of the John Collett's and the Newcomen's Educational Foundation.

Joseph Collier Holiday Fund

Beneficial area: The former Metropolitan Borough of Southwark (generally, the northern part of the present London Borough of Southwark)

Objects: Recuperative holidays for the needy aged who are 60 or over

Type of beneficiary: Individuals

Income: £6,890 (1989)

Grant total: £1,360

Grant details: Cash grants as a contribution to holiday costs. No further information available.

Applications procedure: To the correspondent, Mondays and Thursdays, 10.00 to 2.00.

Correspondent: Mrs J Crossman

Address: Charities Section, Municipal Offices, 151/153 Walworth Road, SE17 1RW (071-703 5464)

Other information: The charity formerly owned a holiday home in Bognor Regis. This was sold for £60,000 and the money invested in a capital fund. The interest on this fund is now used to contribute to the holiday costs of eligible beneficiaries and any excess of income over expenditure is reinvested. This entry was not confirmed by the trust.

The Mayor of Southwark's Common Good Trust

Beneficial area: London Borough of Southwark

Objects: General charitable purposes for the benefit of Southwark residents at the discretion of the mayor

Type of beneficiary: Organisations and individuals

Income: The trust has a permanent fund invested from which it received an income of £8,230 in 1989. In addition, it fundraises actively, raising a further £11,910.

Grant total: £17,540 (1989)

Grant details: Individuals with disabilities are supported with grants for specific items such as electric wheelchairs, and speaking computers for blind people. Smaller donations are given to individuals in situations of emergency hardship, such as elderly people faced with sudden large heating bills or single parent families needing children's clothing. Donations are also made to charity appeals for specific items.

Applications procedure: Applicants can either write directly to the Mayor or via a welfare agency or social worker. Applications can be made at any time of the year and are normally dealt with within one month.

Correspondent: The Mayor

Address: London Borough of Southwark, Mayor's Office, Southwark Town Hall, Peckham Road, London SE5 8UB (071-525 5000 ext 27303)

Other information: This entry was not confirmed.

The Mary Minet Trust

Beneficial area: London Boroughs of Southwark and Lambeth

Main grant areas: Relief of the poor, sick, disabled, handicapped and infirm

Type of beneficiary: Individuals

Income: £13,560 (1991)

Grant total: £10,060

Grant details: Grants in the range of £35 to £600 for such items as telephones, orthopaedic aids, furniture, and nursing costs and convalescent holidays. The trust cannot provide assistance for debts of any kind.

Applications procedure: Via social services, CAB, hospitals, GPs. The trustees meet quarterly.

Correspondent: The Honorary Secretary

Address: 54/56 Knatchbull Road, London SE5 9QY (071-274 2266)

The Peter Minet Trust

Beneficial area: Local charities in Camberwell, Lambeth and Southwark have priority. Occasionally national charities are supported.

Objects: Support of charities with social welfare objectives

Type of beneficiary: Organisations

Grant total: £137,730 (1991)

Grant details: Grants are made only to registered charities, both to national charities and charities local to the London Boroughs of Lambeth and Southwark. Grants are one-off and range from £50 to a maximum of £10,000.

Applications procedure: In writing to the correspondent, including audited accounts. Meetings are usually held in January, April, July and October.

Correspondent: The Honorary Secretary

Address: 54/56 Knatchbull Road, London SE5 9QY (071-274 2266)

The Peckham and Kent Road Pension Society

Beneficial area: Peckham, SE15

Objects: Provision of pensions to residents of at least 5 years who are receiving Supplementary Benefit and are over 60 (women) or 65 (men)

Type of beneficiary: Individuals

Latest figures: 1987

Income: £7,000

Grant total: £6,050

Grant details: Monthly pensions of £6. The correspondent states that the trust's resources are already stretched by its pension commitments.

Applications procedure: To correspondent via social services, GP etc. A recommendation from an existing grantee is helpful.

Correspondent: L R Clayton

Address: 2 Clayhill Cottages, Lamberhurst, Kent TN3 8AY (0892 890247)

Other information: This trust is administered in conjunction with the Camberwell and Dulwich Benevolent Society (see previous entry).

Rotherhithe Consolidated Charities

Beneficial area: Ancient Parish of St Mary's, Rotherhithe

Objects: Payment of pensions and relief of poverty, especially among elderly people

Type of beneficiary: Individuals

Income: £195,570 (1988/89)

Grant total: £24,510 (1988/89)

Grant details: The trust pays monthly pensions of £7 to about 400 pensioners, and gives food vouchers at Christmas time. Donations are sometimes given to organisations and recent beneficiaries include Age Concern, a League of Friends and a minibus project.

Applications procedure: Direct to the correspondent, giving details of age and circumstances

Correspondent: B Claxton

Address: Hardcastle Burton, Amwell House, 19 Amwell Street, Hoddesdon, Herts., EN11 8TS (0992 444466)

Other information: In 1988 the charity sold one of its properties, Millstream House, and £1,258,710 was invested from the proceeds. This sum now generates around £160,000 per annum and explains why the trust's income has more than doubled from £70,290 in 1987 to £195,570 in 1989. Due to this increased income the trustees are proposing to institute a scheme for providing holidays for its pensioners which will probably cost about £60,000 per annum. In November 1991 they were consulting the Charity Commission with a view to broadening the scope of their grant-making.

At the moment the trust is underspending its income and reinvesting the surplus.

Rebecca Flower Squire's Bequest, The Flintoff Charity, and others administered from the church of St Mary Newington, Southwark

Beneficial area: Ancient Parish of St Mary Newington

Objects: Relief of sickness

Type of beneficiary: Individuals

Income: About £2,000 (1991)

Grant total: £2,000

Grant details: One-off cash grants to a maximum of £150 are made.

Applications procedure: To the correspondent. The trustees meet in the Spring and Autumn.

Correspondent: The Rector

Address: 57 Kennington Park Road, London SE11 4JQ (071-735 1894)

St Olave's United Charity, incorporating the St Thomas and St John charities

Beneficial area: Bermondsey and Rotherhithe i.e. SE1 and SE16

Main grant areas: Relief of need; support of local charitable organisations; provision of pensions

Type of beneficiary: Individuals and organisations

Income total: £272,312 (1989)

Grant total: £58,370

Grant details: Grants are made to local groups and charities, including schools, churches, clubs and welfare organisations (e.g. care for the elderly).

Grants to individuals are in the form of pensions or one-off gifts. 650 elderly people are currently receiving pensions, and a further grant is made before Christmas. One-off grants for individuals and families can be made for a wide variety of need, including education, clothes, musical instruments and holidays.

Applications procedure: Pension applications are dealt with four times a year; a waiting list is in operation. Educational grants should be made through a school or other organisation. Applications should be in writing outlining need; applications from organisations should give full details, including income and expenditure.

Correspondent: Mrs S Broughton, Secretary

Address: 6/8 Druid Street, Tooley Street, London SE1 2EU (071-407 2530)

Other information: The trust's income fluctuated a few years ago when the former clerk and three of his associates defrauded it of an estimated £700,000 when selling off some of its property. Now the trustees are reinvesting a sizeable part of the charity's income each year, £182,660 in 1989. This entry was not confirmed by the trust.

The Emily West Temple Trust

Beneficial area: In the following order of priority: Parish of Christchurch, Southwark; former Borough of Southwark; present London Borough of Southwark

Objects: Relief of poor persons under the age of 25 in need of a change of air, convalescence or other assistance.

Type of beneficiary: Individuals

Income: £2,500 (1988, see below)

Grant total: £2,500

Grant details: One-off grants for individuals. Applications from organisations may be considered.

Correspondent: Canon P B Challen

Address: Christchurch Industrial Centre, 27 Blackfriars Road, SE1 8NY (071-928 4707)

Other information: Figures above refer also to the Christchurch Church of England Educational Foundation (see separate entry)

Major Local Companies

IPC Magazines Ltd, Kings Reach Tower, Stamford Street, London SE1 9LS (071-261 5000) supports local charities. The chairman decides on donations.

Matthew Hall Mechanical & Electrical Engineers Ltd, 7-14 Great Dover Street, London SE1 4YR (071-407 7272) gives preference to charities in Southwark. The Charities Committee decides donations on merit. Contact Mr Bowyer, Company Secretary.

Price Waterhouse & Co (Chartered Accountants), Southwark Towers, 32 London Bridge Street, London SE1 9SY (071-939 3000). Contact Reginald Thorne.

Express Newspapers plc, Ludgate House, 245 Blackfriars Road, London SE1 9UX (071-928 8000) mainly donates to national charities but does support local organisations as well. Contact David Tough, Chief Accountant.

Sources of Advice

Southwark Community Care Forum, Pitt Street Settlement, 191 East Surrey Grove, Off Commercial Way, London SE15 (071-252 5776).

Contact: Tamara Essex.

Southwark Arts Forum, 31 Morecambe Street, London SE17 1DX (071-701 9323). Contact Ro Shannon, Treasurer.

Southwark Institute of Adult Education, Queen's Road Centre, St Mary's Road, London SE15 2EA (071-639 1178)

Southwark Youth Office, Sumner House, Sumner Road, Peckham, London SE15 5QF (071-701 8559)

Southwark Education and Training Shop, 175 Rye Lane, London SE15 4TL (071-635 9111)

Sutton

London Borough of Sutton

Civic Offices, St Nicholas Way, Sutton, Surrey
SM1 1EA. (081-770 5000)

Correspondents:

Social Services Department: Stephanie Barnes,
Administrative Officer,

Education Department: Malcolm Brown, Head
of Resources,

Leisure Services Committee: John Fisher, Chief
Administration Officer, (081-770 4600)

Grant total 1991/92: £481,222 main programme
funding

Funding: Sutton does not have a central grants
programme. Some of its support for local voluntary
organisations is practical (see under 'other support'). However, it does make some direct grants
through three committees on a regular basis; in
1991/92 this can be broken down as follows:

Housing and Social Services	£434,902
Education	£11,320
Leisure	£35,000
TOTAL	£481,222

Housing and Social Services: Nearly all of Sutton
Council's grants are given through the Housing and
Social Services Department. This supports a wide
range of welfare agencies, including organisations
for the elderly, children, physically disabled, mentally ill, mentally handicapped, physically disabled
and drug abusers. In 1991/92 funded projects include Sutton Bereavement Service (£25,000), Sutton
Homestart, for families with under fives (£40,000),
Voluntary Fitters, providing back-up services for
carers, (£27,000) and St Raphael's Hospice (£7,000).
Grants in 1991/92 can be broken down into the
following categories:

Welfare of blind people	£780
Welfare of deaf people	£600
Welfare of people with disabilities	£30,440
Day centres	£34,890
Welfare of the elderly	£48,114
Care of mothers and young children	£12,260
Mental health	£4,250
Prevention care and after-care	£3,300
Marriage guidance	£10,940
Other welfare services	£109,373
Sutton Council for Voluntary Service	£179,955
TOTAL	£434,902

The Children Act 1989: In March 1992 Sutton had
not changed its criteria for grant-making but it was
determined to find additional funding for children's
organisations from its own resources.

Education: This committee supports a wide variety of educational projects in the borough. In 1991/
92 it gave grants to about 20 organisations including the Christian Education Movement, the Com-
monwealth Youth Exchange Council, Sutton Council for School Sports, Sutton and District Schools
Music Association, the English Folkdance and Song
Society and Sutton Mencap. Grants ranged in size
from £50 to £2,000 – the largest went to Sutton
School of Gymnastics for £2,000. Most of these
grants are made on a regular basis; however, new
applications can be considered.

Leisure Services: The Leisure Services Department funds organisations which provide leisure
facilities, including arts groups, sports and recreational projects. Grants are available for equipment
as is the subsidised use of council facilities. A
public hall or park can be used for events free of
charge, as the hire fee will be refunded. This fund is
advertised and applications invited all year round
(see under 'Applications procedure'). Applications
for facilities costing less than £250 can, however,
be dealt with at the discretion of the Director of
Leisure Services without being referred to committee.

Although recreational projects were funded to a
total of £35,000 in 1991/92, some were standard
grants given out every year.

Mental Illness Specific Grant: In 1991/92 Sutton
received a central government grant of £74,471 of
which £34,551 was used to fund voluntary
organisations.

Drugs and Alcohol Specific Grant: No bid for funding was made by Sutton in 1991/92.

Applications Procedure: Housing and Social Services Department grants are dealt with annually. The normal deadline for submission of completed application forms falls in September.

There are application forms for grants made by the Education Department. Applications for assistance should normally be submitted by 1 December, as most grants are made early in the financial year. However, urgent requests can be considered at other times.

Applications for Leisure Services grants below and above £250 are invited all year round. Application forms are available from Peter Smithson, Director of Leisure Services, The Old Court House, Throwley Way, Sutton, Surrey SM1 4AF.

Other support: Sutton provides considerable 'hidden' support in kind for local voluntary groups. This can include payment of ground-rent, building and transport maintenance, free access to council vehicles and/or drivers and cheap or free hire of council-owned premises. For example, Social Services and Youth Services have community buses and ambulances for the use of local youth groups and for charities working with the disabled; these can be driven by volunteers or paid workers. In the first instance charities should approach Ian Green, Transport Manager, for further information.

Contracting and the Community Care Plan
In 1992 Sutton Social Services funded voluntary organisations through grants and no contracts were planned for 1992/93. However, consideration was given to the question of contracts for care in future years. Members wish to see 'priorities identified against which difficulties can be judged'.

Sutton Council for Voluntary Service, MIND and a local branch of Carers' National Association were amongst the voluntary groups contributing to Sutton's Community Care Plan.

For further information contact: Paul Chapman, Head of Planning and Review

Merton and Sutton Joint Consultative Committee

Beneficial area: London Boroughs of Merton and Sutton

Funding practices: Many projects are sponsored by the health authority or/and the local authorities. Funding pump-primes new schemes which cater to both health and social care needs of the local population. It is tapered, usually over seven years, after which a sponsoring authority must intend to fund the project from its main allocation.

Total expenditure: £827,000 (1990/91)

Joint finance budget: £931,000 for 1991/92 (please note that the programme is fully committed until 1995/96).

Details of projects: Over 50 different organisations were funded in 1990/91, including MIND (£12,500), MENCAP (£17,000) and Crossroads (£26,400).

Applications procedure: For up-to-date guidance for voluntary organisations contact the Director of Social Services at the London Borough of Merton (081-543 2222) or the Director of Social Services at the London Borough of Sutton (081-770 5000) or the health authority contact given below.

Correspondent: Ms Laura Cummings, Planning Manager

Address: Merton and Sutton Health Authority, Wilson Hospital, Mitcham, Surrey CR4 4TP (081-648 3021)

Other information: The committee meets three times a year but joint finance bids are considered once a year.

Beddington and Wallington Relief Fund For the Sick and Infirm

Beneficial area: Beddington and Wallington

Objects: Benefit of sick and infirm people

Type of beneficiary: Individuals

Income: £866 (1988)

Grant total: £866

Grant details: Grants are made for services or towards the cost of essential items or equipment (no cash grants are given and receipts are needed as proof of purchase). Maximum value of grants has been increased to £30. Christmas parcels are distributed.

Applications procedure: In writing and only on referral from social services or welfare agencies such as Age Concern, WRVS etc.

Correspondent: Miss M Mansfield

Address: 51 Fairlawnes, Maldon Road, Wallington, Surrey SM6 8BG (081-647 9551)

Carshalton Aid in Sickness Fund

Beneficial area: Former urban district of Carshalton

Objects: Relief of sickness, disability, handicap and infirmity

Type of beneficiary: Individuals and organisations

Income: £2,640 (1990)

Grant total: £1,720

Grant details: Grants were made both to individuals and organisations (probably for further distribution) which included a local old people's welfare committee, the Sutton Association for the Blind and the Chest and Heart Association etc.

Applications procedure: To the correspondent.

Correspondent: Mrs Hilda Harding, Clerk and Trustee

Address: 26 Fairlawnes, Maldon Road, Wallington, Surrey SM6 8BG (081-647 7154)

Carshalton (Educational) Charities

Beneficial area: Parish of Carshalton

Objects: Help towards the cost of education, training, apprenticeship or equipment for people under 25 years living in the beneficial area.

Type of beneficiary: individuals

Grant total: £700 (1990/91)

Grant details: Grants between £50 and £70 are made towards payment of fees, travelling or maintenance expenses, outfits, equipment etc

Applications procedure: By letter to the correspondent.

Correspondent: W Barton, Borough Solicitor

Address: Civic Offices, St Nicholas Way, Sutton, Surrey SM1 1EA (081-770 5207)

Other information: Another trust, the Carshalton Charities for the relief of poverty in the Parish of Carshalton, is also administered. In 1988 it has an income of £250 and made 20 grants of about £10.

Collett Trust Fund

Beneficial area: Mainly in the Sutton area

Type of Beneficiary: Individuals and occasionally charitable organisations

Income: £1,500 (1990)

Grant total: £1,200

Grant details: The trust is associated with Sutton Baptist Church and in 1990 ten grants totalling £900 were made to individuals and organisations involved with it and £50 was given to a person unconnected with the church. In addition three grants totalling £250 were made for the furtherance of education and religion.

Applications procedure: Individuals unconnected with the church have been supported in the past, but the trust's limited resources mean that only a few cases can be considered each year. Applications in writing; trustees usually meet in May and October.

Correspondent: D Arkinstall

Address: 18 Highfield Road, Sutton, Surrey SM1 4JX (081-642 9376)

The Sutton Community Chest Fund

Beneficial area: London Borough of Sutton

Objects: Relief of individual hardship

Type of beneficiary: Individuals

Income: About £450 in 1991 (but variable, relying on fundraising)

Grant total: About £540

Grant details: Donations range in size from £5 to £100. Typical grants are to help with the purchase of items of clothing or material for home decoration. Very occasionally, help can be given with tuition fees.

Applications procedure: In writing to the correspondent.

Correspondent: Barry Green, Mayor's Secretary

Address: London Borough of Sutton, Civic Offices, St Nicholas Way, Sutton, Surrey SM1 1EA (081-770 5000)

Sutton Local Lotteries Fund

Beneficial area: London Borough of Sutton

Objects: General charitable purposes of a social, recreational, environmental or cultural nature.

Type of beneficiary: Voluntary organisations with the widest community benefits; preference being given to:

Local charities

Local branches of national charities

Organisations which have received a substantial input from the aforementioned groups.

Income: About £40,000 per annum (plus interest earned on existing balances)

Grant total: £22,000 (1990/91)

Grant details: Grant-aid will be considered for one-off projects and the purchase of equipment. There is no limit on the size of grant made.

Applications procedure: Application forms are available from the correspondent. All applications are considered by an Awards Panel and its recommendations are then forwarded to the council's Resources Sub-Committee for final ratification. These committees meet five times a year.

Correspondent: Director of Leisure Services

Address: London Borough of Sutton, Old Court House, Throwley Way, Sutton, Surrey SM1 4AF (081-770 4658)

Major Local Companies

Unigate Ltd (distribution), 2 Vale Road, Sutton, Surrey SM1 1RF (081-642 7661) donates crates of milk to local fetes, bazaars etc. Contact Eddie Farquharson, Dairy Manager.

M J Gleeson Group plc, London Road, North Cheam, Sutton, Surrey SM3 9BS (081-644 4321) supports a variety of local and national appeals. Preferred areas of support are children, youth, social welfare and medical work. Contact C W McLellan, Financial Director.

Securicor Group plc, 13 Carshalton Road, Sutton, Surrey SM1 4LD (081-770 7000) supports specific charitable projects rather than large general appeals. Children, youth, social welfare and medical work are preferred areas of support. Contact the Secretary to the Securicor Charitable Trust.

Sources of Advice

Sutton Council for Voluntary Service, 31 West Street, Sutton, Surrey SM1 1SJ (081-643 3277)

Director: Anne Burleigh
Opening hours: 10.00-4.00

Sutton Arts Council, 5 St John's Road, Sutton, Surrey SM1 3JA (081-641 2487). Contact Miss Mary Cryer, Secretary.

Sutton College of Liberal Arts (adult education), St Nicholas Way, Sutton SM1 1EA (081-770 6901)

Tower Hamlets

London Borough of Tower Hamlets

The Town Hall, Patriot Square, London E2 9LN (081-980 4831

Correspondents:

Policy and Strategy Committee: Alison Dickens, (081-980 4831 ext 5362)

Education Strategy Committee: David Stone, (071-739 4344 ext 3251)

Social Services Strategy Committee: Voluntary Liaison Officer (to be appointed), (081-980 6311)

External Funding Unit: Francine Miller, Head of External Funding, (borough-wide Urban Programme projects), (081-980 4831 ext 5363)

Bethnal Green Neighbourhood Centre, 22/28 Underwood Road, London E1 5AW (071-377 0872): Jill Crumpton, Economic Development Unit

Bow Neighbourhood Centre, Gladstone Place, off Roman Road, London E3 (081-980 1812 ext 5523): Martin Mason, Community Education Manager

Globe Town Neighbourhood Centre, 62 Roman Road E2 0PG (081-980 8067): Kevin Nolan, Community Development Officer

Isle of Dogs Neighbourhood Centre, Jack Dash House, 2 Lawn House Close, London E14 9WQ (071-555 0533): Judith St John

Poplar NC, Southern Grove, E3 4PN (081-980 7200): Sandra Jennings, Grants Officer

Stepney NC, Cheviot House, 227 Commercial Road E1 2VU (081-790 1818): Jim Staunton, Neighbourhood Chief Executive

Wapping NC, Limehouse Town Hall, 646 Commercial Road E14 7HA (071-987 9200): Brian Oakaby (mainstream grants), Kevin Constable (Urban Programme)

Grant totals 1991/92:

£2,160,418 in main programme funding;

£1,153,000 in Urban Aid;

£405,510 in Joint Funding;

Funding practice: Tower Hamlets is unusual in that much of its grant-making to voluntary organisations has been decentralised and is now carried out by its seven neighbourhood committees. These make grants to groups wholly or substantially serving their neighbourhood, while three central committees Education Strategy, Social Services Strategy and Policy Strategy make grants to organisations providing services on a borough-wide basis. Grants are awarded annually by all committees though some are considering three year service level agreements with certain organisations.

The Children Act 1989: In view of this new legislation Tower Hamlets prioritised grant-making to organisations working with young children from 1992/94.

Urban Programme: Under the council's decentralised structures, initial consideration of applications and the implementation and monitoring of most approved Urban Programme projects is the responsibility of the six Neighbourhoods within the Urban Programme part of the borough (ie Bethnal, Green, Bow, Globe Town, Poplar, Stepney and Wapping). The Education Department administers education related projects. The External Funding Unit, part of the corporate centre, is responsible for the overall coordination and administration of the Programme. The Unit issues all annual application forms.

Projects operating borough-wide should apply to the Neighbourhood in which they are/will be based. Projects which are not yet based in the borough should sent their completed forms to the External Funding Unit (Room 114, the Town Hall, Patriot Square E2).

City Challenge: In 1992 the government agreed to implement the City Challenge Action Plan submitted by the London Borough of Tower Hamlets for parts of Bethnal Green Neighbourhood (mainly the Spitalfields area), and to provide £37.5 million over five years (£7.5 million p.a.).

A company in which Tower Hamlets Council will have a minority interest, is being set up to administer and monitor the implementation of the Action Plan. Any project ideas should be referred to the (Acting) Chief Executive of the Company, which is based at 91 Brick Lane, E1 (071-247 3748).

Mental Illness Specific Grant: In 1991/92 Tower Hamlets received £170,000 from the Department of Health and funded the Working Well Trust (an employment initiative for people with long-term mental illness) and Tower Hamlets Consortium Limited in which the Mental Health Care Association and Victoria Park Housing Association are collaborating (running a post-discharge house for adult mentally ill people).

Drugs and Alcohol Specific Grant: Tower Hamlets received £103,000 from the DoH and funded B Sharp (a voluntary alcohol project) for work with women and people from black and ethnic minority communities, NACKO, a project providing supported housing for recovering drug users and the Association for Prevention of Addiction for its Community Drugs Team.

All funding from these specific grants went to voluntary sector projects except for one specialist advisor on dementia, working with homecare staff, carers and community groups, based within the Social Services Department. For further information contact Lady Kina Avebury (081-980 6311).

Applications procedure: Mainstream grants are considered once a year. Application forms are available from the appropriate neighbourhood/departmental contact in November; the deadline for submission normally falls in January.

Other support: Tower Hamlets sometimes allows local voluntary groups to use its premises on a low-rent basis. It can also give advice and information and is currently funding a programme of training courses for the voluntary sector via the Urban Programme.

Contracting and the Community Care Plan

In 1992 Tower Hamlets Social Services mainly funded voluntary organisations through grants but was introducing contracts/service agreements for large voluntary agencies. These contracts were reasonably specific about services required and usually lasted for three years.

In 1992/93 Social Services expects to enter into contracts with voluntary organisations for mental health services, (MIND in Tower Hamlets, £259,000), provision for respite care and learning difficulties (Barnardos) and facilities for people with disabilities (Crossroads £175,000).

All local voluntary groups, major national organisations and users were involved in consultation meetings and an open day concerning Tower Hamlets' Community Care Plan.

For further information contact: Ann Symes, Coordinator of Care in the Community, Social Services Strategy Group (081-980 6311)

Tower Hamlets Joint Consultative Committee

Beneficial area: London Borough of Tower Hamlets

Objects: The Joint Consultative Committee (JCC) supports schemes which provide care for people in the community and which contribute more in terms of total care for the individual than if applied directly to health services. Groups supported include those with learning difficulties, the mentally ill, the elderly, children and primary care services.

Funding practices: Projects are funded as part of a three-year programme and each October the JCC considers bids for the next joint finance programme. For each new project a lead agency is appointed which undertakes the responsibility to evaluate the project with a view to continuing its funding beyond the period of joint finance support if the project is seen to give value for money.

Expenditure on voluntary organisations: £410,510 (1991/92) out of total of £725,900

Details of projects: In 1991/92 support was given to the following voluntary groups: NEWPIN, new parent infant network, (£35,700); Families Together, (£42,000); Youth Counselling Service (£16,200); Infant Feeding Project (£18,500) Informal (£20,000), a black and ethnic community alcohol abuse project; Elderly Family Placement scheme (£34,870); Magic Me, school children visit and share stories with old people in homes (£11,000); What-it-means-to-us, parents support group for children with disabilities (£2,000); Speakeasy, speech therapy for under fives (£23,000); Somali Youth Counsellor (£10,000); MACA, (Mental Aftercare Association) respite for carers of mentally ill (£44,000); Linkage (£14,600); Age Concern Respite Care (£50,000); St Hilda's Bengali Elders Day Centre, (£26,900); Refugees from Vietnam: Elders' Project (£16,740) Welfare Rights (£20,000).

Applications procedure: Applications should be sent to the correspondent in mid-September who then forwards them to the relevant Joint Development Group. All bids are considered by the JCC's October meeting.

Correspondent: Pamela Siann, Joint Planning Administrator

Address: Tower Hamlets District Health Authority, Tredegar House, 97-99 Bow Road, London E3 2AN (071-377 7934)

Other information: The JCC is made up of members of the health and local authorities, the Royal London Trust and associated community services, the City and East London Family Practitioner Committee, and, representing the voluntary sector, Age Concern, MENCAP and Maternity Services Liaison Scheme. The committee meets on a Monday afternoon in January, March, May, July, October and November at various sites in Tower Hamlets.

The Aldgate Lordship Foundation

Beneficial area: Former Parish of St Botolph Aldgate and elsewhere

Objects: General benefit of the poor

Type of beneficiary: Individuals

Income: £1,900 (1980)

Grant total: £1,300

Grant details: Pensions and payments for nursing and sick relief

Applications procedure: To the correspondent

Correspondent: Peter Davies

Address: 27 Dangan Road, Wanstead, E11 2RF (081-989 5946)

Other information: This entry was not confirmed by the trust.

The Aldgate and Allhallows Barking Exhibition Foundation

Beneficial area: City of London and the London Borough of Tower Hamlets

Objects: Grants for those in further and higher education.

Type of beneficiary: Individuals

Income: £155,000 (1990)

Grant total: £105,000

Grant details: The applicant's parents must live or work in the beneficial area. The applicant must be under 25 years old. No further information available.

Applications procedure: To the correspondent. Preliminary enquiries welcome.

Correspondent: M Sparks, Clerk to the Governors

Address: 31 Jewry Street, London EC3N 2EY (071-480 5884)

Other information: See entry for Sir John Cass's Foundation

Samuel Butler's Educational Foundation

Beneficial area: Specific parishes in the London Borough of Tower Hamlets (Spitalfields, Limehouse, Stepney, Shoreditch, Whitechapel, Christchurch, Bethnal Green, Covent Garden, Ratcliffe, London Docks, Sandwich in the County of Kent, and Wapping) Please check parishes in question with the clerk.

Objects: Educational grants for young residents under the age of 25

Type of beneficiary: Organisations and individuals

Income: £10,250 (1990/91)

Grant total: £5,960

Grant details: Whilst the trust makes a few individual grants for school pupils to help with books, equipment, clothing or travel, the bulk of its income is given to educational establishments with donations ranging from £100 to £1,000.

Applications procedure: To the correspondent

Correspondent: Michael Sparks, Clerk

Address: 31 Jewry Street, London EC3N 2EY (071-480 5884)

Other information: The trust only used to make grants to individuals but decided to support educational establishments as well. 'Collective enterprises by schools and other organisations have proved the best way of allocating funds. It enables the assessment of needs to be made by those that provide the services.

See also the entry for Sir John Cass's Foundation

Samuel Montagu Charitable Trust

See section for the Corporation of the City of London

The William Davis Trust

Beneficial area: London Boroughs of Tower Hamlets and Hackney

Objects: Educational grants for those living, working or studying in the beneficial area

Type of beneficiary: Individuals

Latest figures: 1990

Grant total: £12,000

Grant details: Cash grants, to a usual maximum of £250, were made to help with school, college or university fees, or for books, equipment or field trips etc. which will be of educational benefit to the applicant.

Applications procedure: To the correspondent

Correspondent: Mrs Jean Walker, The Deputy Director, the London Diocesan Board for Schools

Address: 30 Causton Street, London SW1P 4AU (071-821 9311)

East London Nursing Society Trust

Beneficial area: Tower Hamlets

Objects: Welfare of the sick poor

Type of beneficiary: Organisations

Income: £9,900 (1990/91)

Grant total: £10,910

Grant details: Grants usually ranging between £200-£500 are made to welfare organisations such as special schools either towards their own work in the relief of sickness and poverty or for direct distribution to needy individuals or groups. Grants can only be made where funding is not readily available from statutory sources. Many grants have been given to alleviate poverty and sickness among the Bangladeshi and other deprived communities.

Application procedure: From organisations, social workers or vicars, in writing to the correspondent. The trustees meet three times a year, but emergencies can be dealt with as they arise.

Correspondent: D M Collins, Honorary Secretary

Address: 92 Crown Woods Way, Eltham, London SE9 2NN

Help-in-Need Association

Beneficial area: Tower Hamlets Health District

Objects: Relief of sickness

Type of beneficiary: Organisations

Grant total: £9,000 (1988)

Grant details: The association usually gives money to organisations involved with the relief of sickness for specific equipment or certain projects, which have included holidays and parties. Grants are one-off and usually for about £500, although amounts up to £2,000 are sometimes given.

Applications procedure: In writing to the correspondent. Processing of applications takes 2-3 months.

Correspondent: See below

Address: See below

Other information: The last known correspondent for the trust was C L Scholtz at the Department of Anatomy, The London Hospital, London E1 1BB. Attempts to contact him were unsuccessful. Further information would be welcomed.

The Henderson Charity

Beneficial area: Hamlets of Ratcliff and Shadwell, and the Parish of St George's-in-the-East Stepney

Objects: Provision of pensions

Type of beneficiary: Individuals

Grant total: About £10,000 (1991)

Grant details: Pensions of £15 per month for single people and £20 per month for married couples are given. Pensioners must be long-standing residents of the beneficial area, and there is a maximum income requirement.

Applications procedure: Vacancies are advertised locally and through social services and appropriate welfare agencies. Application forms when an election is due can be obtained from social services or the correspondent.

Correspondent: Charles Westover

Address: Taylor Joynson Garrett Solicitors, 10 Maltravers Street, London WC2R 3BS

Trevor Huddleston Fund for Children

Beneficial area: Isle of Dogs

Objects: Relief of poverty among children and where necessary by helping their parents and families

Grant total: About £5,000 in 1989

Grant details: The trust makes about 100 grants a

year between £10 and £150 to cover clothing, holidays and school outings, fuel debts, Christmas gifts, funeral expenses, rent arrears, special projects.

Applications procedure: Mostly through schools, social services and churches, but individuals may also apply directly.

Correspondent: Rev Nicholas Holtman

Address: Christ Church Vicarage, Manchester Road, London E14 9BN (071-987 1915)

Other information: This entry was not confirmed by the trust.

Isle of Dogs Community Trust

Beneficial area: Isle of Dogs Neighbourhood

Objects: To benefit local people through the promotion of social, recreational, educational and training opportunities

Type of beneficiary: Organisations and projects

Income: Not available

Grant total: about £52,000 (1991/92)

Grant details: There are three grant schemes:

The Small Grants Fund: Grants are awarded on a one-off basis, normally for amounts less than £1,000. They must fall within one of the following priority areas:

- provide social, recreational or educational opportunities
- promote the development of self-help through voluntary activity
- assist those learning new skills
- new initiatives for meeting social needs in the community

Development Fund: Grants are awarded to projects providing facilities or services of strategic importance which require funding over a two year period to undertake new work or develop a fresh approach to securing income. For the time being this fund is limited and preference is shown to projects which have raised a minimum of 30% of total costs from private or charitable sources and which can demonstrate potential for a lasting contribution to the Isle of Dogs Neighbourhood.

Challenge Fund: Grants are awarded to assist projects with their fundraising. A 'challenge' is made to any group whose members believe they can fundraise through their own efforts any sum of up to a maximum of £5,000 over a 12 month period, with the trust matching £1 for £1 the monies raised.

Examples of grants made in 1991/92: Mudchute

Farm received £4,900 towards the salary of a development worker; the Island Advice Centre received £5,000 towards running their counselling services; the Island Neighbourhood Project was granted £1,500 towards a women's support group; Docklands Handicapped Group received £1,100 for transport; George Green Table Tennis Club was given £350 for general support.

Office furniture and equipment service: From time to time the trust is offered desks, chairs and filing cabinets from various business sources and supplies them to groups working in the area.

Applications procedure: An application form is available from the correspondent who is happy to have an informal talk with applicants before they submit their proposal. Applications for a grant from the development fund also entail members of an organisation to make a personal presentation before the Grants Committee during the final selection process and each short-listed submission will be visited.

Correspondent: Mr Pat Ward, Director

Address: The Innovation Centre, 225 Marsh Wall, London E14 9FW (071-454 1066)

Other information: The trust was established at the beginning of 1990 as the successor of the East End Community Trust and is now developing a new on-going role.

Lester Trust Fund

Beneficial area: Bow, Barking and Dagenham

Objects: Religious, educational or social work

Type of beneficiary: Organisations

Income: £19,360 (1990/91)

Grant total: £14,800

Grant details: In 1989/90, the last year for which accounts are on file at the Charity Commission, £5,000 was given to Kingsley Hall. The remainder was distributed among a wide range of charities, including Christian Aid, Quaker Peace and Service, Citizens Advice Bureau, Voluntary Service Association, Barking Council for Racial Equality, Alcohol Advisory Service and Help the Aged. Most of these grants are recurrent and ranged from £250 to £2,000.

Applications procedure: To the correspondent

Correspondent: C Snelling

Address: Midgley Snelling & Co, IBEX House, Baker Street, Weybridge, Surrey, KT13 8AH (0932 853393)

The London Dispensary Fund

Beneficial area: United Parish of Christ Church with All Saints, Spitalfields

Objects: Welfare of the sick poor

Type of beneficiary: Individuals

Income: £650 (1986)

Grant total: £550

Grant details: No cash grants are given. The trust's income is spent on Christmas food parcels, food and comforts, arrangement of transport and outings to the seaside.

Applications procedure: To the correspondent

Correspondent: Mrs I B Stride, Clerk to the Trustees

Address: The Rectory, 2 Fournier Street, Spitalfields, London E1

Other information: The fund was founded in 1777 for the provision of free medical attention and medicine. Its present work dates from the inauguration of the NHS.

Attempts to contact the correspondent were unsuccessful. Further information would be welcomed.

Norton Folgate Foundation

Beneficial area: The London Borough of Tower Hamlets

Objects: To make grants to girls and women under 25 years old who live in, or whose parents live in the beneficial area

Type of Beneficiary: Individuals (girls and women)

Grant total: about £950

Grant details: Grants are made to a usual maximum of about £100 to school pupils to help with the cost of books, equipment, clothing or travel. Grants to a maximum of £100 are also made to help with school, college or university fees or to supplement existing grants.

Applications procedure: On a form available from the correspondent.

Correspondent: Head of Awards Section

Address: Education Offices, 27 Birkbeck Street, London E2 6LA (071-739 4344).

Other information: This trust will be administered by the local council but is currently awaiting legal procedures since transfer from the former ILEA and no grants can be considered at the moment.

The Ratcliffe Pension Charity

Beneficial area: London Borough of Tower Hamlets

Objects: Benefit of needy residents

Type of beneficiary: Organisations

Income: £23,000 (1991)

Grant total: Unknown

Grant details: The bulk of the income is distributed to organisations within the area of benefit which make provision for needy persons suffering hardship or distress. Pensions are no longer paid but occasionally small gifts in cash or kind are made to individuals who are brought to the attention of the trustees by local welfare organisations.

Applications procedure: As above, only through welfare organisations in exceptional circumstances

Correspondent: J A Newton, Clerk

Address: Coopers' Hall, 13 Devonshire Square, London EC2M 4TH (071-247 9577)

Other information: The charity has stated that "annual demands invariably exceed income and we do not encourage personal applications which serve only to stretch even further our limited staff resources."

St Katharine & Shadwell Trust

Beneficial area: The wards of St Katharine and Shadwell in the London Borough of Tower Hamlets (ie Wapping Neighbourhood)

Objects: To improve the quality of life for the people of Wapping

Types of beneficiary: Organisations

Income: This is an uncertain figure as the trust's capital sum is yet to accrue interest

Grant total: £100,000 in 1991 (This was an exceptional figure because the trust had only just been formed and trustees decided to spend some of its capital)

Grant details: Grants are awarded for projects in the following categories:

Education and Training

Recreation and leisure

Easing poverty and sickness

Public Education in the arts

Housing the needy

In 1991 examples of grants awarded are as follows:

the Tower Hamlets Advanced Technology Trust received £7,500 to move to Wapping and provide training in computer technology and electronic engineering for women. Schools such as St Paul's Junior School received £1,000 towards sound equipment and the English Martyr's Primary School received funding of £1,000 for a computer. Tower Hamlets Community Transport was awarded £5,480 to run the shopping bus service for pensioners. Cable Street Community Gardens received £500 to improve the pathways between its garden plots and the mobile playgroup, Playbus, was awarded £2,500 to make regular visits to the Bangladeshi community on the Berner Estate.

However, applicants should note that grants were made across such a broad spectrum for 1991 only. The trust intends to concentrate its resources on education, training and employment skills in the next few years.

Applications procedure: In writing to the correspondent, with the name and address of your organisation, contact name, day time telephone number, a short description of your project, the amount of money you need and how you plan to spend it.

An application should consider the following questions:

Can you say how many people are likely to benefit?

Have funds been sought from anyone else?

What efforts have been made to raise money?

What are your long-term plans?

Where will financial support come from in the future?

Jenny Dawson, the Director, is happy to have an informal discussion with applicants before they apply.

Correspondent: Jenny Dawson, Director

Address: PO Box 1779, London E1 8NL (071-782 6962)

Other information: The trust is the result of a joint initiative between Wapping Neighbourhood and News International plc. As a founder member, News International has contributed £3.5 million which has been invested to provide an income for the charity.

Stepney Relief in Need Charity

Beneficial area: Former Metropolitan Borough of Stepney

Main grant areas: Relief of hardship and distress.

Type of beneficiary: Individuals

Income: £15,400 (1990/91)

Grant total: £4,880

Grant details: Direct assistance was given to individuals in need in the form of Christmas parcels (£125), fuel allowances (£280) and 12 monthly payments to pensioners (£220). Grants were also made to Stepney Neighbourhood Social Services (£4,200).

Applications procedure: To the correspondent. The trustees usually meet four times a year.

Correspondent: Mrs J Partleton, Clerk to the Trustees

Address: Rectory Cottage, 5 White Horse Lane, London E1 3NE (071-720 3598)

Tower Hamlets Further Education Trust

Beneficial area: The London Borough of Tower Hamlets

Objects: To make grants to students in further education who are not eligible for a mandatory award

Type of beneficiary: Individuals living in the London borough of Tower Hamlets

Grant total: Over £300,000 in 1991

Grant details: The trustees will normally only consider assistance towards those expenses which are necessary to enable the student to undertake their course of study. However, supplementary assistance over and above the standard level of support may be considered for both award holders and non award holders for expenses such as childcare, essential books and equipment or special clothing needed in connection with the course of study being undertaken.

The trustees are normally prepared to consider assistance towards travel expenses.

Applications procedure: On a form available from the correspondent

Correspondent: Jackie Feehan, Education Department

Address: Education Offices, 27 Birkbeck Street, London E2 6LA (071-739 4344)

Tower Hill Improvement Trust

Beneficial area: Great Tower Hill, Tower Hill, St Katherine's Ward in the London Borough of Tower Hamlets

Objects: The relief of the aged, impotent and poor. Relief of distress and sickness. The provision of leisure and recreation facilities for social welfare and the support of education. The provision and maintenance of gardens and open spaces.

Type of beneficiary: Organisations

Income: £63,000 (1990/91)

Grants: £35,000

Grant details: Grants were made to the All Hallow Church (£25,000) and St George in the East (£9,500).

Applications procedure: To the correspondent

Correspondent: Dr Roy Harris

Address: Attlee House, 28 Commercial Street, London E1 6LR (tel: 071-377 6614 fax: 071-377 9822)

Trivial Pursuits Fund

Beneficial area: London Borough of Tower Hamlets

Objects: Old age pensioners, general charitable purposes

Type of beneficiary: The elderly, organisations

Income: Variable

Grant details: The mayor fundraises by organising a trivial pursuits evening and encouraging donations from businesses. The funds are used to provide an old age pensioners' party each year and the remainder is distributed to one or two charities chosen by the mayor. In 1990/91 the Mildmay Mission was supported and in 1991/92 the Mildmay Mission and the Globe Centre received funds.

Application procedure: The Mayor, Councillor Barry Blandford

Address: Town Hall, Patriot Square, London E2 9LN (081-980 4831)

Miss Vaughan's Spitalfields Charity

Beneficial area: Ecclesiastical Parishes of Christchurch with All Saints, Spitalfields, St Matthew, Bethnal Green and St Leonard, Hoxton

Objects: Originally the clothing and support of poor mechanics and weavers in Spitalfields, unable from illness or any calamity to work. Now relief of need generally.

Type of beneficiary: individuals and families

Income: c£1,130 (1990/91)

Grant total: c£980

Grant details: Grants to individuals and families. In the past people who were convalescing, unemployed or invalids and large families on a low income, received support.

Applications procedure: to a member of the clergy from the above mentioned parishes

Correspondent: Mr E T Wheeler

Address: 24 Burghill Road, Sydenham, London SE26 4HN (081-778 2764)

Other information: The trust never keeps any surplus in its account as it prefers to allocate all its income.

Alice Clare Woodthorpe Williams Charity

Beneficial area: The St Mary's and Spitalfields Wards of the former Metropolitan Borough of Stepney

Objects: Relief of poverty

Type of beneficiary: Individuals

Income: £1,850 (1987)

Grant total: £820

Grant details: Food vouchers and food parcels were distributed. No further information available.

Applications procedure: To the correspondent

Correspondent: See 'Other information'

Other information: Stuart Lee, former Clerk for the above trust, left Tower Hamlets Social Services Department and no one there knows who is currently administering the charity. Further information would be welcomed.

Local Major Companies

Gibbs Hartley Cooper Ltd (Insurance Brokers), 27/33 Artillery Lane, London E1 7LP (071-247 5433) responds to local and national appeals. In the past it helped provide equipment for local schools and assisted the Lloyds Initiative, a Business in the Community project. Contact Mr Ledsam, Company Secretary.

Hogg Group plc, 1 Portsoken Street, London E1 8DF (071-480 4000) gives to local groups such as the church fund, Saint Botolph's and local hospitals. Contact Doris Barker, Secretary to the Hogg Group Plc Charitable Trust.

Leslie & Godwin Group Ltd, 6 Braham Street, London E1 8ED (071-480 7200) supports national charities and local appeals such as the special baby unit and cancer scanner appeals of the local hospital. The company also has a seven year covenant with Saint Botolph's Church in Aldgate which looks after homeless people. Contact Lesley Reynolds, Secretary to the Managing Director, The Leslie and Godwin Charitable Trust.

Sources of Advice

Tower Hamlets Arts in Education Forum, Limehouse Town Hall, 646 Commercial Road, London E14 7HA (071-987 9200). Contact Brian Oakaby, Coordinator, (Opening hours: 9.00-5.00).

Tower Hamlets Community Education Service consists of Neighbourhood branches and is decentralised. For further information contact Wapping Neighbourhood, Shadwell Centre, The Highway, E1 9HT (071-790 3358)

Waltham Forest

London Borough of Waltham Forest

Walthamstow Town Hall, Forest Road, London E17 4JF (081-527 5544).

Correspondents: Administration:
Secretariat: Judy-May Brandy, Assistant Committee Manager (grants)

Information and Advice:
Community Liaison Unit: John Whitfield, Community Liaison Officer

Women's Unit: Sharon Hanooman, Acting Head of Unit

Social Services Dept: Shaheen Westcombe, Principal Officer (Voluntary Organisations Liaison) Steve Peacock, Planning Adviser (Mental Illness and Drug/Alcohol Specific Grants)

Race Relations Unit: Lyn Brown, Voluntary Sector Co-ordinator

Housing Dept: Jane Foley, Tenant Liaison Officer

Consumer Protection Dept: Robin Middleton, Assistant Controller - Chief Trading Standard Officer

Dept of Economic Development: Jeremy Chandler, Principal Planning Officer

Grant totals 1991/92: £3,626,968 in main programme funding.

Funding practice: Waltham Forest makes grants to the voluntary sector through a variety of committees. The Secretariat co-ordinates most grant-aid to voluntary organisations.

Grants given by the individual committees in 1991/92 can be broken down approximately as follows:

Social Services:	£1,383,620
Under Fives:	£80,550
Grant Aid Members Panel:	£1,048,813
Race Relations:	£271,400
Women:	£249,000
Economic Development:	c£13,360
Education:	£287,795
Housing:	£182,000
Leisure:	£99,200
Planning (historic buildings):	£11,230
TOTAL	£3,626,968

Policy: Any organisation seeking a grant from Waltham Forest must sign a copy of the council's grant-aid conditions. These are fairly standard, relating to the applicant's non-profit-making and non-party-political status, amongst other staffing and financial criteria. Applicants should note that a copy of their organisation's constitution or articles of association must be submitted prior to an application for grant-aid being considered.

The Children Act 1989: In March 1992 Waltham Forest formed the Children Committee in response to this new legislation The new committee has grant-making powers but the funding policy towards organisations working with children will probably remain the same.

Mental Illness Specific Grant: In 1991/92 Waltham Forest received a grant from the Department of Health and funded Waltham Forest MIND (£10,500) to evaluate a council project, MIND (£11,000) to run a Sunday drop-in luncheon club, Waltham Forest African Caribbean Mental Health Organisation (£5,500) to run a Saturday drop-in luncheon club, an Asian mental health group (£5,500), Waltham Forest Asian Centre (£5,000), and the Black People's Mental Health Association (£84,000) to provide support, advocacy, daytime activities and weekend respite care.

Drugs and Alcohol Specific Grant: In 1991/92 Waltham Forest received £50,505 in funding from the Department of Health and supported Waltham Forest Alcohol Counselling Services (£71,935). Joint Finance funds were also allocated to this voluntary group.

Applications Procedure: In the first instance enquiries and applications should be addressed to the Secretariat. Grants are made annually and forms are automatically sent to previous applicants. The grant cycle is advertised in both local and selected ethnic minority newspapers. Deadlines for applications are under review.

Other support: Each year the council runs a number of seminars to advise local groups how to complete their applications forms. Waltham Forest also gives discretionary rate relief to local voluntary organisations. The application procedure for this is under review.

Contracting and The Community Care Plan
In March 1992 Social Services was 'looking to shift from a position of funding voluntary organisations purely through grants to using service level agreements with larger organisations.' Grant-aid will probably be maintained to promote innovation and to encourage new voluntary organisations to form a relationship with the council.

Service Level Agreements will probably be specific about a service required of a voluntary group but they would be open to review. Their duration was being debated in early 1992.

Social Services consulted its local voluntary sector about community care, and Waltham Council as a whole was reassessing its relationship with the voluntary sector.

For further information contact: Steve Peacock, Planning Adviser

Waltham Forest Joint Consultative Committee

Beneficial area: The area is co-terminous with the London Borough of Waltham Forest and the Waltham Forest Health Authority but includes Wanstead/Woodford for acute hospital services and services for elderly people.

Objects: To encourage voluntary groups to submit bids for joint finance monies for projects which provide an independent life for people in their own homes who otherwise would be in hospital or other institutional care.

Funding practices: The Joint Consultative Committee (JCC) does not have direct control over joint finance expenditure for care in the community projects but makes recommendations to the Waltham Forest Health Authority.

Expenditure on voluntary organisations: c£200,000 (1991/92)

Details of projects: Voluntary projects supported include Crossroads Care Attendant Schemes, Bereavement Support Project, Waltham Forest Alcohol Counselling Service, Carers' Support Network, Age Concern and MENCAP.

Applications procedure: All bids from voluntary organisations must be considered via the Opera-
tional Planning procedure which involves consideration by the service development groups, the joint finance group, the joint consultative committee and finally the district health authority. The initial information submitted by the voluntary organisation should include a statement of costs, how the people in Waltham Forest will benefit from the proposal and whether it will require capital or revenue funding, one-off or recurring. The applications procedure is under review. For further details contact the correspondent below or David Jobbins, Waltham Forest District Health Authority, PO Box 13, Claybury Hall, Woodford Green, Essex IG8 8DB (081-520 8971).

Correspondent: Roy Gopaul, Health Services Adviser, Chief Executive's Dept

Address: Walthamstow Town Hall, Forest Road, London E17 4JF (081-527 5544 ext 4805)

Other information: The JCC currently meets six times a year.

Waltham Forest Arts Council

Beneficial area: London Borough of Waltham Forest

Type of beneficiary: Organisations and individuals in the borough

Grant details: Like all arts councils, this is primarily an advisory and co-ordinating body which promotes and develops arts in the borough. A small grants budget is available for affiliated societies and individuals.

Correspondent: Bill Parkinson, Secretary

Address: The William Morris Gallery, Lloyd Park, Forest Road, Walthamstow, London E17 4PP (081-527 8750)

The Sir William Mallinson Scholarship Fund

Beneficial area: London Borough of Waltham Forest

Objects: Educational grants for residents under 19 years old

Type of beneficiary: Individuals

Grant total: About £500 per annum

Grant details: The trust sponsors students or groups of students who wish to undertake a special course of study or project.

Applications procedure: Applications can be made at any time, on a form available from the correspondent.

Correspondent: The Chief Education Officer

Address: London Borough of Waltham Forest, Education Department, Municipal Offices, High Road, Leyton, London E10 5QJ (081-527 5544 ext. 5015)

Other information: A number of other educational trusts (the Henry Green Scholarship Fund, The Sir George Monoux Exhibition Foundation and Walthamstow Fund, and the Robert Ozler Trust) are administered from the same address. They are established for the benefit of present and former pupils of 16 specific schools in the borough. Their combined grant total in 1991 was about £1,300.

The Walthamstow Charity for Children

Beneficial area: Former Borough of Walthamstow

Objects: Promotion of the physical and moral well-being of children under five

Type of beneficiary: Organisations

Grant total: £250 (1991)

Grant details: Grants of about £50 are made to playgroups.

Applications procedure: To the correspondent

Correspondent: Administration Officer (to be appointed)

Address: London Borough of Waltham Forest, Education Department, Municipal Offices, High Road, Leyton, London E10 5QT (081-527 5544)

Other information: The most recent accounts on file at the Charity Commission are for 1967, when the charity's income was £370. See also the entry for The Sir William Mallinson Scholarship Fund.

Waltham Forest Handicapped Trust

Beneficial area: London Borough of Waltham Forest

Objects: Welfare of handicapped people whose needs cannot be met under statutory provisions

Type of beneficiary: Individuals and organisations

Income: £360 (1990/91)

Grant total: £1,100

Grant details: The trust makes grants for a variety of needs, and can also give applicant advice about sources of statutory funding.

Applications procedure: In writing via social services, welfare agency etc.

Correspondent: Mrs L Bell

Address: c/o Community Services, 154 Blackhorse Road, Walthamstow, London E17 6NW (081-527 5544 ext. 4757)

Waltham Forest Mayor's Fund

Beneficial area: London Borough of Waltham Forest

Objects: To raise money for individuals in need whom statutory bodies are not able to assist.

Type of beneficiary: Local charities in the borough. It is not usual to give to local branches of national charities unless they help residents of the borough directly.

Income: Varies from year to year as it depends on local support for fund-raising events.

Correspondent: The Mayor

Address: Town Hall, Forest Road, London E17 4JF (081-527 5544)

Major Local Companies

Bush Boake Allen Ltd (Flavours, Fragrances & Aroma Chemical Manufacturers), Blackhorse Lane, London E17 5QP (081-531 4211) supports some local charities. Contact Norma Venn, Secretary to the Personnel Director.

Jermyn Street Shirt Makers Ltd (formerly the Eagle Shirt Co Ltd), Sutherland Works, St Andrew's Road, Walthamstow, London E17 6BD (081-527 8376) is now part of the House of Fraser plc. Collections are made amongst staff for the Heart Foundation and the hospice at Hackney. Contact Mr Mizbah, Management Accountant.

Thorn Security Ltd, 160 Billet Road, Walthamstow, London E17 5DR (081-527 5533). Contact Mrs Bouchard in the Personnel Department.

Sources of Advice

Waltham Forest Council for Voluntary Service, Greater London House, 547/551 High Road, Leytonstone, London E11 4PB (081-558 6011)

General Secretary: Ms Nors Jackson
Opening hours: 10.30-4.30

Waltham Forest Education Advice Shop for Adults, 398 Hoe Street, Walthamstow E17 6AA (081-521 4311)

Wandsworth

London Borough of Wandsworth

Wandsworth Town Hall, Wandsworth High Street, London SW18 2PU (081-871 6000)

Correspondents:

Economic Development and Grants Office (Policy and Finance Committee): Mike Brook, (general multipurpose grants for voluntary organisations and the economic development programme, Naaznim Khaki (small grants across the borough), Rasjid Craig (Urban Programme),

Social Services Committee: Alan Young, Director of Social Services,

Leisure and Amenity Services Committee: Urszula Creedon (for holiday playschemes), or Pauline Gibbs, (for small holiday grants)

Housing Committee: Dick Bunting, Housing Resources Officer,

Education Committee: Julia Prescott, Education Grants Officer,

Arts Grants Panels: Ivor Fry, Arts Officer.

Grant totals 1990/91: 5.9 million main programme revenue funding

Funding practice: During the course of 1991 Wandsworth Council devolved its grant programme to a number of service committees: Social Services, Education, Leisure and Amenities, Policy and Finance, and Housing. This was done to allow clear policy decisions to be made by the appropriate committee and to allow voluntary organisations to be clear about which officer was dealing with an application and subsequent enquiries. All committees will be looking to formulate clear policies for grant-making during the course of 1992.

At the time of going to press Wandsworth Council was reorganising its Economic Development and Grants Office.

Wandsworth has a fairly standard grants policy. In order to receive a council grant, a voluntary organisation must operate for the benefit of Wandsworth and its inhabitants and must be able to demonstrate proper conduct of its general and financial affairs. The activity for which funds are sought should be a response to a demonstrable need which is not otherwise provided for.

The majority of grants are recurrent, although a number of one-off grants are also made. All new applications are first considered for Urban Programme funding, and if unsuccessful, will be submitted to the appropriate committee. Organisations already in receipt of a grant will be considered a priority.

Officers also operate a Small Grant Funds Scheme to meet one-off requests for necessary items. There are three types of Small Grants Funds: General (£15,000), Arts and Leisure (£10,000) and Social Services type grants (approximately £5,000).

The Children Act 1989: As a result of the new legislation Wandsworth Council increased its grants to certain children's organisations in 1992. For example, Share A Family which provides respite care for disabled children received increased support. Service Level Agreements were also made to provide additional services identified by the new legislation. For example, Wandsworth entered into a SLA with the National Children's Home for a family aid/centre.

Urban Programme: Wandsworth is an Urban Programme Authority. Capital projects are funded almost exclusively through the Urban Programme (UP). Organisations in receipt of UP capital funding tend to be those concerned with economic and/or environmental affairs. Would-be applicants should contact the Urban Programme Co-ordinator in the Economic Development and Grants Unit.

Mental Illness Specific Grant: In 1991/92 Wandsworth was successful in its bid for funding from the DoH and made grants to Unity Centre of South London and Wandsworth MIND.

Drugs and Alcohol Specific Grant: Wandsworth's application for funding from central government was unsuccessful in 1991/92.

Applications procedure: The closing date for applications from organisations not already in receipt of council grant-aid and UP applicants is July each year; the closing date for organisations already in receipt of council grant-aid is September.

Other support: Wandsworth assists local voluntary organisations in practical ways such as providing accommodation in council owned premises and conducting lease negotiations with landlords, giving discretionary rate relief, offering advice on financial, fund-raising, personnel and constitutions. It also runs training courses for voluntary organisations in financial management and hopes to run other courses in good personnel practices for voluntary organisations and fund raising.

Two booklets have been printed: *Premises Advice Notes* and *Guide to Staff Recruitment and Selection for Voluntary Groups*. A directory listing all voluntary organisations in the borough is also to be published. A general information pack providing good advice for the voluntary sector may also be produced during 1992. The Grants Unit is also developing a library of resource material for voluntary organisations.

Contracting and the Community Care Plan
In 1992 Wandsworth Social Services funded voluntary organisations through grants but was considering introducing service level agreements (SLAs) and contracts.

It is concerned to ensure that smaller, less well-organised groups are not disadvantaged in the development of contracts for care and wishes to provide a sound financial base for all organisations to allow them a greater certainty in planning. Grant-aid will probably be maintained for some groups and performance targets set for them.

The voluntary sector was involved in developing Wandsworth's Community Care Plan, primarily through the Wandsworth Community Alliance which was established for this purpose.

For further information contact: Alan Young, Director of Social Services

Wandsworth Joint Consultative Committee

Beneficial area: London Borough of Wandsworth

Objects: No stated policies but will fund voluntary sector initiatives consistent with joint care strategies.

Funding practice: Joint finance for capital and revenue. Schemes to support informal carers, housing for people with learning difficulties, families of people with learning difficulties.

Expenditure on voluntary organisations: £255,000 (1991/92)

Details of projects: In 1991/92 Wandsworth Community Care Alliance (£5,000), Volunteer Bureau

(£22,000), Crossroads Care Attendants (£56,000) and Contact-a-Family (£51,000) were among the voluntary organisations supported.

Applications procedure: Application forms are sent to local voluntary groups.

Correspondent: Sue Redmond, Joint Planning Officer

Address: London Borough of Wandsworth, Lyon House 104 High Street, Wandsworth SW18 (081-871 6271)

Other information: The committee meets quarterly, approximately the second week in each quarter.

Battersea United Charities

Beneficial area: Former Metropolitan Borough of Battersea

Objects: Educational grants; relief of need

Type of beneficiary: Individuals

Grant total: £4,500 (1990)

Grant details: The largest of the charities that make up the Battersea United Charities, the John Edmonds Charity, makes educational grants to residents under 25 years old. These can cover clothing and travel expenses for younger children and fees and books for older students.

The smaller Charlotte Despard Charity makes grants to older women who are taking up training for employment after divorce, widowhood or bringing up children.

Christmas parcels are distributed to elderly people.

Applications procedure: In writing direct to the correspondent, although referrals from the education welfare service are common in the case of the John Edmonds Charity, for which also an interview will sometimes be arranged.

Correspondent: T W Ottway, Clerk to the Trustees

Address: Battersea District Library, Lavender Hill, London SW11 1JB (081-871 7466)

Harold Carter Bequest

Beneficial area: North Battersea

Objects: Relief of need

Type of beneficiary: Individuals and organisations

Income: £3,000 (1990/91)

Grant total: £2,500

Grant details: The trust is centred on the church in North Battersea, and makes grants of up to £250 annually to meet any special circumstance or need of an individual or a charitable organisation in the area.

Applications procedure: Through referral from social services, charities and schools. A preliminary telephone call to discuss the application is welcomed.

Correspondent: David Jesson-Dibley

Address: St Mary's Parochial Church Council, 72 Albany Mansions, Albert Bridge Road, London SW11 4PQ (071-228 7506)

Other information: In January 1991 the Parochial Church Council of St Mary's Parish Church, North Battersea decided to make a portion of the Harold Carter Bequest available to local charities and services. There will be a policy review in January 1993.

The Children's Health Centre Samaritan Fund

Beneficial area: London Borough of Wandsworth

Objects: Relief of necessitous child patients not older than 14 at any health centre in the Borough

Type of beneficiary: Individuals

Latest figures: 1987

Income: £1,000

Grant total: £900

Grant details: Grants can cover food and clothing, commodities, services, Christmas extras and holidays, and are normally limited to a maximum of £20. Grants are made for items essential for the child's well-being regardless of whether other members of the family will benefit equally. Sympathetic consideration is given to one-parent families and those whose sole income is from social security benefits.

Applications procedure: On the application obtainable from the correspondent. Trustees meet four times a year; emergency payments can sometimes be made.

Correspondent: G Drake

Address: 3 Wayside Road, Basingstoke, Hants, RG23 8BH

Other information: Attempts to contact the correspondent proved unsuccessful. Further information would be welcomed.

The Mayor of Wandsworth's Appeal Fund

Beneficial area: London Borough of Wandsworth

Objects: General charitable purposes at the discretion of the mayor

Grant details: The fund runs from May to May, when all its revenue is distributed in a large one-off grant to one charity nominated by the Mayor.

Correspondent: The Mayor

Address: The London Borough of Wandsworth, Mayor's Parlour, Town Hall, High Street, London SW18 2PU (081-871 6044)

Peace Memorial Fund

Beneficial area: London Borough of Wandsworth

Objects: To provide financial assistance towards holidays (mainly in the UK) for needy children not more than 16 years old

Type of beneficiary: Individuals

Grant total: £6,000 (1991)

Grant details: 139 grants were made to children towards the cost of holidays and educational visits.

Applications procedure: Through organisations only - these can include Wandsworth Borough Council, and school, Scouts and Cubs groups and local churches.

Correspondent: Gareth Jones, Administrative Officer

Address: Town Hall, Room 153, Wandsworth High Street, London SW18 2PU (081-871 7520)

The Putney Crèche

Beneficial area: Putney and Wandsworth areas

Objects: Welfare of mothers and their children up to the age of 7

Type of beneficiary: Individuals

Income: £6,500 (1990)

Grant total: £6,500

Grant details: Grants are made to mothers who might have experienced matrimonial problems and are now experiencing financial difficulties in bringing up infant children. Grants may be up to £35 where there is one child in the family and up to £60 where there are two or more. Should further requests for grants be made after six months then, providing funds are available, a further payment to half the above values can be made.

Applications procedure: For economic reasons distributions are only made through recognised welfare organisations in the area. Application forms can be obtained from the correspondent.

Correspondent: Mrs A Smalley

Address: Messrs. Russell-Cooke Potter & Chapman, 2 Putney Hill, London SW15 6AB (081-789 9111)

Other information: The charity derives its income from a freehold property which is at present let to Wandsworth Council as a day nursery.

Putney Relief Committee

Beneficial area: Putney

Objects: Assistance to the elderly and families in need

Type of beneficiary: Individuals

Income: £2,500 (1988)

Grant total: £2,500

Grant details: Monthly payments, fuel allowances and Christmas gifts are distributed. Grants for Special Cases are also available.

Applications procedure: By personal recommendation from clergy, social workers, health visitors, doctors. Note that the address below is for mailing purposes only.

Correspondent: The Secretary

Address: c/o Eileen Lecky Health Centre, 2 Clarendon Drive, London SW15 1AA

Betty Rawson Putney and Roehampton Children's Fund

Beneficial area: Putney and Roehampton

Objects: Convalescent treatment and holidays for deserving children.

Type of beneficiary: Individuals

Grant total: £3,000 (1990/91)

Grant details: About 120 grants are made annually to a maximum of £100 per family for help with convalescent holidays and school journeys.

Applications procedure: Via health visitors, social workers or head teachers to the correspondent

Correspondent: Mrs E Russell (see 'Other information')

Address: 197 Roehampton Lane, London SW15 4HN (081-788 9925)

Other information: In 1992 Mrs Russell was retiring from the trust and the trustees were vainly searching for someone to replace her.

The Bertha Smith Charity

Beneficial area: Parish of St Michael and All Angels, Southfields,

Objects: Relief of need

Type of beneficiary: Individuals

Income: £660 (1990/91)

Grant total: £480

Grant details: Grants were given to 12 people, sometimes to assist in the payment of heating bills during severe weather.

Applications procedure: To the correspondent

Correspondent: Rev D J Casiot

Address: St Michael's Vicarage, 73 Wimbledon Park Road, London SW18 5TT (081-874 7682)

Other information: This entry was not confirmed by the trust.

The Wandsworth Children's Fund

Beneficial area: London Borough of Wandsworth, and those parts of the old borough which included Streatham and parts of Clapham

Objects: Relief of needy children less than 16 years old

Type of beneficiary: Individuals

Income: £3,160 (1989/90)

Grant total: £1,480

Grant details: A total of 18 grants were made, towards the cost of baby equipment, clothing and convalescent holidays. Grants cannot be made for general furnishings, to pay debts or for adult holidays.

Applications procedure: Children are usually brought to the attention of the trustees by social workers, health visitors, education social workers, education welfare officers, school teachers and youth club leaders. Application forms are available from the correspondent, and applications are considered three or four times a year.

Correspondent: Mrs B Giles, Clerk

Address: 42 Rosemead Avenue, Mitcham, Surrey, CR4 1EY (081-764 1690)

Wandsworth Combined Charities

Beneficial area: Ancient Parish of Wandsworth, i.e. the present wards of Fairfield, Earlsfield, Southfield, West Hill, Springfield, part of Thamesfield and part of East Putney.

Objects: Provision of pensions to long-standing residents

Type of beneficiary: Individuals

Income: £9,620 (1989)

Grant total: £7,140

Grant details: The trust pays pensions and only in exceptional circumstances makes grants.

Applications procedure: Via social services, Age Concern, local clergy or by direct enquiry to the correspondent. Vacancies are locally advertised from time to time

Correspondent: A V Rashbrook, Clerk

Address: H E Rashbrook & Son, 91 East Hill, Wandsworth, London SW18 2QD (081-874 2211)

Other information: The Wandsworth Consolidated Charities, the Charity of Francis Millington and a small educational charity were amalgamated in January 1992 to form the Wandsworth Combined Charities.

Major Local Companies

Arding & Hobbs, Clapham Junction, London SW11 1QL (071-228 8877) supports a local charity each year and in 1992 chose Trinity Hospice. Contact Patricia Young, Customer Services.

Planned Maintenance Engineering Ltd, 12-14 Lombard Road, London SW11 3AY (071-228 6400) donates about 30% of its donations budget to local charities. Money is allocated to more or less the same charities each year. Contact Dawn Mapes, Assistant to the Company Director.

Young & Co Brewery plc, The Ram Brewery, Wandsworth High Street, London SW18 4JD (081-870 0141). Contact John Young, Chairman.

Sources of Advice

Wandsworth Adult College, College HQ, Sutherland Grove SW18 5PT (081-871 8333)

The Wandsworth Education Shop (free advice to adults), 86 Battersea Rise, London SW11 1EJ (071-350 1790)

Westminster

City of Westminster

PO Box 240, Westminster City Hall, Victoria Street, London SW1E 6QP (071-828 8070)

This council has a centralised grant-making system. In the first instance all enquiries should be addressed to the correspondents below:

Correspondents:
Grants Unit: Margaret Leask, Principal Arts Officer, Nicky Mills, Principal Grants Officer, Sarah Carter, Administrative Assistant (071-798 2735/3133)

For central government specific grants: ie HIV/AIDS, Mental Illness or Drugs/Alcohol grants contact:

Social Services: Ray Boyce, Principal Officer for Drugs/Alcohol and HIV/AIDS (071-798 3830)

Social Services: Graeme Tweedale, Assistant Divisional Director (Mental Health) (071- 828 8070)

Social Services: Suzann Hill, Assistant Director (Elderly Services) (Mental health for the elderly) (071-828 8070)

Grant totals 1991/92:
£6,500,000 in main programme funding
£97,900 Urban Programme funding
£27,200 in Joint Finance

Funding: The City of Westminster funds voluntary organisations in two main ways:

- non-arts organisations are funded by the Grants Sub-Committee;
- arts organisations are funded by the Arts Sub-Committee.
- In 1991, £1,500,000 was given to arts organisations and £5,000,000 to non-arts organisations.

The main purpose of Westminster's grant-aid is to enable voluntary organisations to provide direct services complementary to those offered by the council.

The priorities for grant-aid are:
- to help the underprivileged, people with disabilities and those in need;
- to provide recreational and leisure facilities and opportunities.

Preference is given to organisations which involve the greatest number of volunteers and members of the community. Applicants are encouraged to seek private funds through the council's matching funding incentive.

In addition, two committees provide limited funding to voluntary groups, but all enquiries should be directed to the Grants Unit.

Education Committee, this committee funds mother tongue projects and specific education projects in the voluntary sector (approximately £77,000 in 1991).

Social Services Committee, this committee funds services for alcohol and drug misusers through the Department of Health grant.

The Children Act 1989: In 1992 the new legislation led the council to prioritise the funding of children's organisations and to make additional one-off grants for the upgrading of their premises.

Mental Illness Specific Grant: Westminster received and funded joint projects involving the health authorities, social services and a voluntary agency.

Drugs and Alcohol Specific Grant: In 1991/92 Westminster received DoH funding and supported the CORE Trust (£40,000) to set up a residential unit and Rugby House Project (£20,000) for a mobile alcohol project in Westminster.

Applications procedure: Application forms are available each August (September for arts groups) for grants to be made during the following financial year. Forms should be returned to the council by the beginning of October (or the end of November for arts groups). Decisions regarding all non-arts applications are taken in December; those regarding arts applications are taken in January.

Contracting and the Community Care Plan
In 1992 grants were awarded through the Grants Subcommittee but the Social Services department was reviewing the council's funding arrangements with a number of voluntary organisations providing social welfare services in Westminster. This was

with a view to making these arrangements more formal by introducing Service Level Agreements.

Social Services will not be implementing Service Level Agreements until April 1993, and those drafted in 1992 run for a year and are very general.

All local voluntary organisations which the Community Care Forum identified were approached for suggestions. A Community Care Coordinator based within Voluntary Action Westminster worked closely with users, carers and a wide range of voluntary organisations through the Community Care Forum.

For further information contact: John Morgan, Assistant Divisional Director, Social Services (071-798 1894)

Westminster Joint Consultative Committee

Beneficial area: City of Westminster

Objects: The Joint Consultative Committee (JCC) sets priorities for funding each year. Generally projects are supported which assist people in the community or help them return to the community. In 1992/93 projects had to contribute to a mixed economy of care and priority was given to service provision for people with mental health problems, the elderly, the physically disabled, people with a learning disability and children.

Funding practices: Grants may be made for schemes requiring revenue or capital or both. The amount available for new schemes varies year by year. Sometimes there is a high level of funds already committed to continuing schemes, so that the amount available for funding to start in April is limited.

Total expenditure: £685,000 (1990/91)

Expenditure on voluntary organisations: £96,000 (1990/91)

Details of projects: Voluntary organisations receiving support in 1990/91 include: Volunteer Stroke Scheme (£7,240), St Mungo's Clubhouse (£20,000), Westminster Society (£7,580) and Voluntary Action Westminster (£2,180).

Applications procedure: An application form can be obtained from Claire Davies at Parkside Health Authority, 16 South Wharf Road, London W2 (071-725 1284) or from Liz Fenton, Voluntary Action Westminster, 1 Elgin Avenue, London W9 3PR (071-286 3451). Applications should be sent in before the end of December for funding the follow-

ing year, and are approved in February.

Correspondent: Ian Gregory, Secretary to the JCC

Address: Parkside Health Authority, 16 South Wharf Road, London W2 (071-725 1284)

Other information: The committee meets three times a year, in February, May and October. Its members include representatives from Westminster City Council, the two health authorities within Westminster City Council's boundaries (Parkside and Riverside), Kensington, Chelsea and Westminster Family Health Services Authorities, and three voluntary sector representatives.

City of Westminster Arts Council

Beneficial area: The London Borough of Westminster

Objects: To promote small-scale, community-based arts activities

Type of beneficiary: Organisations and individuals

Income: £127,000 (1990/91)

Grant total: £63,700

Grant details: The City of Westminster Arts Council only supports arts events which benefit Westminster residents and fall into one or more of the following categories:

1. Take place in areas relatively lacking in arts facilities, resources, and events, e.g. residential areas, the North of the borough;

2. Respond to the needs and interests of the local communities;

3. Develop the range of cultural traditions and/or reach members of ethnic minority communities;

4. Encourage new users to the arts or bring existing users into contact with new work and different cultural/artistic traditions;

5. Reach groups which do not have ready access to the full range of arts resources and events; (e.g. disabled people, the elderly, young people, children)

6. Reach new audiences by using unusual venues;

7. Involve the direct participation of a large number of Westminster residents.

No core funding is given, only one-off grants for short-term projects. In 1990/91 grants ranged between £100 and £4,500 and were made under the following categories: Combined Arts and Festivals; Drama, Dance and the Spoken Word; Art, Craft and Design; Music; Photography and Video (bursaries only, see application procedure). Examples of projects funded are: Pimlico Arts and Media, Pimlico Festival (£4,500), Path Productions, Drama workshops for disabled people (£200), St James's Opera, Dido and Aeneas (£500).

Most funding takes the form of a guarantee against loss which can include matching funding if sponsorship has been raised. The amount matched will be £1 for £1 to a maximum of £1,000 for sponsorship already raised and £500 for anticipated sponsorship. However this only applies if the request for matching funding is included in the initial application.

There is also a Video and Photographic Bursary Scheme whereby individuals and groups working in these media can receive funding. Conditions for eligibility are very similar to those already mentioned for grant-aid and matching sponsorship.

Applications procedure: Application forms for grant-aid and matching sponsorship are available from the correspondent and must meet the following deadlines:

30 September for events in November – February;

31 January for events in March – April;

31 March for events May – July;

31 May for events August – October.

No application forms are used for the Photographic and Video Bursary Scheme but guidelines are available. The deadline for these applications is 30 November each year.

Correspondent: Fran Little, Administrative Officer

Address: Marylebone Library, Marylebone Road, London NW1 5PS (071-798 1017)

Other information: The CWAC has a close working relationship with Westminster City Council which funds it. Westminster City Council also funds arts activities but arts groups cannot apply to both authorities. An informal chat with Fran Little or Margaret Leask, Principal Arts Officer at Westminster City Council (071-798 2498), is recommended before any application is made.

Arundell Street Fund

Beneficial area: City of Westminster

Objects: General charitable purposes

Type of beneficiary: Organisations only

Income: £2,700 (1988)

Grant total: about £6,300

Grant details: The average size of grant is £1,500. Only one-off grants are made.

Applicants should note that this fund is administered together with the Edward Harvist Trust (see separate entry). Groups should only apply to one of these and beneficiaries will receive a grant from only one of the trusts at any one time.

Applications procedure: Applications should be made in writing to the correspondent. No forms are available. (See also under 'Grant details').

Correspondent: Kevin Taylor, Head of Grants and Arts

Address: City of Westminster, PO Box 240, Westminster City Hall, Victoria Street, London SW1E 6QP (071-798 3133).

The Lord Ashdown Charitable Trust

Beneficial area: National; City of Westminster

Objects: General charitable purposes

Type of beneficiary: Organisations

Income: £885,000 (1989)

Grant total: £999,930

Grant details: The work of this trust has already been described in detail in the companion Guide to the Major Trusts. It is however worth noting that the Lord Ashdown Charitable Trust has supported groups operating locally in Westminster. Recent beneficiaries included the Westminster Action Team, Paddington Migrants' Unit, Westminster Medical School and Inner City Studies on Self-care.

Applications procedure: The trust states that resources are already heavily committed and the chances of success for unsolicited applications are small.

Correspondent: CM Marks

Address: c/o 44a New Cavendish Street, London W1M 7LG (071-486 4663)

Other information: This entry was not confirmed by the trust.

City of Westminster Charitable Trust

Beneficial area: The City of Westminster

Objects: General charitable purposes

Type of beneficiary: Organisations only

Income: £26,300 (in 1990/91 but this figure is variable as this is a fund-raising charity.)

Grant total: £39,580

Grant details: Grants ranging from £200 to £2,000 were made to tenants' and community associations, counselling groups, charities working with the homeless, and organisations providing services for young people, the elderly, people who are disabled, physically or mentally ill.

Applications procedure: No application forms. Telephone first for guidance.

Correspondent: Kevin Taylor, Head of Grants and Arts

Address: City of Westminster, PO Box 240, Westminster City Hall, Victoria Street, London SW1E 6QP (071-798 1864).

Other information: This trust was established in 1987 as a channel for charitable donations to benefit the borough. It also raises money for charity through events such as the annual New Year's Day Lord Mayor of Westminster's Parade. As yet it has no fixed grant-making policy.

The Dean's Gift

Beneficial area: Westminster area

Objects: Benefit of poor men and widowed women

Type of beneficiary: Individuals

Grant total: £250 (1988)

Grant details: This fund, an amalgam of charities established by statute under the reign of Elizabeth 1, paid for the distribution of beef, mutton and bread to the poor who assembled at the porter's lodge on Thursdays and Saturdays. It now pays a monthly pension of £1 to about 12 pensioners, with a small grant in October towards fuel and heating and a small gift to the 12 beneficiaries on Ash Wednesday. There are one or two vacancies for pensions.

Correspondent: Rear-Admiral K Snow, Receiver General

Address: Chapter Office, Westminster Abbey, 20 Deans Yard, London SW1P 3PA (071-222 5152)

The Arthur John Graham Cross Charity

Beneficial area: City of Westminster

Objects: Relief of need in cases of sickness, distress, disablement or handicap among residents

Type of beneficiary: Individuals

Grant total: £5,780 (1991)

Grant details: One-off grants, averaging about £70 to a maximum of £100, are made for heating, fuel, clothing, convalescence, holidays, travel, home repairs, aids, appliances. Grants towards more expensive items e.g. electric wheelchairs, can also be considered (see below).

Applications procedure: The charity does not deal directly with individuals. Applications should be submitted via social workers, or occupational therapists, physiotherapists, hospitals and welfare organisations such as Age Concern etc. Applications for sums up to £100 are dealt with as and when received; larger amounts are considered twice yearly at the trustees' meetings. All grants are distributed only through social services, hospitals etc., most of whom have application forms.

Correspondent: Mrs E Garwood

Address: 68 Arncliffe Drive, Heelands, Milton Keynes, MK13 7LH (0908 319460)

Emanuel Hospital

Beneficial area: Former Parishes in Westminster, and the former Parishes of Chelsea and Hayes (now in Hillingdon), as constituted in 1894.

Objects: The payment of pensions to poor, sober and honest people under the age of 56 years, who are members of the Church of England and who have lived in the beneficial area for at least two years.

Type of beneficiary: Individuals

Income: £69,720 (1989/90)

Grant total: £19,100

Grant details: The charity can pay "Lady Dacre" pensions of £258 a year to elderly people who, in addition to the qualifications listed above, have a maximum income of £60 per week in the case of single applicants and £96 per week for married couples. Small grants are also made.

Applications procedure: Direct to the correspondent. There is an application form which should be returned along with supporting documentation. Help and advice may be sought from local welfare agencies (e.g. Age Concern) and churches.

Correspondent: Mr Lee, Clerk to the Governors

Address: Emanuel Hospital, PO Box 270, Guildhall, London EC2P 2EJ (071-260 1405)

Other information: With the charity's income doubling in a few years, it has a surplus of income over expenditure of about £50,570 per annum which it reinvests. It is now able to provide more pensions and publicises its activities, and details of its pension vacancies in local papers and through welfare agencies and churches within the beneficial areas.

Emanuel Hospital itself was established at the end of the sixteenth century on land owned by Lord and Lady Dacre. When the hospital's land and assets were sold in 1895 the charity was started under its present scheme.

This entry was not confirmed by the trust.

The Forrest and Grinsell Foundation

Beneficial area: City of Westminster, with a preference for the former united Parishes of St Margaret and St John the Evangelist

Objects: Residents, 25 years old or under, in need of financial assistance for education (including musical education), training, or for entry into a trade or profession

Type of beneficiary: Individuals

Income: £27,880 (1987)

Grant total: £16,500

Grant details: The foundation helps young people resident in Westminster, including young unemployed people, with a wide range of educational and other activities, both through direct grants and through schools, youth clubs and other organisations. Assistance can take the form of book grants, travel allowances for educational trips abroad and for university interviews, grants to study music or the arts, providing uniforms or special clothing, helping towards the cost of tools and instruments.

Applications procedure: In writing to the correspondent

Correspondent: Sir Reginald Pullen

Address: Warden's House, 42 Rochester Row, London SW1P 1BU (071-828 3131)

Other information: This trust is administered alongside Vacher's Endowment and United

Westminster Almshouses (see separate entries). This entry was not confirmed by the trust.

The Charity of Edward Harvist (Westminster)

Beneficial area: City of Westminster

Objects: General charitable purposes

Type of beneficiary: Organisations only

Income: £57,000 (1991/92)

Grant total: £42,400

Grant details: Grants to local organisations, mainly for equipment, furniture, specific items. Grants tend to range in size from a few hundred pounds to £5,000.

This trust is administered interchangeably with the Arundell Street Fund (*see separate entry*). It is therefore pointless for any voluntary organisation to apply to more than one of the two.

Applications procedure: No application forms.

Correspondent: Principal Grants Officer

Address: c/o City of Westminster, PO Box 240, Westminster City Hall, Victoria Street, London SW1E 6QP. (071-798 3133)

Other information: This charity is one of the grant-making arms of Edward Harvist's Estate. This was founded by the will of Edward Harvist in 1610 for the repair of the Edgware Road between Tyburn and Edgware. The scheme has since been adjusted and is now run for the benefit of needy people living in the five boroughs through which the Edgware Road passes: namely, Barnet, Brent, Camden, Harrow and Westminster (see separate entries). Harrow administers the charity's income; each of the councils concerned is then itself responsible for making grants in its borough.

Hyde Park Place Estate Charity (Civil Trustees)

Beneficial area: London Borough of Westminster

Objects: Relief of sick, convalescent, handicapped or infirm residents, and for education in the area

Type of beneficiary: Individuals and organisations

Income: £132,000 (1990/91)

Grant total: £116,000

Grant details: For individuals and families grants can be made for domestic expenses, special equipment, holidays for the disabled and training expenses for young people. Organisations may also apply - recent beneficiaries include nursery schools, youth clubs, refuges for those rendered homeless, and projects for handicapped people and the victims of crime.

Grants, which may range from a few pounds to several thousands, are made at the discretion of the trustees and decided according to circumstances. No recurrent grants are made, but beneficiaries can reapply if there is further need.

Applications procedure: By letter to the correspondent. Applications on behalf of individuals need the recommendation of a trustworthy person or organisation.

The trustees meet twice yearly, usually mid-May and mid-November. Applications can often be processed within a few days but may be held over to the next half-yearly meeting if large-scale funding is involved.

Correspondent: Miss E Crichton, Clerk to the Trustees

Address: St George's Vestry, 2a Mill Street, London W1R 9LB (071-629 0874)

Other information: Two much smaller trusts are administered from the same address, the Charity of Matthew Tomlinson and St George's Hanover Square Charitable Trust.

Paddington Charitable Estates Educational Fund

Beneficial area: The former Metropolitan Borough of Paddington (roughly the north-west corner of the City of Westminster bounded by the Edgware Road and Bayswater Road)

Objects: Support of voluntary schools; support of organisations involved in education; educational grants for residents under the age of 25

Type of beneficiary: Individuals and organisations

Income: £152,130 (1990)

Grant total: £76,800

Grant details: The work of the charity falls into two areas: about three-quarters of the grants are made to voluntary schools in the beneficial area, with the remainder of the grant budget allocated to individuals, organisations and to eight local schools.

This latter category saw grants made to youth and educational clubs and groups for such needs as a computer and a programme of teaching dyslexic children. About £13,960 was awarded in grants.

Direct support of residents under 25 accounted for about £20,220 of which £15,900 was given in educational grants and £4,320 was donated through a pocket money scheme. Children of school age received assistance towards clothing and holidays, although occasionally grants were made towards higher education. £18,000 was donated to eight local schools which receive funding every year.

Grants totalling £15,620 were awarded to voluntary schools for major development schemes.

Applications procedure: Applications should be in writing by social services or a welfare organisation on behalf of a client. If in doubt a telephone call to the correspondent would be useful to establish if a case is eligible.

Correspondent: Sarah Carter, Assistant Clerk to the Trustees

Address: 16th Floor, Westminster City Hall, Victoria Street, London SW1E 6QP (071-798 2735)

Paddington Welfare Charities

Beneficial area: The former Metropolitan Borough of Paddington (roughly the north-west corner of the City of Westminster, bounded by Edgware Road and Bayswater Road)

Objects: Relief of need, sickness and distress

Type of beneficiary: Organisations and individuals

Income: £34,000 (1990)

Grant total: £35,000

Grant details: The main way that relief is given is by paying for items, services or facilities which would alleviate the person's situation. There is no maximum or minimum grant; as long as the need is clear, the trustees have a wide scope in the sort of relief they can give, provided that the beneficiary is a resident of the beneficial area and the money is not being used for the relief of public funds (rent, rates etc).

Individuals may be supported through pensions, which have recently been increased to £12 per month and account for £11,500 of the grant total. A fuel assistance scheme is also operated (£3 vouchers) and gifts are distributed from local churches at Christmas.

A small proportion of the grant total (about £4,000) is allocated to organisations such as Age Concern to help them in their work with needy and sick people.

Applications procedure: In writing through social services and welfare agencies only. Applications are normally dealt with within two to three weeks.

Correspondent: Sarah Carter, Assistant Clerk

Address: City of Westminster, PO Box 240, Westminster City Hall, Victoria Street, London SW1E 6QP (071-798 2735)

Other information: See also the Paddington Charitable Estates Educational Fund.

Rumsey Charity

Beneficial area: Parishes of St Barnabas and St Mary, Pimlico

Objects: Benefit of poor residents

Type of beneficiary: Individuals

Latest information: 1983

Income: £1,600

Grant total: £1,125

Grant details: 19 donations were given for clothing, shoes, sheets, holidays, parties, outings, youth club, football gear, craft apparatus, groceries.

Correspondent: Miss H A Lynes, Clerk

Address: See 'Other information'

Other information: Miss H A Lynes moved from 256 Wellington Flats, Ebury Bridge Road, London SW1W 8RZ about six years ago. We would be grateful if anyone could inform us of her new address. The trust's last accounts on file at the Charity Commission are for 1983.

William Shelton's Educational Foundation

Beneficial area: Ancient Parishes of St Giles in the Fields, St Martin in the Fields and St Paul, Covent Garden

Objects: Benefit of young people living or being educated in the beneficial area

Type of beneficiary: Individuals

Latest figures: 1978

Income: £4,300 (including income from a Tercentenary Account and from properties at Parker St, WC2)

Grant total: £1,860

Grant details: Grants were made under clause II (1) of the Scheme (Scheme not on file at the Charity Commission). Educational grants are made - no further information available.

Applications procedure: To the correspondent

Correspondent: Mrs J Rustage, Secretary

Address: 17a Macklin Street, Drury Lane, London WC2V 5NR (071-405 1878)

Other information: With moves underfoot for the disposal of its properties, the foundation's income is expected to increase substantially in the not too distant future.

See also The Bloomsbury Dispensary and the Dibdin Brand Charity. On unknown grounds the chairman of these charities withheld his approval for the appearance in this guide of any information about the charities' work.

This entry was not confirmed by the trust and further information would be welcomed.

The Ancient Parish of St Andrew Holborn – charities administered from the Guild Church of St Andrew

The Guild Church of St Andrew Holborn is the administrative base for the five grant-making charities described below. The limited beneficial area and objects of these charities were making it increasingly difficult for beneficiaries to be found and for all the money to be spent. The trustees have therefore simplified and extended the charities' schemes.

Isaac Duckett's Charity

Beneficial area: The former Parish of St Andrew, Holborn and the former Metropolitan Borough of Holborn, and the former Parish of St Clement Danes and the former Metropolitan Borough of the City of Westminster.

Trustees: The vicars of the Guild Church of St Andrew Holborn and St Clement Danes, two church wardens from each church and two others from each beneficial area

Objects: To provide relief in need

Type of Beneficiary: Men and women who are or have been employed in or live in or have a special knowledge of the beneficial area. Its constitution states that it must spend 8/9ths of its income on one-off grants and pensions and 1/9 on the St Andrew Holborn City Foundation

Income: £80,150 (1990/91)

Grant total: £70,200

Grant details: The charity does not make grants directly to individuals in need; rather, it gives financial support to its two branches (St Andrew Holborn and St Clement Danes) and to the St Andrew Holborn City Foundation to support the needy.

Address: St Andrew's Vicarage, 5 St Andrew Street, London EC4A 3AB (071-583 7394)

Correspondent: The Clerk (to be appointed)

Other information: For many years Isaac Duckett's Charity owned and obtained rental income from houses in Crayford Road and Ducketts Road and much of its expenditure went on maintaining this rented accommodation. In 1989 it sold two of its properties generating £94,050 and this sum was added to the capital fund. The future income of the trust should be greatly increased.

Isaac Duckett - St Andrew Holborn Branch

Beneficial area: The former Borough of Holborn, with preference for the Parish of St Andrew, Holborn

Trustees: The Vicar of the Guild Church of St Andrew Holborn, the two churchwardens and two others

Objects: Relief in need

Type of beneficiary: Men and women who are or have been employed in the area of the former parish of St Andrew. Preference is given to those who are qualified as, who are or have been domestic servants, housekeepers or resident caretakers.

Income: £31,120 (1988/89)

Grant total: £2,320

Grant details: Both one-off grants and pensions are given. In 1988/89 ten pensions were made to old people, mostly for £208 per annum and three grants were made ranging from £50 to £200.

Applications procedure: Applications should be in writing, either directly or via welfare agencies and social services.

Correspondent: The Clerk (to be appointed)

Address: St Andrew's Vicarage, 5 St Andrew Street, London EC4A 3AB (071-583 7394)

The St Andrew Holborn City Foundation

Beneficial area: The City of London and that part of the ancient Parish of St Andrew, Holborn which lies outside the City.

Objects: The relief in need of persons resident or employed in the beneficial area. Preference is given to people resident or employed in the former London or City liberty of the ancient Parish of St Andrew, Holborn.

Type of beneficiary: Individuals and organisations

Grant total: About £8,000 per annum

Grant details: Grants can be made to:

School children to further their artistic careers

Social welfare agencies working for the relief of needy people in the beneficial area

Individuals in need for specific items such as carpets and television licences

Applications procedure: In writing to the correspondent

Correspondent: The Clerk (to be appointed)

Address: St Andrew's Vicarage, 5 St Andrew Street, London EC4A 3AB (071-583 7394)

Other information: The trust is trying to widen the scope of its scheme to be able to help more people in need.

In the 1988/89 accounts on file at the Charity Commission the charity's General Fund had an accumulated surplus of £34,140 and its Capital Fund had an accumulated surplus of £11,240. This surplus appears to be carried forward every year.

Bromfields Educational Foundation

Beneficial area: The ancient Parish of St Andrew, Holborn (excluding those parts falling within the parish of St George the Martyr, Holborn)

Governors: The vicar and wardens of the Guild Church of St Andrew, Holborn and four others

Objects: To enable students of higher education to prepare for (or enter) a trade, profession or calling by means of scholarships, bursaries, maintenance allowances or cash grants

Type of beneficiary: Young people under the age of 25 who live or work or whose parents/guardians live or work in the beneficial area. Organisations or groups of people cannot be assisted.

Income: £16,560 (1989/90)

Grant total: £4,420

Grant details: The foundation can support young people in a variety of ways, including:

Grants for children or young people to attend courses at any school, college, university or other place of learning approved by governors of the foundation;

Help with the cost of suitable clothing, books etc. for young people leaving education to enter a profession or trade;

Help with travel costs if it can be proved to be a vital part of the furthering of the education of a young person;

Help to enable young people to study music or other arts;

Help with items not provided by the local education authority for special facilities for training in athletics, sports and games.

Grants in 1989/90 ranged from £100 to £1,000 and many were recurrent.

Applications procedure: Application forms are available from the correspondent; all applications should be made in writing only (no telephone calls).

Correspondent: The Clerk (to be appointed)

Address: St Andrew's Vicarage, 5 St Andrew Street, London EC4A 3AB (071-583 7394)

Other information: Applicants must be prepared for the foundation to check with their school, college or university to ensure that they are attempting a course which is within their capabilities. The foundation will not consider applications from a young person whose parents or guardians are sufficiently well-off for the applicant not to be in real need of help.

As with previous years, an excess of income over expenditure, £10,230 in 1989, was reinvested. The foundation now has considerable accumulated, unspent funds, mainly through rental income from its property in Wimbish, Essex.

Hoxton Estate Charity

Beneficial area: The liberties of Saffron Hill, Hatton Garden and Ely Rents, all in the ancient Parish of St Andrew, Holborn, and now in the London Borough of Camden

Objects: The relief in need of people resident in the beneficial area

Type of beneficiary: Individuals in need

Income: £35,950 (1989/90)

Grant total: £35,440

Grant details: After administrative costs, Hoxton Estate Charity allocates its money in the following proportions:

15/20ths in pensions to elderly people in need

3/20ths on holidays for elderly people in need

2/20ths in educational grants to children of needy parents in cases where local authority support is not available

Applications procedure: In writing to the correspondent.

Correspondent: The Clerk (to be appointed)

Address: St Andrew's Vicarage, 5 St Andrew Street, London EC4A 3AB (071-583 7394)

Other information: The charity's income used to come from rental income from property in Kingsland Road, north London. In 1989 all properties were sold for the net amount of £170,200. This was then invested in a capital fund which now yields interest of about £35,950 per annum.

Isaac Duckett – St Clement Danes Branch

Beneficial area: The City of Westminster, with preference for the Parish of St Clement Danes

Type of beneficiary: Men and women who are or have been employed in the beneficial area. Preference is given to those who are qualified as, who are or have been domestic servants, housekeepers or resident caretakers.

Income: £27,480 (1987/88)

Grant total: £3,650

Grant details: Both one-off donations and pensions are given. In 1977/88 17 pensions of £200 were made and one for £50. Two donations of £200 were also given.

Correspondent: Michael Thatcher, Clerk to the Trustees

Address: Winkworth and Pemberton, 35 Great Peter Street, Westminster SW1P 3LR (071-222 7811)

Other information: This charity is a branch of Isaac Duckett's, from which it receives its income. This entry was not confirmed by the trust.

St Clement Danes Educational Foundation

Beneficial area: The Diocese of London with preference for the City of Westminster

Objects:

1. The maintenance of the St Clement Danes Church of England School in Westminster

2. The payment of exhibitions at any secondary school or place of further education

3. Assistance to promote the education or training of people entering a trade or profession

Type of beneficiary: For 2 and 3, above, beneficiaries must be needy individuals under 25 years old who are or who have been pupils at the St Clement Danes Church of England School or who are resident in the beneficial area.

Income: £113,140 (1989/90)

Grant total: £570

Grant details: The St Clement Danes Educational Foundation supported a large building programme at the St Clement Danes Church of England School in 1989 and has little or no surplus income for the time being. In 1989/90 the bulk of the trust's income was spent on educational supplies, equipment and maintenance of the aforementioned school.

Applications procedure: In writing to the correspondent

Correspondent: Michael C Thatcher, Clerk to the Trustees

Address: Winkworth and Pemberton, 35 Great Peter Street, Westminster, London SW1P 3LR (071-222 7811)

Other information: This entry was not confirmed by the trust.

St Clement Danes Parochial Charities

Beneficial area: The Parish of St Clement Danes in Westminster, but if there are no suitable applicants, then the City of Westminster

Objects: The relief of needy residents

Type of beneficiary: Individuals in need

Income: Between £8,000 and £10,000 (1987)

Grant total: £2,000

Grant details: Both one-off grants and quarterly pensions are given. In 1987 the charity awarded 25 pensions of £80 a year each.

Applications procedure: Application forms are available from the correspondent.

Correspondent: Michael C Thatcher, Clerk to the Trustees

Address: Winkworth and Pemberton, 35 Great Peter Street, Westminster, London SW1P 3LR (071-222 7811)

Saint Marylebone Educational Foundation

Beneficial area: The former Borough of St Marylebone and the City of Westminster

Objects: Grants to school pupils and students under 25; schools.

Type of beneficiary: Organisations and individuals

Grant total: £85,000 (1990/91)

Applications procedure: Individuals should write to the correspondent for a standard application form for completion by the applicant's parent(s) or self if over 18. Applications are considered in January and June. Schools should just write in with details of the purpose of the requested grant and the amount needed.

Correspondent: Mrs P Le Gassick

Address: 39 Burbage Road, London SE24 9HB (071-274 5886)

St Marylebone Health Society

Beneficial area: Former Borough of St Marylebone in the City of Westminster

Objects: The health and well-being of families with children of school age and under

Type of beneficiary: Individuals

Income: £15,810 (1990)

Grant total: £17,270

Grant details: Holidays for parents and their children are arranged and paid for, although grants are also sometimes made for holidays arranged by the family. Holiday grants are usually sufficient to pay for a one week holiday in a caravan or holiday camp, including fares and food allowance if self-catering. Please note that overseas holidays and families without children cannot be funded, and that applicant should have lived in the beneficial area for two years.

Other grants (length of residence qualification not necessary) to a total of £5,440 were made for beds, bedding, household equipment, children's equipment, clothing etc. Grants tend to be to an average of £100, with a maximum limit of about £300. Small Christmas grants were made, payable in the form of grocery vouchers. They ranged from £10 for a single parent and small child to around £40 for a large family.

Applications procedure: Via social workers, educational welfare officers and health visitors, using the application form available from the correspondent. Holiday applications by March if possible. Other applications at any time.

Correspondent: Mrs M North, Honorary Secretary

Address: 9 Hunting Gate Close, Enfield, Middlesex EN2 7EF (081-367 6704)

St Mary-le-Strand Charity

Beneficial area: The City of Westminster, with priority for the Parish of St Mary-le-Strand

Objects: The relief in need of residents in the beneficial area

Type of beneficiary: Organisations and individuals

Income: £98,760 (1990)

Grant total: £41,290

Grant details: The St Mary-le-Strand Charity gives one-off grants to organisations, and individuals in need. It also gives regular allowances to the needy elderly and occasional limited one-off assistance for education or training to young people under the age of 25.

In 1990 it gave grants worth £20,900 to 20 organisations. Donations ranged from £250 to £3,500 and beneficiaries included a youth club, church organisations, family workshop, voluntary groups providing services for the homeless, mentally handicapped, or people with HIV/AIDS. It also provided £4,900 of pensions and made one-off grants of about £100 to people in need.

Applications procedure: Applications must come from organisations themselves or, in the case of individuals in need, from social workers or welfare agencies where a case worker is already working with the potential beneficiary.

Correspondent: Mrs Anne Butters, Clerk

Address: 171 Strand, London WC2R 2LS (071-836 3205)

United Charities of St Paul's, Covent Garden

Beneficial area: City of Westminster

Objects: General benefit of the poor

Type of beneficiary: Individuals and organisations

Income: £4,160 (1990/91)

Grant total: £4,020

Grant details: Trustees favour applications from individuals rather than organisations and in 1990 most donations were made to people, sometimes through hospitals, health authorities, family service units or an early intervention service. These one-off grants ranged from £50 to £180. Payments on a monthly basis were also made to about twelve people.

Correspondent: C G Snart, Clerk

Address: William Sturges, Alliance House, 12 Caxton Street, London SW1H OQY (071-222 1391)

United Westminster Almshouses

Beneficial area: City of Westminster

Objects: Almshouses; payment of pensions to needy elderly people; general relief in need

Type of beneficiary: Organisations and individuals

Income: £340,860 (1988/89)

Grant total: £6,620

Grant details: The charity's total expenditure in 1989 was £124,782 and almost all of it went on maintaining its almshouses. £6,620 was given in out-pensions and grants and £4,690 was given in benefits to its almspersons.

Applications procedure: Application forms for out-pensions are available from the correspondent.

Correspondent: Sir Reginald Pullen

Address: Warden's House, 42 Rochester Row, London SW1P 1BU (071-828 3131)

Other information: The charity's income is derived from investments, and property in London, Solihull, Newbury and Preston. Currently an annual excess of income over expenditure of about £216,000 is being reinvested each year. This entry was not confirmed by the trust.

See also the entries for Vacher's Endowment and the Forrest and Grinsell Foundation.

Vacher's Endowment

Beneficial area: Greater London

Objects: Provision of pensions and grants to residents over 50 years old in need, hardship or distress who are living or have lived in Greater London, and their dependants.

Type of beneficiary: Individuals

Income: £24,000 in 1987 (mainly from investments and property in East Ham and Haringey)

Grant total: £7,380

Grant details: Quarterly allowances of £50 or £75, or one-off grants.

Applications procedure: Application forms and further information may be obtained from the correspondent in writing.

Correspondent: Sir Reginald Pullen

Address: Warden's House, 42 Rochester Row, London SW1P 1BU (071-828 3131)

Other information: The objects of the charity were broadened by schemes in 1989 and 1991. This entry was not confirmed by the trust.

Waterloo Parish Charity For The Poor (formerly the Kirchner Fund)

Beneficial area: Parish of Waterloo, St John, and St Andrew

Objects: Benefit of the poor

Type of beneficiary: Individuals, organisations

Income: about £1,000 in 1990/91

Grant total: Unknown

Grant details: Small grants can be made to individuals for living expenses and domestic items, although the charities' combined income (about £1,000) is already overstretched. Organisations which provide services for people in need can apply for funding as well.

Applications procedure: Through social workers

Correspondent: Rev R Yeomans

Address: St John's Vicarage, 1 Secker Street, London SE1 8UF (071-633 9819)

Other information: In 1989 the Charity Commission approved a new scheme whereby The Kirchner's Fund for the Poor of St John the Evangelist, Kirchner's Fund for the Poor of St Andrew and The Reverend Nathaniel Ernest Muggeridge Charity were amalgamated to become 'The Waterloo Parish Charity for the Poor'.

Westminster Amalgamated Charity

Beneficial area: London Borough of Westminster

Objects: Relief of Sickness, infirmity and poverty among people living, working or studying in the beneficial area

Type of beneficiary: Individuals and organisations

Income: £272,970 (1989/90)

Grant total: £197,420

Grant details: £33,350 was given in grants to individuals, mostly for heating, in cash or in kind, or for holidays and holiday fares.

Grants totalling £155,570 were made to 48 organisations. The largest donation was £31,060 and went to Age Concern, Westminster. The C.O.R.E. Trust (£8,000), Westminster Society for Mentally Handicapped Children and Adults (£7,000), the St Peter's Eaton Square Appeal (£7,500) also received substantial funding. Smaller grants of about £2,000 were given to organisations like Blenheim Project, Marylebone Bangladesh Society, Mozart Estate Tenants' & Residents' Association and North Westminster Victims' Support Scheme. 13 grants were made for under £1,000 and totalled £7,220.

Applications procedure: In writing to the correspondent. Individuals' applications should be made through a welfare agency, doctor, social services etc.

Correspondent: P Bircher, Clerk to the Trustees

Address: 4/5 Gough Square, London EC4A 3DE (071-353 9991)

Other information: The Westminster Amalgamated Charities united seven former charities: Earl Craven's Pest House Charity, Westminster General Aid in Sickness Charity, Albert Reitlinger Charity, Drury Lane Public Dispensary Fund, Henry Convalescent Fund, Jonathan Barlow Charity and the Louie and Cecilia Holiday Fund.

This entry was not confirmed by the trust.

The Westminster Foundation

Beneficial area: Central London and the North West

Type of beneficiary: Registered charities only

Income: £792,128 (1989/90)

Grant total: £637,740

Grant details: Grants can only be made to registered charities and never to individuals. A total of 110 donations were made, the largest being awarded to the NSPCC, (£200,000), Business in the Community (£88,920), The Game Conservancy Trust (£75,300), the Outward Bound Trust and the Royal National Institute for the Blind (£45,000). 69% of donations were made to organisations working in social welfare and most were for £5,000 and under.

A number of specifically London organisations were assisted including the Second Great Sutton Scout Troup (£500), The Lincoln's Inn Heritage Fund (£1,000), Westminster Cathedral Choir School Parents' Association (£100), The Wishing Well Appeal, Great Ormond Street Hospital (£2,000), The International Shakespeare Globe Centre (£2,000) and Lord Mayor of Westminster's Christmas Appeal (£500).

These grants represent a small proportion of the total. Beneficiaries include charities based in the North West, central London and national organisations.

Applications procedure: In writing to the correspondent

Correspondent: J E Hok, Secretary

Address: 53 Davies Street, London W1Y 1FH (071-408 0988)

Trustees: The Duke of Westminster, J N C James, M D T Loup

Miss Hawkins Woodfield Foundation

Beneficial area: The former Metropolitan Borough of Paddington

Objects: To help residents of the area with the costs of education

Type of beneficiary: Individuals under the age of 25

Grant total: About £250

Grant details: Each grant depends on circumstances but will not usually exceed £100. Trustees meet three times a year.

Correspondent: Henry Spector, Chairman

Address: 44 Wolmer Gardens, Edgware, Middlesex HA8 8QD

Other information: The trust went through some upheaval recently when its secretary retired and then his replacement died suddenly. The Chairman, Henry Spector, is looking to appoint another secretary.

Major Local Companies

The following represent a few of the many major companies located in the borough.

St James's Place Capital plc (head office), 15 St James Place, London SW1A 1NW (071-493 8111) has a policy of donating a certain amount to charities working in London and gives about £25,000 a year to groups in this category . Appeals should be addressed to Miss M Fiddle, Secretary of The J Rothschild Group Charitable Trust.

Esso UK plc, Esso House, Victoria Street, London SW1E 5JW (071-834 6677) sometimes gives charities working in the Westminster area. Educational work, training and environmental projects are preferred areas of support. Contact Mr Peter Truesdale, Contributions Manager.

Dunhill Holdings plc, 30 Duke Street, St James's, London SW1Y 6DL (071-499 9566) sometimes makes donations to charities working in the Westminster area. Preferred areas of support are children, youth and people with disabilities. Contact Richard Dunhill, President.

Pearson plc, Millbank Tower, Millbank, London SW1V 4QZ (071-828 9020/071-411 2000) has a small charitable budget to support voluntary organisations working in the Millbank Tower area. Contact Gerald Collett, Company Secretary.

Sources for Advice

Voluntary Action Westminster, 1 Elgin Avenue, London W9 3PR (071-286 3451)

Director: Liz Fenton
Opening hours: 10.00-5.00

Westminster Education Advice Shop (free advice for adults over 19 years old), 30 Church Street, London NW8 8EP (071-724 5051)

City of Westminster Arts Council, Marylebone Library, Marylebone Road, London NW1 5PS (071-798 1017) For details about grants see entry towards beginning of Westminster section.

Westminster Adult Education Institute, Amberley Adult Centre, Amberley Road, London W9 2JJ (071-286 1900)

Index of funding sources